THE STATE OF PSYCHIATRY

By the same Author

INQUIRIES IN PSYCHIATRY

Clinical and Social Investigations

SIR AUBREY LEWIS

*A Monochrome reproduction of a portrait
by Ruskin Spear*

THE STATE OF PSYCHIATRY

Essays and Addresses

by

Sir Aubrey Lewis

Emeritus Professor of Psychiatry
University of London

LONDON

ROUTLEDGE AND KEGAN PAUL

First published 1967
by Routledge & Kegan Paul Limited
Broadway House, 68–74 Carter Lane
London, E.C.4

Printed in Great Britain
by Butler & Tanner Limited
Frome and London

CONTENTS

CONTENTS

INTRODUCTION

IN OCTOBER 1966, Professor Sir Aubrey Lewis, a leading figure in the world of psychiatry for more than a generation, retired from the Maudsley Hospital, where he had joined Dr Edward Mapother's staff in 1928. After qualifying in medicine in his native Australia, he had first made some anthropological studies of aborigines and then turned to psychiatry, working in some of the most famous clinics in America and Europe before coming to London. In 1936, he was appointed Clinical Director of the Maudsley Hospital, and, in 1945, Professor of Psychiatry in the University of London. He was knighted in 1959. During these years, the healthy development of psychiatry, in Britain and abroad, has owed much to his guidance and encouragement: while the Maudsley Hospital, which was combined with the Bethlem Royal Hospital in 1948, has flourished and expanded into a psychiatric centre of international renown.

To mark his retirement, his present students have arranged for the publication of some of his best-known writings. These have ranged considerably beyond the confines of clinical psychiatry, wherein many of his contributions are now recognized as classics. Two volumes have been prepared. This one contains articles on the history of psychiatry, the ways in which it should be taught, and some of the important general issues with which every psychiatrist must inevitably concern himself, but which very few can clarify. Professor Lewis's closely argued essays have always been highly valued by those interested in these fascinating and complex topics for providing some firm ground in an area notorious for soft generalizations. The other volume is devoted to clinical and social psychiatry. Both include a complete bibliography of all Professor Lewis's publications.

Our selection, as the bibliography shows, is only a small sample, but it reflects the breadth of his scholarship and the vigour of his critical mind. For his past students, now scattered throughout the world, these essays will, we hope, be something more: refreshing reminders of their training. For athletes training involves not only a gain of muscular strength, but a loss of excess fat. For psychiatrists Professor Lewis provided its intellectual equivalent. It has been through his teaching, with its challenging mixture of scholarship and common sense, that his influence has been most widely felt, and it is this which we, his present students, gratefully commemorate.

THE EDITORS

The Junior Common Room
The Bethlem Royal and the Maudsley Hospital
November 1966

ACKNOWLEDGMENTS

IN the collection of these papers invaluable help has been given by Miss Helen Marshall, M.A., secretary to Professor Lewis for nearly twenty years. Her exceptional range of precise information and her constant readiness to assist immensely facilitated the task of preparing the books.

The articles first appeared in the following publications and we would like to express our thanks to their Editors for permission to reproduce them.

American Journal of Psychiatry, Athlone Press, Blackwell Scientific Publications Ltd., *British Journal of Sociology, British Medical Journal*, British Broadcasting Corporation, *Discovery, Journal of Analytical Psychology, Journal of Mental Science, Lancet*, Oxford University Press, *Philosophy*, Pitman Medical Publishing Co. Ltd., *Proceedings of the Royal Society of Medicine, Psychiatrie der Gegenwart, Times Literary Supplement, Yale Journal of Biology and Medicine.*

HISTORY

I

THE STORY OF UNREASON

PSYCHOLOGY said Ebbinghaus, has a long past but a short history. If the history of psychiatry is somewhat longer, and more eventful, it is because medicine is psychiatry's other parent, and because society has had some strange and painfully memorable ways of dealing with its irrational members. Perhaps it is better, with M. Foucault, to speak not of the history of psychiatry, but of the history of insanity. His *Histoire de la Folie à l'Âge Classique* is concerned with that history, especially in France during the period that stretched from the middle of the seventeenth to the end of the eighteenth century.

*   *   *

The story in its broad outlines is familiar and dramatic, like the story of slavery. After the tortures and judicial murders of the Middle Ages and the Renaissance, which confounded demoniacal possession with delusion and frenzy, and smelt out witchcraft in the maunderings of demented old women, there were the cruelties and degradation of the madhouses of the seventeenth and eighteenth centuries, in which authority used chains and whips as its instruments. Humanitarian effort put an end to the abuses. Pinel in France, Chiarugi in Italy, Tuke in England inaugurated an era of kindness and medical care, which prepared the way for a rational, humane approach to the mastery of mental illness.

In the nineteenth century the pathology of insanity was investigated, its clinical forms described and classified, its kinship with physical disease and the psychoneuroses recognized. Treatment was undertaken in university hospitals, out-patient clinics multiplied, social aspects were given increasing attention. By the end of the century the way had been opened for the ideas of such men as Kraepelin, Freud, Charcot and Janet, following in the paths of Kahlbaum and Griesinger, Connolly and Maudsley.

In the twentieth century psychopathology has been elucidated, and psychological treatment given ever widening scope and sanction. Revolutionary changes have occurred in physical methods of treatment, the regime in

This article is a review of *Histoire de la Folie à l'Âge Classique* by Michel Foucault. It is reprinted from *The Times Literary Supplement*, 6 October 1961.

mental hospitals has been further liberalized and the varieties of care articulated into one another, individualized, and made elements in a continuous therapeutic process that extends well into the general community, beginning with the phase of onset, *stadium incrementi*, and proceeding to the ultimate phase of rehabilitation and social resettlement.

* * *

This is the conventional picture, one of progress and enlightenment. It is too much of one hue, it is not dappled enough. But as a brief conspectus it is not far out: the chronicle is gratifying indeed when set alongisde the parallel story of our prisons. Latter-day medical historians have been concerned with elaborating the detail, and trying to pierce beneath the crust of these changes to see what movements of thought and culture occasioned them. In his difficult and often obscure but subtly reasoned book M. Foucault gives free rein to a highly individual conception of these forces and of the dialogue which went on century after century as Western societies tried to fix the limits which separated reason from unreason—a dialogue which ended, or was interrupted, when a rational and scientific approach to the problem, in the form of modern psychiatry, gained the primacy. M. Foucault makes it clear that he does not like doctors and their pretensions; he takes a more tragic, Nietzschean, view than theirs of what constitutes insanity.

In the Middle Ages the fool and the madman were at large: the leper was confined. But from the fourteenth century the lazarettos emptied and other outcasts took the leper's place as objects of fear and reprobation, chief among them the sufferers from venereal disease. It was some time before the madman joined them. The fool retained for a while his privileged place at court and elsewhere: in the morality plays and satires his was the voice of bitter, unwelcome truth discoursing of death and the folly of the wise. But with the Renaissance another figure symbolic of irrationality appeared in Germany and France—the traveller in the Ship of Fools, the ironist's targets in the *Encomium Moriae*: man's weakness and absurdity, his dreams and illusions were set in a moral frame, and contrasted with the nightmare hallucinations and phantasms that crowd the canvases of Bosch and Breughel.

In the next period, when the Renaissance merged into the age of reason— the 'classical' age in literature and the plastic arts—society ceased to tolerate the fool and to let the insane go about freely. Bounds were set, and institutions created for the isolation of those who were thought unfit to be retained in the general community. Don Quixote was no longer at large. The institutions were big, and those lodged in them heterogeneous. They were the poor, the delinquent, and the insane.

In France the Hôpital Général and Bicêtre, in Germany the Hamburg Zuchthaus, in England Bridewell, were the models on which houses of correction were rapidly developed. They combined the functions of hospital and hospice, prison and workhouse. In them charity was secularized, vice was punished, and madness found its place of exile. Sometimes quartered in

4

the old leperhouse and made the beneficiary of its endowments (as at St Lazare), more often supported out of public funds and voluntary gifts, these institutions arose from complex origins, in part economic. Vagrants had to be punished, the unemployed had to be made to work, the insane had to be supported since they could not support themselves: so they were all herded together.

*   *   *

The consequences of this policy were obviously bad: John Howard remarked on it, 'many of the bridewells are crowded and offensive, because the rooms which were designed for prisoners are occupied by the insane'. It was hard to say who suffered more: the criminals who were tormented by the madmen, or the madmen abused and ill-treated by the criminals. In the earlier part of the eighteenth century it was chiefly the plight of the former that excited compassion and demands for reform; by the time of Reil and Esquirol it was the outrages put upon the mentally sick by this heartless juxtaposition that were denounced.

For this widespread practice of confining the culpable offender and the innocent imbecile or psychotic in a common institution, the simplest explanation would be that organized society thereby extruded, in a crudely simplified act, all those who would or could not conform to its requirements. M. Foucault refines upon this explanation and expands it.

*   *   *

At the beginning of the classical period Tom O'Bedlams, imbecile beggars and licensed eccentrics had been familiar in the social landscape. But soon mendicancy came to be proscribed and indiscriminate charity was forbidden: thus in the Edict of 1657 which established the Hôpital Général it was laid down that anyone who gave alms to street beggars, whatever the pretext, should be fined four livres, to be handed over to the Hôpital. As the seventeenth century proceeded, there was a regrouping of those whom society wished to expel and exorcize. It paid regard chiefly to the moral aspect of conduct. Along with the beggars it included the mentally ill, the profane, the free-thinkers, libertines, and dabblers in sorcery. Into the closed world which it thought suitable for their aberrations, not then differentiated as they later were, it banished all who dealt in magic practices, blasphemy or perverse sexuality—conduct which seemed to have much in common with frenzy and delusion. Venereal disease bridged the gap between disease and immorality: the logic of the time did not find the gap wide or essential. All the conditions which the seventeenth and eighteenth centuries shut away had, in contemporary eyes, some moral fault, to be punished and cleansed away from impure mind or peccant flesh.

It seems strange and improbable that impiety and insanity, homosexuality and sorcery should have been confounded in one category of wrongdoing, calling for isolation and punishment with the hope of reformation. But we are

5

not so remote from it. The spirit informing the treatment then accorded the would-be suicide—prolonged imprisonment in a small wicker cage or upright box—is not so far removed from the attitude that has allowed suicide to be a punishable offence in our day. Compassion and condemnation are not incompatible even when ill-assorted, nor is it easy to refrain from moral judgments where they are least applicable.

Moral judgments are, by common consent, out of place when those judged are themselves incapable of exercising moral judgment because of infirmity. This aspect of mental disorder was recognized, however inconsistently, by some in the classical period. Notable authorities on canon and civil law, like Zacchias, acknowledged diminished culpability of the insane and held that it required medical skill to assess it—a view that Immanuel Kant was to contest a century or so later. During the greater part of the 'classical' period two contradictory aspects of mental alienation were accepted without misgiving: the psychotic's alienation from moral responsibility, and his alienation from the fulfilment of social obligations, carrying with it a clear implication of shortcomings and default. Determinist views prevailed when the legal issue of responsibility was weighed, but free will was taken for granted when moral obliquity was being adjudged. The antinomy was partly resolved in the nineteenth century, with the creation of a category of 'moral insanity' (to be translated in our century into 'psychopathic personality'); but perhaps the resolution was only verbal.

*　　　*　　　*

Besides the moral factor, other non-medical influences conspired to shut away the insane. The medieval terror of what was uncanny in their conduct had not been entirely dispelled: vestiges of old animistic rituals and half forgotten myths could be discerned in their delusions and vagaries, obscure reminders of bygone beliefs and repressed horrors. There were also the fears of infection: gaol fever was a peril to healthy society, to be guarded against by stricter measures of segregation permitting closer medical surveillance. Yet another reason for isolating these unfortunates lay in the fear of disclosure: insanity in a family meant scandal and dishonour; it had therefore to be hidden—another sample of eighteenth-century muddle-headedness which is not difficult to understand even in the twentieth.

Finally there was the fear of the madman's animality, his violent passions unsubordinated to reason, his unchecked restlessness, his unpredictable outbursts. He was consequently treated like a caged animal, put behind bars, chained and bedded on straw, whipped when disobedient, often left naked in all weathers; and he was credited with having the powers of resistance to pain, hunger and exposure commonly attributed to wild animals. Patients were also put on show at Bethlem, Bicêtre and many other institutions; Hogarth's engraving records it. This exhibition of unfortunates, paraded as in a menagerie, prodded and goaded to amuse the onlookers with their futile rage, was a further assertion that they did not belong to humankind—they were monsters in the literal sense, to be shown for warning and for entertainment. Men otherwise kindly saw no harm in this, and found rationalized excuses for all the brutality and neglect; but there were older fears—of werewolves and other lycanthropes—which reinforced the motives for shutting away the insane.

*   *   *

In their classification of the varieties of mental disorder the physicians of the seventeenth and eighteenth centuries included hysteria and hypochondria —conditions thought due to an excessive sensitiveness to the noxious effect of immoderate pleasures (such as theatre-going, novel reading, study, love-making, and other assorted diversions) and misuse of the non-naturals: air, food, sleep, movement and rest, and excretion. Not only were the hysterics thus brought within the bounds of culpability (as excess in alcohol, or drug-addiction, would likewise have brought them) but their inclusion served to emphasize the role of the environment in causation and treatment. Hence the subsequent vogue of hydrotherapy, shock, and violent movement, change of air, and disguised punishments, such as the administration of asafoetida for hysteria. Something of this punitive itch clung to the 'moral treatment' or psychotherapy which was elaborated in the first half of the nineteenth century. Fear and anger were used as therapeutic agents, and ingenious means of provoking them were devised, some ludicrous, some abhorrent.

M. Foucault is hostile to the popular view that reformers like Tuke and Pinel deserve the full credit of having liberated the mentally ill from the rigours and degradation to which they had been exposed in the classical period. There had already been, as he rightly points out, strong denunciations of the system and proposals for thoroughgoing reform, from several humane and enlightened men (including Mirabeau and Cabanis): but it is one thing to denounce established infamies, and another to demonstrate that it is safe to give them up, and that better measures will work.

Tuke, Chiarugi and Pinel by their bold experiments provided plain evidence that the old ways were bad ways, from every point of view. Their task was made possible by the gradual separation of the mentally ill from the malefactors and other unfortunates with whom they had been confounded. Given an autonomous status, recognized as distinct from others whose conduct was socially disallowed, they could be more closely studied and more individually treated, on medical rather than moral lines. They could at last speak for themselves. Psychiatry was thus born, and oscillated between abstract theorizing—some of it regressive, like Heinroth's concept of sinfulness in insanity—and authentic recognition of the diversity and the claims of mental illness. The motive for confining them was reversed. Instead of being segregated in order that society might be protected from them, they were given asylum in order that they might be protected from a world that could be uncomprehending and hurtful.

The outlooks of the French physician Pinel and the English Quaker Tuke were in many respects different, though in humanitarian sense they were alike. Tuke insisted on the advantages of family life, in the calm and simple surroundings of a country retreat. Pinel put more weight on the reformed society of the mental hospital, which would enable the wildness and wickedness of acute insanity to subside into temperance and virtue. Neither, in the opinion of M. Foucault, realized that he was substituting one kind of restraint for another.

*　　　*　　　*

Since the Age of Reason came to a close the face of psychiatry has changed; no one could doubt that it has changed for the better. But how much of this change is the work of doctors and how much the product of the *Zeitgeist*, or rather of social and technological movements working powerfully on the course of human affairs? This is a common question, inviting a partisan or a philosophical answer. M. Foucault, as a philosopher-historian with some animus against doctors, would have no hesitation about his reply. His brilliant book, erudite, but overloaded with antithesis and abstruse generalizations, is the most original contribution that has been made to the wretched story of unreason in the Age of Reason. Carried to a later period, his studies might illuminate problems that have contemporary urgency.

2

PHILIPPE PINEL AND THE ENGLISH

PINEL IS remembered today because he showed that cruelty and neglect play no part—except a shameful one—in the care of the mentally ill. This was indeed his greatest achievement, and it is right that he should be honoured as one of those 'sainted pioneers' who relieve the miseries of humanity. But he has other claims to our respect and interest. He was, in his intellectual outlook as well as in his humane impulses, a product of the Age of Enlightenment, a younger brother of the Encyclopaedists, and like them he was indebted at some crucial points to English influence and example.

In the second edition of Pinel's *Traité Médico-Philosophique sur l'Aliénation Mentale* [28] there is a passage which I should like to quote:

In medicine everybody tends to vaunt the results of his own experience and to quote only the facts which support it. But if experience is to provide an authentic and conclusive basis for any method of treatment, then it must be derived from a large number of patients, on whom observations have been made with extreme care, according to a fixed and regular plan, and repeated for some years on exactly the same lines: favourable and unfavourable results must both be reported equally and the respective numbers of each given. In other words, it must depend on an application of the theory of probability, which has been so happily used in studying other matters of importance to society. If methods of treating disorder are to be solidly based, they must henceforward depend on the results of applying this theory of probability: otherwise medicine cannot take on the character of a true science.'

How obvious all that is, and how often the warning has had to be repeated. The history of therapeutic efforts and fashions, controversies, successes and disappointments in psychiatry might have been less jerky if Pinel's principles had been heeded. It is still a valid charge against psychiatry that its most characteristic methods of treatment, the psychological, have not been appraised by the method which Pinel judged essential [28].

'A continual comparison must be made of the proportion that obtains between recoveries and admissions, at different times in the same place or in different hospitals over the same period of time. If the comparison is to be sound, several requirements must have been satisfied: namely, extreme care in supervising the manner in which registers are kept and tables constructed; regular notes compiled

This paper was read to the Section of Psychiatry with the Section of History of Medicine of the Royal Society of Medicine in February 1955. It is reprinted from the *Proceedings of the Royal Society of Medicine*, (August 1955), **48**, 581–6.

with particular detail on those patients who leave the hospital apparently recovered; and precise figures for the number of recoveries, and relapses, and, of course, failures. The elementary mathematics of probability should be applied to the analysis of these data.'

How did Pinel come to attach so much importance to this use of the theory of probability? The reasons, I think, are both particular and general. He had been bred in the tradition of the liberal arts and especially the quadrivium: mathematics and philosophy were his chief sustenance as schoolboy and during the formative years, from 17 to 22, which he spent in the seminary at Lavaur. When he turned from the Church to medicine, mathematics provided him with his daily bread. At Toulouse and later at Montpellier he gave lessons in mathematics: and after he had removed to Paris in 1778 he chose the same means of livelihood. He could have begun to practise, but the intrigues which he noted, with aversion, among the members of his profession in the capital, and his poverty and comparative youth, made him prefer to meet his needs by teaching and medical journalism. It was not until 1785 that he gave up the lessons in mathematics; and from his letters it can be inferred that he did not regard them, any more than his translations and editorial labours, as hack work. His interest in mathematics was therefore keen, and his knowledge probably commensurate. He consorted at any rate with d'Alembert and other men of distinction in mathematics: he was the friend of Condorcet, whom he helped to hide at Mme Vernet's during the Terror; and the bent of his mind is shown by the title of his Master's thesis: 'On the certainty which the study of mathematics instils into the judgment of scientific problems.'

When Pinel studied at Montpellier [1] Barthez was teaching there and Boissier de Sauvages had not long retired. Vitalist doctrines were put forward with versatile brilliance and convincing dogmatism, as Pinel tells us in his description of Barthez as a teacher, but he also tells us of his own preference at that time for the mechanistic or mathematical approach to physiology and medicine which derived from such men as Borelli and Baglivi, Hoffman and Jurin. But his preference was discriminating. In his *Nosographie Philosophique* [29] he wrote, apropos of de Sauvages:

'What gratuitous assertions! One cannot read them without disgust if one's taste has been purified by the study of geometry. . . . Are we not entitled to think that the cultivation of the exact sciences has a happy influence on the study of medicine leading to a surer tact and discernment in distinguishing true observations from those which are equivocal or obscure. But I must add that the principles of the exact sciences cannot be applied unmodified to the course and treatment of disease. All the efforts of Boerhaave, Pitcairne, Jurin and others during the last century have only made one realize how vain were their claims, apart from some of Borelli's work and the physiomathematical theories of sight and hearing.'

And, appealing to the judgment of mathematicians, he quotes the well-known passage in which d'Alembert had ridiculed the '*médicins algébristes*' who treated the human body as a very simple machine.

10

It is evident that Pinel was not in the camp of the followers of Stahl, nor happy among the iatro-physicists: but he betrayed a strong leaning to the latter during his earlier professional years. Between 1787 and 1792 he published a number of papers on the application of mathematics to the mechanism of bony dislocation, and during the same period he prepared his annotated translation of Baglivi's works.

Now although Baglivi had been elected to the Royal Society, I have so far brought no evidence that English influences acted upon Pinel directly. Indirectly English influence was, of course, great. Isaac Newton had given that impetus towards quantitative studies in every branch of knowledge which was powerful in scientific thought during the eighteenth century. The French humanists, in their reaction against Descartes, derived views from Locke and other English and Scottish empiricists which influenced the humanitarian movements of which Pinel's reform was an example. And, as d'Alembert pointed out, it was from such sources that the distrust of systems and facile explanations took its origin [4].

'The physicists must guard above all against seeking to account for what is outside his grasp. He must distrust this passion for explaining everything which Descartes introduced into physics. . . . Facts, and no verbiage, that is the great rule. . . . But in banishing this mania for explaining everything, we are far from condemning either the spirit of conjecture, which in its cautious discernment often leads to discoveries; or the spirit of analogy, which with wise audacity penetrates what Nature seems to wish to conceal and anticipate facts before perceiving them.'

The sense of the first part of this extract was reiterated over and over by Pinel: it is his weakness that he could pay little regard to the spirit of the latter part.

But Pinel had made a more immediate contact with English writings and outlook. While at Montpellier he became friendly with an English doctor studying there, and learnt English from him [23]. Thenceforward he read English medical writings attentively, as his references to British works and journals testify. More significant, he translated Cullen's *Institutions of Medicine*, relating them constantly to the teaching of Boerhaave and Sydenham, and translated also a selection of papers from the *Philosophical Transactions of the Royal Society*. The introductions he wrote to the three volumes of this translation for which he was responsible, and the articles he chose to include, are indicative of the mathematical bent.

In the introduction to the volume on Medicine and Surgery [25], which appeared in 1791, he wrote:

'Medicine and Surgery would have always had the first place among the natural sciences if they had been treated with the same thoroughness as they are in the *Philosophical Transactions*. In the studies reported there, observations are rigorously marshalled. . . . The papers are valuable because the authors have limited themselves to reporting facts and the inferences that can legitimately be drawn from these, without wandering off into vague theories and conjectural systems.'

And in the Avertissement prefixed to the volume on Anatomy and Physiology [24] he deplores how men of inexact mind, who prefer brilliant hypotheses

11

and the sterile verbiage of metaphysics, have held up the progress of physiology: but, he goes on,

'Certain Memoirs in the *Philosophical Transactions* serve as a remedy for this malady of the mind, which has been the cause of so many errors. I have tried to make these memoirs more widely known, as much for their firm logic and experimental rigour as for the novelty and importance of the facts they report.'

Among the articles he selected are several concerned with vital statistics. Thus in the Anatomy volume he publishes a long extract, with tables, bearing on the disproportion between male and female births; and in the Medicine volume he translates a lengthy paper on the same subject taken in conjunction with statistics of death and accidents after confinement, to determine the chances of survival. After another paper of demographic interest, he wrote:

'I thought I ought to present first this interesting research on population, public health, and the means of determining the growth or decline of nations. The English seem further advanced than any other people in calculations of mortality, which have been made among them with the greatest precision, and from which they have been able to draw very useful conclusions. . . . It is much to be desired that these studies, hitherto so neglected in France, should now be cultivated with zeal.'

His zeal, indeed, for making these papers known was so great that he reproduced two of them—Dr White's 'Observations on the Tables of Mortality in York', and Dr Percival's similar 'Observations' in Manchester, published six years earlier—twice over, in separate volumes. Both the papers were evidently translated afresh for the Medicine volume, which appeared a year after the Anatomy and Physiology volume, for there are between the two translations many differences of minor detail. It would seem that Pinel, who was notoriously absent-minded, forgot that he had included these articles in the 1790 volume and in his eagerness to set them before his colleagues put himself to the trouble of turning them into French twice over.

In none of these papers is there any sophisticated mathematical treatment of the data. They carry us back, not to Halley or De Moivre, but to Graunt and Petty, and Gregory King. Pinel makes no reference to his fellow-countryman, Deparcieux, nor in this context to Laplace, d'Alembert, Lagrange, Condorcet or other illustrious Frenchmen who applied the mathematics of probability to social and scientific problems. Although he selects several statistical articles on the mortality of smallpox and the evidence that inoculation is beneficial, he does not refer to Daniel Bernoulli's famous memoir, nor to the notable contributions to the same subject by Trembley, d'Alembert and Laplace [18, 33]. Evidently mathematical arguments interested him little for their own sake but he responded warmly to the promise that by calculating probabilities and departures from probability the efficacy of treatment for particular diseases might be firmly determined. There are passages in his writings which echo or paraphrase the eloquent and prescient statements in which Condorcet in the '*Discours Préliminaire*' of his *Essai*, and Laplace in the Introduction to his *Théorie Analytique des Probalilités*,

12

proclaimed the advantages of applying statistics to the social as well as to the physical sciences:

'The calculation of probabilities can make us estimate the advantages and defects of methods that are employed in the less exact sciences. Thus, to find out the best among various treatments used for a disease, it is sufficient to try each of them on the same number of patients, keeping all the circumstances perfectly identical. The superiority of the most helpful treatment will become more and more manifest as the number of patients increases, and calculation will reveal the corresponding degree of probability that will be beneficial' [20].

Pinel [28] with an excess of confidence, assures us that 'the fundamental principle of the calculation of probability will always be easy and simple to apply: one will only have to make in each hospital, where the criteria of cure and failure have been worked out, a simple enumeration of the cases falling into these two groups.... Such an analysis, carried out in relation to treatment at the Salpêtrière, shows how experimental medicine can advance firmly and steadily by means of a statistical study of probabilities; but medicine will forfeit this advantage if regard is paid only to favourable outcomes.'

Pinel underrated the difficulties and arrived at some mistaken conclusions from his simple calculation of percentages, but his basic principle was sound. He particularly avoided the mistake of omitting failures and including relapsed patients as though they were new ones admitted during the period reported—a potent source of error even in our own time. He passed on his enlightened views to his pupil and friend, Esquirol [12], who wrote:

'There are honest and sincere doctors who do not like statistics. Have they sufficiently considered that the sciences of observation cannot advance except by statistics?... I like statistics in medicine, because I am convinced of their usefulness;'

and who bore witness to his faith by the figures that he provided annually from Charenton and the inquiry he made into the supposed increase in the number of insane persons in France [9, 11]. Moreover, many of Pinel's non-medical contemporaries knew of his statistical efforts: thus Cuvier spoke of them appreciatively in his report to the Institute on the progress of the Natural Sciences between 1789 and 1807 [3].

But Pinel's statistical example and precepts bore dubious fruit. Mental hospitals did, it is true, begin to publish annual statistics, but the analysis of the figures showed those errors which he had deplored—prejudice, sophistry and uncritical claims. The grossest examples of this occurred in the United States where, as Albert Deutsch [5] has described, therapeutic optimism went hand in hand with careless treatment of numerical data during the first half of the nineteenth century. In England Burrows was an example of the same irresponsible pretensions, and it was not until the 'forties that William Farr [13, 14] and then Dr John Thurnam [32] of the Retreat examined and reprobated the methods of calculating recoveries that had been employed. It would be tempting to digress here in order to examine the contribution of these two men, and particularly of Thurnam, towards putting the published statistics of mental disorder on a good footing. Farr's outspoken and vigorous

13

onslaught was along a wide front, and deserves to be re-read. But limiting myself to what concerns Pinel, I must record that Thurnam, though well acquainted with Esquirol's use of statistics, evidently knew Pinel's work only from the first edition of the *Traité* [27], in which statistical matters receive but the briefest mention. He consequently makes only slight and inaccurate references to Pinel's efforts in this field, and it must be conceded that he goes far beyond Pinel in the careful analysis of his figures: he had, of course, much ampler data to draw upon, and the guidance of men like Farr and Quetelet. Thurnam's book appeared in 1845; Pliny Earle [6, 7] somewhat later (1875 and 1887) wrote a correspondingly critical examination of mental hospital statistics for American psychiatrists. Thereafter the form of statistical tables improved; no superintendent claimed that 90 per cent of his patients were cured; and the mental hospital figures remained for the most part undistorted—and unquarried. At intervals, however, claims have been put forward for this or that method of treatment, which have betrayed the erroneous habits of mind which Pinel tried to correct. If the rules he laid down had been followed, we should have been in less doubt about the efficacy of some methods of physical treatment introduced more than a century after his time, and we are still woefully troubled because psychotherapeutic methods have not been evaluated in accordance with the requirements he stipulated. It need hardly be said that Pinel with all his fervour in 'moral' treatment was cool in appraising remedies [29]:

'It is true of mania as of many other disorders: if there is an art in administering drugs, there is an even greater art in knowing how to do without them on occasion.'

It is hard to say whether Pinel's teaching on the use of statistics affected directly the outlook or practice of his successors, apart from Esquirol. The statistical method was brought to bear on many problems of nosology and pathology, but P. C. A. Louis and others who tilled this field owed nothing directly to Pinel, as far as I know, and the same is very likely true of those in England, like Sir Henry Holland [17], who expected much from medical statistics. Holland, in his 'Essay on Medical Evidence', writes about pitfalls in judging the value of treatment and about the need for numerical inquiry in language which reads like a paraphrase of Pinel, but although it is likely enough that Holland, who spent so much time abroad, was acquainted with Pinel and perhaps attended his lectures, he makes no reference to him in this connexion.

Another feature of Pinel's outlook was his insistence on the value of such psychology as was then available. Locke and his follower Condillac, were the two men to whom he most often appealed as sure guides in the study of the insane [26]:

'Can one describe the symptoms of insantiy if one has not analysed with Locke and Condillac the functions of human understanding?' . . . 'So I had to retrace my steps and study the writings of our modern psychologists, Locke, Harris, Condillac, Smith, Stewart.'

14

Stewart was, of course, Dugald Stewart; Smith, less obviously, Adam Smith. No doubt at the salon of Madame Helvétius, which Pinel frequented, he heard recollections of Adam Smith who had associated with Helvétius, Turgot and Quesnay during the time he lived in Paris as bear leader to the young Duke of Buccleuch; it is evident, moreover, that Pinel was acquainted with the 'Theory of Moral Sentiments', and was much taken with the conception of sympathy as the universal source of moral feeling and emotion that is there put forward. His friend, the widow of Condorcet, translated this work, and it is her version, published in 1798, that Pinel cites in the Traité.

What I have said so far suggests, I think, that Pinel received more from England than England from him, and that what he got was sometimes first-hand, but more often at one remove, mediated through Condillac and other *philosophes* and mathematicians of his own country. At all events the stamp of Locke and of the English pioneers of political arithmetic was on him. He was well versed moreover in the English and Scottish medical writings of his time. This was especially true of the writers on insanity, whom he quotes frequently, and of Cullen, whom he translated.

For Cullen he expressed much admiration, and some sharp criticism, as he did for Boerhaave. For Sydenham his admiration was greater, and his criticism milder. Sigerist [31] has pointed out how closely his views of disease followed those of the great Englishman. It is not usual now to regard Pinel's views on general medicine any more respectfully than one would those of a contemporary psychiatrist. But specialism was not then what it is now, and besides being the most eminent alienist in France, Pinel was also one of the two most eminent physicians and teachers in Paris. In a memoir which appeared in the *Lancet* [19] a few months after his death, his *Nosographie Philosophique* is described a 'a work which became a classical one not only in France but almost in all Europe and which caused him to be regarded as one of the most imposing authorities in medicine'. That this was not uttered in the spirit of obituary flattery is clear from many other testimonies, during his lifetime and since [15, 22, 30]. The *Nosographie Philosophique* is a remarkable book, whose Introduction shows clearly how Pinel valued observation and distrusted theory, how he ranged with confidence through the whole field of European medicine, and rejected among much eighteenth century lumber the illusory efforts at a Linnaean classification of disease. He harked back constantly to Hippocrates, whose works he had read systematically with his friend Chaptal when they were young men together at Montpellier, and he extolled the exact sciences, particularly geometry, as purifying agents in medical thought. We have moved so far in clinical medicine since Pinel's day that the actual content of his *Nosographie* has little interest—far less than the content of his *Traité de l'Aliénation Mentale*, for we have not moved quite so far in psychiatry in the last 150 years. But the 'Nosographie' reminds us of his cool and critical intellect, whereas in psychiatry we are more apt to dwell on his warm heart and courageous humanity.

I would add only a few words about the effects of Pinel's Treatise upon

English thought and practice. Because the York Retreat was founded in complete ignorance of Pinel's work at the Bicêtre, and exerted such a powerful effect thereafter on public opinion and asylum practice in England, we are prone to think that Pinel's influence upon people in this country was negligible. I doubt if this view can be sustained. As early as 1803 [8] an anonymous writer in the *Edinburgh Review* thought Pinel's work well enough known to need to be decried: and a scurrilous, chauvinistic job the reviewer made of it. Then in 1806 Davis's translation of the *Traité* was published at Sheffield. After Pinel's death, lengthy accounts of him appeared; a full translation of Pariset's *Éloge* [22], for example, ran through the *Medical Times* [21], from June to September 1845. More important, English writers on mental illness wrote of him, as they did of Esquirol, with admiration, and there is good reason for believing that the 'non-restraint' movement owed something to Englishmen's notion of his benevolent aims. In June 1838 R. Gardiner Hill [16] delivered a lecture on 'Total Abolition of Personal Restraint in the Treatment of the Insane'. In it he described at length what Pinel did at the Bicêtre, and the horrible conditions that had obtained before. 'I turn with pleasure from this picture to the more humane and enlightened system which followed the attempt of the intelligent and immortal Pinel, and in which the Quakers took the lead in this country in their admirable Institution, the Retreat. . . . Still, however, much remains to be done: and it is mainly with the view of stating what may yet be accomplished, and not merely stating, but proving that statement by incontestable examples, that I now address you. I wish to complete that which Pinel began. I assert then in plain and distinct terms, that in a properly constructed building, with a sufficient number of suitable attendants, restraint is never necessary, never justifiable, and always injurious, in all cases of Lunacy whatever.' Sentiments expressed less vehemently but to the same effect were stated by Connolly [2]. It was not, I think, Pinel's opinions but his practice, that made these reformers feel that they were travelling on his road. Before him men like Daquin and Chiarugi, and indeed the writers of antiquity, had extolled kindness in dealing with the insane, but it was his signal merit that he demonstrated its efficacy beyond all dispute. Gardiner Hill, likewise, and Connolly, had to demonstrate the truth of what they claimed for treatment without mechanical restraint, and to fight for it.

The man who knew Pinel best called him the La Fontaine of Medicine—'the same nicety of observation, the same quickness in seeing relationships, the same knowledge of the human heart, the same simplicity and good nature, the same disinterestedness' [10]. Esquirol went on, after making this affectionate comparison, to call him 'one of the luminaries of our time'—an exemplar of that troubled and distinguished age which produced men like Lavoisier and Laplace, Bichat, Fourier and Lamarck. He was also, we may well conclude, an exemplar of the qualities that make up the character of the good psychiatrist —qualities of intellect as much as of character, that are required now just as they were when Pinel entered on his charge at the Bicêtre in 1793.

REFERENCES

1 CHARVET, S. 'Esquisse d'une Étude sur Philippe Pinel,' Thèse de Montpellier, No. 47, 1881.

2 CONOLLY, J. *The Treatment of the Insane Without Mechanical Restraints*, London, 1856.

3 CUVIER, G. *Histoire des Progrès des Sciences Naturelles Depuis 1789*, Paris, 1808.

4 D'ALEMBERT, J. *Discours Préliminaire de L'Encyclopédie*, Paris, 1754.

5 DEUTSCH, A. *The Mentally Ill in America*, New York, 1937.

6 EARLE, P. Annual Report of Northampton State Hospital, Massachusetts, Boston, 1875.

7 — *The Curability of Insanity*, Philadelphia, 1887.

8 *Edinburgh Review*, 1803, **2**, 160.

9 ESQUIROL, J. E. D. *Mém. Acad. Méd. Paris* (sect. de médecine), 1828, **1**, 32.

10 — *Mém. Acad. Méd. Paris* (partie historique), 1828, **1**, 224.

11 — *Ann. Hyg. publ., Paris*,1830, **4**, 332.

12 — *Des Maladies Mentales Considérées sous les Rapports Médical, Hygiénique et Médico-légal*, Paris, 1838.

13 FARR, W. *On the Statistics of English Lunatic Asylums and the Reform of their Public Management*, London, 1839.

14 — *J. R. statist. Soc.*, 1841, **4**, 17.

15 FLEURY, M. de. *Ann. méd-psychol.*, 1927, **85**, 72.

16 HILL, R. G. *Total Abolition of Personal Restraint in the Treatment of the Insane*, London, 1839.

17 HOLLAND, H. *Chapters on Mental Physiology*, London, 1852.

18 JOHN, V. *Geschichte der Statistik.* Stuttgart, 1884.

19 *Lancet*, 1827, **12**, 262.

20 LAPLACE, P. S. *Théorie Analytique des Probabilités*, 2nd ed., Paris, 1814.

21 *Med. Times, Lond.*, 1845, **12**, 227.

22 PARISET, E. *Mém. Acad. Méd. Paris* (partie historique), 1828, **1**, 189.

23 PINEL, C. *Gaz. hebd. Méd. Chir.*, 1859, **6**, 273.

24 PINEL, P. *Abrégé des Transactions Philosophiques de la Société Royale de Londres*, 6e partie, *Physiologie et Physique Animale*, Paris, 1790.

25 — *Abrégé des Transactions Philosophiques de la Société Royale de Londres*, 7e partie, *Médecine et Chirurgie*, Paris, 1791.

26 — (an 8) *Mém. Soc. méd. Emulations*, 1799, **3**, 1.

27 — (an 9) *Traité Médico-Philosophique sur l'Aliénation ou la Manie*, Paris, 1801.

28 — *Traité Médcio-philosophique sur l'Aliénation Mentale*, 2nd ed., Paris, 1809.

29 — *Nosographie Philosophique ou Méthode de l'Analyse Appliquée à la Médecine*, 6th ed., Paris, 1818.

30 SEMELAIGNE, R. *Les Grands Aliénistes Français*, vol. 1, Paris; 1894.

31 SIGERIST, H. E. *Grosse Aerzte*, Munich, 1933.

32 THURNAM, J. *Observations and Essays on the Statistics of Insanity, Including an Inquiry into the Causes Influencing the Results of Treatment*, London, 1845.

33 TODHUNTER, I. *A History of the Mathematical Theory of Probability*, London, 1865.

3

J. C. REIL'S CONCEPTS OF
BRAIN FUNCTION

REIL HAS long been a name and nothing more in English-speaking countries—the forgotten eponym of an island, like Juan Fernandez or Baffin. This
shadowy fame was not what his contemporaries expected for him: nor did he
foresee it: in his farewell address to the University of Halle he reviewed his
life's work and recalled that it would be hard to find a cultivated region of the
earth in which there was not a pupil of his practising or teaching: and he
gloried in being one of those whose ideas had produced a scientific revolution
in medicine. Competent scholars, from Johannes Müller to Diepgen and
Neuberger, have indeed thought him an outstanding man—not only for his
anatomical studies but for his physiological speculations. He is in any case a
significant figure, for in the development of his ideas we can see the transition
from the era of Willis to the era of Bell and Magendie. Reil's inconsistencies
and mistakes epitomize the difficulties of that transition: some of them are
still with us.

The indifference with which his work has been treated by English writers
has doubtless been a consequence of his cloudy philosophical leanings and his
reputation as an advocate of cruelty in the treatment of the insane. The French
on the other hand were alive to his achievement, and the discriminating
appraisal by Jourdan which appeared in the *Journal Universel des Sciences
Médicales* in 1817 acclaimed his contribution to the advancement of nosology,
psychiatry and anatomy.

Reil's professional life was bound up with the University of Halle, where he
received his medical education and occupied the Chair of Medicine for
twenty-three years. His efforts to study and interpret the functions of the
brain were clearly dependent on the influence of the tradition and teachers of
that University. It had been founded, less than a century before he entered it,
by the Pietists, who gave it an impetus and character impregnated with the

First delivered as part of an Anglo-American Symposium on *The History and Philosophy of
Knowledge of the Brain and its Functions* given in London in July 1957. It is reprinted from
a book of a similar title published by Blackwell Scientific Publications in 1958 under the
editorship of Dr F. N. L. Poynter, pp. 154–66.

Puritan ethos which, as Professor R. K. Merton's sociological analysis has shown, promoted scientific activity in the seventeenth and eighteenth centuries. The first two professors of medicine were Stahl and Friedrich Hoffman; one of the early professors of philosophy was Christian Wolff, the rationalist protégé of Leibnitz; and among Reil's contemporaries as professors at Halle were Kurt Sprengel in the faculty of medicine, and the philosophers Steffens and Schleiermacher. These men were his friends, who played a considerable part in moulding his ideas. Steffens in particular, whom Reil had been active in bringing to Halle from Copenhagen, was responsible for much of Reil's later attachment to 'Naturphilosophie'. Reil's activities as a physician also brought him into contact with some notable patients, including Goethe, who admired him 'zugleich als Praktiker, als denkender, wohlgesinnter und anschauender Mann'.

The outward events of his life can be briefly recalled. He was appointed Professor at the age of twenty-eight: he established his reputation by his *Memorabilia Clinica* (1792), his essay on the vital force (1795), his anatomical studies of the crystalline lens and the nerves (1796), his treatise on fevers (1797–1815), his psychiatric texts (1803 and 1805), and his anatomical studies of the brain (1807–8). When in 1806 the University of Halle was closed by Napoleon, Reil used the ensuing two years of freedom from teaching to carry through his dissections of the cerebellum and other cerebral structures. As a fervent patriot he found the atmosphere of Halle intolerable during Jerome Bonaparte's rule, and he accepted a call to Berlin, but he was unhappy there, because of antagonism between him and Hufeland and Langermann. In the War of Liberation which followed the retreat from Moscow Reil took over the organization of field hospitals: he wrote vivid, angry reports describing the terrible conditions to which the wounded were exposed: it was in the course of his duties, in charge of the lazarets after the battle of Leipzig, that he contracted typhus and died. He was a many-sided man, strongly conscious of his obligations as teacher and citizen, energetic in practical affairs, and with a philosophic bent.

His views about the functions of the brain appear first in his *Tractatus de Polycholia* (1783) and there bespeak essentially the traditional Galenic views: thus melancholia is due to viscid biliary juice clogging the vessels in the interior of the brain and compressing the nervous tubules; 'Portiuncula peccantis materiae, parva quidem sed eo majori acrimonia armata ad intimum cerebri meditullium penetrat, stimulat, perversos motus inducit, animae functiones subvertit et humores superiora versus invitat. Num tenuior pars nervorum canaliculos ingrediatur fluidoque nerveo misceatur?' The emphasis here on the centrum ovale or meditullium as the seat of mental functions and on the flow of nervous fluid through channels in the nerves attest the influence of Willis, with whose works he was well acquainted.

The same conceptions appear nine years later in his *De Crisibus Morborum Nervosorum*, now with strong evidence of the influence of Albrecht von Haller. In the final analysis, he asserts, all diseases are nervous diseases, the nerves contain all the strength and animal essence of the body. 'Nervi sane solae corporis humani partes sint quae omnem vim essentiamque animalem continent.'

In 1794, however, his elaborate work on Gemeingefühl—coenaesthesis—showed an advance in his thought. He emphasized that perception of bodily events is a cerebral function mediated through the nerves: 'es ist wahrscheinlich, dass die pulpösen Spitzen der Nerven, womit dieselben in die organischen Theile sich endigen, und die in Verhältniss desjenigen Theils, in welchem sie sich endigen, die äussersten Fortsetzungen vom Gehirn sind, die Eindrücke aufnehmen und den Anfang unserer Gefühle hervorbringen.' The qualities of the brain determine a man's temperament: feelings related to the state of the body are coloured by the degree of irritability of the brain when it receives messages from the organs. Older ideas about the effect upon temperament of black bile, of tension and atony, overlook the essential cerebral element in the whole process which has sensory information at one end and character, passions and habits at the other. Also, Reil insisted, cerebral stimulation exerts an effect throughout the body: 'die Thätigkeiten des Seelenorgans sind gleichsam ein zufälliger Reiz aller Organe des ganzen Körpers. Schmerz erregt die Thätigkeit des Seelenorgans, das auf alle Theile zurückwirkt.' This theme had been also developed by his pupil Büttner in a dissertation written under Reil's close direction.

The following year (1795), reporting his observations on the structure of the brain and nerves, he declared that every nerve has its own energy and independence; the brain is distinct, it is not just the site of origin of the nerves but is an organ with definite functions. Nothing is secreted in it which is to be distributed through the nerves, as though through channels.

Another concept, however, becomes very prominent in his writings, and his exposition of the matter has been regarded by Sudhoff as a classical contribution to medical thought. He was preoccupied with the great question of the nature of the living processes. He examined this closely in his monograph *Von der Lebenskraft*, in which the influence of Kant can be readily discerned. Reil veered towards the mechanist yet dynamic conceptions of Hoffman rather than the animism of Stahl (but this, of course, oversimplifies the standpoints of the two early Halle professors as well as the standpoint taken up by Reil). He held that all phenomena of the living animal body which are not ideas, or consequences of ideas, are derived from animal matter: the anima sensitiva had become a superfluous concept. Besides crude matter, as we become aware of it through our senses, there is a finer matter, subtle, easily movable and volatile (flüchtig) which flows in and out of various parts of the body: it may be oxygen (as John Mayow had in effect suggested, in language very close to Reil's), or electricity, or light. The simplest organic structure is the fibre—and the fibre is a type of the crystallization of animal matter; all fibres possess three qualities—excitability (Erregbarkeit), irritability (Reizbarkeit) and sensibility (Empfindlichkeit).

Although in this essay Reil was not concerned particularly with the functions of the nervous system, his later views are at many points fore-shadowed, especially his emphasis on physical and chemical changes in the nervous system, which ebb and flow regularly so long as healthy balance is maintained.

In the same year he expressed an opinion about the action of the brain as a whole to which he often subsequently turned. After dwelling like La Peyronie in 1741 and Koiter in 1573 on the evidence that the brain could continue to exercise all its functions, including mental operations, when its various parts had been damaged, he wrote 'there is no special part of the brain concerned with psychic functions'. 'Diese Erfahrungen bestätigen bei Rec. immerhin die Idee dass im Gehirn keine besondere Abteilung für einzelne Geistes-operationen vorhanden sind, welches ausserdem noch aus der ein-fachen Bauart des Gehirns wahrscheinlich wird.' This view inhibited him from considering localization with the ardour that he showed in his anatomical studies. Because of it he was driven to some awkward shifts: visual images, he said, for example, can originate in any part of the brain and are projected into the optic nerve. ('Wirkungen von Gehirnthätigkeiten die in irgendeinem unbestimmten Theil des Gehirns anfingen und zu einem bestimmten Nerven, zum Beispeil zum Sehnerven fortgesetzt würden.')

When Reil wrote his *Rhapsodien* in 1803 he based his advocacy of psycho-logical treatment upon his conception of brain function. The cure of insanity, he said, must be through psychological means— 'dies scheint aus der ganzen Einrichtung des Seelenorgans hervorzugehen'. Its mechanism is extremely complex, the dynamic balance of its parts varied.

Diese Beziehungen der Theile des Seelenorgans unter einander sind auf eine eben so bestimmte Vertheilung der Kräfte im Gehirn und dem gesammten Nerven-system gegründet. Wird dies Verhältnis gestört, so entstehen Dissonanzen, Sprünge, abnorme Vorstellungen, ähnliche Associationen, fixe Ideenreihen und inhen ent-sprechende Triebe und Handlungen.

The brain could be influenced by asthenia or asthenic states in the vegeta-tive system, and consequently by drugs which allay excitement or arouse from torpor; but drugs cannot act directly on mental activity.

Nun werden aber die Kräfte durch zwechmässig erregte Thätigkeiten abgeändert. Denn sie sind Resultate des Stoffs und der Struktur; und die Natur wechselt den Stoff wenn sie wirkt, ändert also durch ihre Thätigkeiten die Qualität und Quan-tität der Kräfte ab . . . Wenn daher die alienirten Kräfte des Gehirns in Wahnsinn rectificirt werden sollen, so . . . kann dasselbe . . . durch keine anderen Erregungs-mittel in seine specifisch eigenthümliche Action gebracht werden, als durch solche in deren Gefolge Gefühle, Vorstellungen, Triebe u.s.w. entstehn. Dies geschieht durch die psychische Kurmethode.

Reil's detailed argument indicates his acceptance of the view that the brain's psychological functions have to be integrated into a harmonious concert, or temperature as he calls it.

Dadurch wird der Intemperatur der Reizbarkeit des Gehirnes eine andere Rich-tung gegeben. So sind wir im Stande Gleichgewicht und normales Kraftverhältnis in den verschiedenen Getrieben des Seelenorgans, Einklang und richtige Beziehung (rapport) derselben zu einander . . . wiederherzustellen.

To the brain as a whole he ascribes a special energy, and a power of integrating varied bodily activities.

Es (das Gehirn) reiht die zerstreuten Organe des Körpers an seine Aeste auf, verbindet sie durch untergeordnete Heerde zu eignen Getrieben und sammelt diese endlich alle in seinen grossen Mittelheerd auf. Hier ist der Knoten der Organisation geschürzt durch welchen sie sich als Naturzweck über die leblose Natur erhebt.

If, however, the dynamic balance in the brain is disturbed, the varied functions cease to act together, and a whole world of phenomena become manifest which we did not know we had it in us to produce.

Sobald dies Verhältnis der dynamischen Temperatur in Seelenorgan wankt, so wankt auch die normale Receptivität für äussere Gegenstände; . . . einzelne Getriebe wirken für sich, Nebelsterne dringen aus der Tiefe zur Klarheit hervor, und es wird in uns eine Welt sichtbar, von der wir nicht ahndeten dass sie in uns vorhanden sey.

He assumes that in an area of the brain which is active there is a turgor which accompanies chemical activity, and that there is possibly an oscillation of the fibres. The brain may, on the other hand, be deprived of the necessary materials for its metabolism. In either case symptoms may ensue. Reil describes a system in which normally messages from the sense-organs and viscera reach the brain, and promote ideas, perceptions and feelings there ('die Vorstellungen breiten sich im Gehirn aus nach den Gesetzen der Association') which in turn are followed by impulses sent out along the motor nerves (Bewegungsnerven). It is remarkable that although Reil was certainly familiar with Soemmerring's views, and those of Prochaska and other speculators about the sensorium commune, he passes the matter by silently. Ten years earlier he had written: 'As to a special sensorium commune limited to a small part of the brain, I think it exists only in people's imagination. . . .'

In the Rhapsodies Reil is struggling with the old problem of how to relate mental with physical events. His standpoint on this is more clearly expressed in the fourth volume of his Fieberlehre. He declares roundly that the mind must not be thought of as essentially different from the body but that there is a mutual interaction. The detailed structure of the brain, the proportion of its constituent parts, its metabolism (die Lebens- und Vegetationsprocesse im Gehirn, der Wechsel des Stoffes durch den sie sich offenbaren) and the relation of all these to its mental activity are for the most part still unknown, he insists, but we may suppose that there is a single organ or organism, which develops in two directions: physiological and psychological.

Then he draws some physiological inferences. The cerebral peduncles and their continuation over the pons into the cord are the meeting-place of all the nerves of the body: at most the olfactory can be excepted. The reticular carfax of the nervous system seems to be, he says, the focus of all nervous activity. Though brain and nerves are conjoined for reciprocal communication, each nerve has an independent life of its own, made possible by the quality of the nervous medulla which is secreted from the neurilemma. The more a nerve has ganglia along its course, as the sympathetic chain has, the more independent of the brain it seems to become.

He reviews briefly the chemical findings of Fourcroy and the anatomical findings of Vicq d'Azyr and Soemmerring, but sadly recalls that at the end of their labours the nervous system was still a physiological puzzle. Though he makes appreciative reference to Gall, he adopts none of his views about localization of physiological functions in the cortex, nor his ill-advised classification of mental faculties. He prefers other formulations, such as his favourite picture of the nervous system as an anatomically independent and complete entity. It is our real body: the rest is the nutritive, protective bark around this delicate, precious pith.

The brain has four main functions: it initiates voluntary movement; it receives coenaesthetic sensations which are transformed into ideas (Vorstellungen); it perceives external objects; it has the power of imagination, which includes remembering and fantasy. A change in the internal condition of the brain is the proximate and adequate cause of all mental disorders. So long as the brain is able to preserve balance in its vital activities, abnormal stimuli can produce only illusions, and other phenomena which we recognize as deceptive: when the brain's balanced functions cease to act together, insight is lost, ideas do not follow the normal rule of association (in which he followed Hartley), and partial activities are set off by stimuli from the nerves, resulting in delusions and hallucinations. It is, he says in one of his numerous similes, as though everything is reflected in a distorted mirror. This mirror —the brain—is distorted and distorting because something has gone wrong in its chemistry and its organization; but alas, he adds in a familiar plaint of his, 'nun ist uns aber sowohl die normale als abnorme Mischung und Organisation des Gehirns an sich unbekannt'. Detectable changes in the structure of the brain can be found only in idiocy and dementia, on theoretical as well as empirical grounds they cannot be responsible for the bulk of mental disorder. Although Reil still lays great weight on the excitability of the nervous tissue in the brain, he subordinates this to integration and balance, which he stresses as the condition of normality.

In gesunden Zustande erregt eine Action des Seelenorgans und des übrigen Nervensystems eine andere nach einer festen Regel, die sich theils auf die nächste mechanische Verbindung der Theile des Nervensystems zu einem Ganzen, theils auf den Normalgrad der Vitalität seiner Theile gründet ... Wenn sich also die Temperatur der Reizbarkeit des Nervensystems, als eines Moments seiner normalen Association und Sympathie, ändert: so wird auch die Regel umgestossen, nach welcher die Theile desselben sich auf einander beziehen, auf einander einwirken und sich gegenseitig erregen, und statt derselben wird eine neue, abnorme Regel gesetzt.

After this came Reil's series of reports on the structure of the brain, in 1807 and 1808. He introduced the bald anatomical narrative with one of his boldest rhetorical flights. He extolled the brain as the organ in which all the mishaps of humanity, everything great and noble and everything small and bad, has its roots: and he proclaimed that in so far as the organization of the brain approaches that of the prototype eternally ordained for it, human reason approaches its prototype; but if the structure of the brain is incomplete, man sinks to the animal level and becomes the slave of sensuality. Man's reason is mirrored in the structure of the nervous system as God is in the structure of the cosmos. From this exalted passage he rises to a still higher plane:

staunend und ehrfurchtsvoll stehe ich vor diesem Heiligthum, das bey allem Leben und Weben, bey allem Thun und Treiben des Menschengeschlechts, von Anbeginn bis auf unsere Zeit sein geheimes Spiel mitgetrieben hat . . . Hier entsprang die Idee des Belveder'schen Apolls! Ohne dieses marmorweisse Gewölbe, das seine Bögen hoch über die Quellen des sinnlichen Lebens hinspannt, wäre Homer's Iliade, Keppler's Zoonomie der Gestirne nicht! Was in diesen maeandrischen Hallen unter denselben oscillirt, geht mit Blitzes-schnelle von Einem auf Alle über, versenkt den Einen als Seele in das All, und das All als Kraft in den Einen. . . .

And in a last fervid apostrophe he calls on Erato—the Muse, you will remember, of amorous poetry—to sharpen his gaze so that he may see the mysterious bridal bed where body and soul celebrate their nuptial orgies.

These bold flights are reminiscent of Robert Burton—'the most noble organ under heaven, the dwelling-house and seat of the soul, the habitation of wisdom, memory, judgment, reason, and in which man is most like unto God'. But descending from these exalted heights into the plain, Reil displays his real strength, in his matter-of-fact account of the structure of the cerebellum. On the functions of the cerebellum he is, however, silent. When he comes to the cerebral hemispheres, he stresses the peduncular system, stretching from the pyramids through the crura and the corona radiata to the frontal lobes, but he attaches even more importance to the basal ganglia. Near the optic thalami, he says, the great cerebral ganglion with its two portions conjoined is one of the most remarkable parts of the brain. But, by a rapid and fatal transition, he goes on to call it the source or the solar centre of the brain. In it is secreted a powerful and copious spirit or essence (Lebensgeist) which spreads out in all directions, gives every organ a feeling and reactive capacity which makes full vital activity possible. This passage, isolated in a sea of straightforward descriptive prose, is a relapse into the vitalism he had abjured when he was younger: one can understand the regret with which Hufeland and many German writers since then have noted the effects upon Reil's thought of Naturphilosophie during the last few years of his life. Its tenor is in striking contrast to the famous letter of Kant to Soemmerring ten years before, in which the philosopher distinguished between the possible location of the sensorium commune as the material structure making possible conscious representation of sensory impressions, and the fundamentally insoluble problem, as Kant saw it, of finding a local habitation for the mind.

The theme of integration is prominent, as in all Reil's speculations about the brain. Thus after describing the increasing complexity of the nervous system as one passes from molluscs and leeches to mammals, he asserts its essential unity: it has everywhere the same sort of basic chemistry and structure, the whole is like the parts, and something of the whole is implanted in every part. The whole is in a state of dynamic tension, which accounts for differentiated functions for different parts: the spherical structure of the brain bespeaks an opposition between contractile and expansive forces. These latter speculations are, of course, derived from Schelling and proved scientifically profitless.

The influence of Schelling, and of Steffens, continues to be painfully evident in Reil's subsequent writings on this matter, published in the Beiträge which he and Hoffbauer edited. The concepts of polarity, tension, individuality, potentiation, ideality and what he calls centricity are woven into a loosely expressed tissue of philosophical and biological speculation, in which it is often difficult to find an intelligible meaning. Comparisons drawn from astronomy are frequent, and spheres and foci are taken to be the universal type of material structure, in macrocosm and microcosm alike. But amid these philosophical excursions Reil expresses some views that are an advance on his earlier opinions. We cannot, he says in 1808, separate body and mind, they are in perfect parallelism: every mental activity is necessarily accompanied by an inconceivably rapid change in the brain which is not accessible to available means of observation. The brain can be regarded as an aggregate of many different structures, which are not independent but are subordinated to yield a unitary activity; only in disease or in dreaming can the separate parts function in isolation.

His evident devotion to holistic views is well illustrated in his remarks about the value of autopsy findings. In spite of the emphatic assertions of his demigod Haller regarding the necessity for examining the brains of the insane and comparing the findings with the mental abnormalities the patients had displayed, Reil declared categorically, in a review of Joseph Mason Cox's *Practical Observations on Insanity*, that psychiatric observations have been too closely directed to the affected brain, and have consequently not surveyed the total organism: autopsies are futile, because we know so little about the relation of mind and body that we could not interpret the findings.

This feeling of nescience about the detailed relation between mind and brain, appearing so frequently in his writings, bears witness to a frustrated preoccupation with the question rather than to a negative, sterile attitude of mind: it was at this time that he was pursuing his anatomical investigations, in the leisure forced upon him by the closing of the University. That he was working under difficulties can be guessed from the petulant outburst against Herr Langermann: 'I have not been able to investigate whether the fibres of the anterior commissure disintegrate in dilute hydrochloric acid into more delicate fibrils because a certain Herr Langermann, who is himself in danger of disintegrating in his own slime, got a police order against me, forbidding me to macerate tissues—in a place where streams of blood from the slaughter-house foul the public ways!' The inherent difficulties of his task were well known to him: earlier, at the end of his anatomical work on the crystalline lens (1794) he had written: 'In investigating the brain I have met the greatest difficulties and made the least progress.' And in 1809 he is still aware of the enormous problems. After a modest statement of what he believes he has achieved in unravelling the cerebral structures, he admits to gaps and defects in his account:

auch hier ist mir, wie beym kleinen Gehirn, die Verbindung der Windungen mit dem Kern dunkel geblieben. An der Enträthselung der Ganglienkette, die durchs Rückenmark heraufkömmt, von der hintersten bis zur vordersten Hirnhöhle durch die Axe des Gehirns fortgeht, nemlich des Grundes der vierten Hirnhöhle, der Vierhügel, Sehhügel und des gestreiften Gangliums bin ich fast verzweifelt.

But, he goes on, 'I have lately learnt a few tricks which will enable me, I hope, to clear this up too.'

It is something of a paradox that a man who was so painstaking an inquirer into the structure of the brain, and who used chemical methods for facilitating these studies, should have been sweeping in his guesses about the brain's functions and chemistry. But this was imposed on him after all by the state of knowledge in his time. Fourcroy and Vauquelin, with whose writings he was well acquainted, could not help him in his efforts to understand the metabolic processes. His contemporaries were still battering their heads at questions like the seat of the sensorium commune and the nature of the vis nervosa. In Italy Rolando, pursuing kindred aims to Reil's, declared that cerebral operations are true movements of the cerebral fibres, that the seat of the soul is in the medulla oblongata, and that the vis nervosa, or nervous fluid responsible for movement, is secreted in the cerebellum (which, like Reil, he conceived as a voltaic pile), while Chiarugi, an enlightened psychiatrist, was asserting that 'all modifications of the body are caused by the immediate action of the soul on the sensorium commune'; and in England Alexander Walker, the contentious opponent of Charles Bell, was of the opinion that the cerebellum is the organ of volition, and that 'the intensity of the intellectual functions is as the length of their organs and the permanence of these functions as the breadth of their organs'. Reil had at least passed beyond these echoes of Aristotle and the medieval scholars.

Reil was not an original thinker, nor an experimental physiologist: his philosophy was therefore second-hand, and his physiology conjectural. But he was critical: he did not, for example, embrace the diffuse Brownian doctrine of irritability, then so attractive to German physicians, and he was discriminating in his attitude towards Gall's theories: but his determined effort to steer a middle course between the vitalists and the materialists led to his unhappy adoption of Schelling's idealist system, with its analogizing key to every problem.

Reil aimed high. He wanted to penetrate the mysteries of form in living organs, and to relate form to function. He made very few experiments, but he reflected constantly on the nervous system. In his University and in the larger world men whom he admired had been long preoccupied with the peculiar features of vital activity: he tried to reduce the argument to scientific terms.

26

When Steffens, soon after his arrival in Halle, contested Reil's beliefs about the chemical determinants of organic form and activity, Reil answered that he had to make do with the explanations at hand: if he were offered better ones, he would not reject them. Unfortunately, Steffens offered him, in his philosophical system, an explanation which after much hesitation Reil adopted. That he hesitated is clear, from the sharp criticism he expressed in 1800. 'Faulty application of transcendental philosophy to medicine would, I fear, do more harm than good . . . we misuse our reason if we apply it to thinking out possibilities *ad lib.* and juggling with concepts that have no other proof of their objective reality than that they do not contradict one another.' If he fell into that error himself, it was a late aberration, influenced, probably, by the turmoil of his personal life during its closing years. The aberration represented, I think, mainly the same eagerness to utilize fresh ideas as leads many in our time to look to the concepts of, say, communication theory, to elucidate some aspects of cerebral activity. We turn to the language and analogies of electronic engineering, Reil turned to the analogies of electricity and mechanics. It is too early to tell whether we are more cautious in our borrowings than he was. If we compare him with his older contemporaries like Unzer, his merits are not diminished: it is when we set him alongside younger men, working on the same problems—Charles Bell, Flourens, Magendie—that his failings appear: failings derived from the legacy of eighteenth-century views and disputes in which he was brought up. They did not prevent him from making exact observations and just inferences, as in his demonstration that the sympathetic nervous system works independently and is concerned in the regulation of vegetative processes. Reil was a great anatomist and physician, an inexperienced but thoughtful psychiatrist, and he was an unresting theorist who propounded in about equal measure truths for which he had not full evidence and errors which were based on correct observations too boldly encompassed in a single formula.

REFERENCES

BRUGSCH, TH. 'Die Klinik in Halle (historisch),' *Sudhoffs Arch.*, 1928, **20**, 17–32.
DIEPGEN, P. *Geschichte der Medizin*, Band 2, 1. Hälfte, Berlin, De Gruyter, 1951.
D'IRSAY, S. 'Der philosophische Hintergrund der Nervenphysiologie im 17 und 18. Jahrhundert', *Sudhoffs Arch.*, 1928, **20**, 181–97
GREGOR, A. 'Johann Christian Reil', in Kirchhoff (ed.), *Deutsche Irrenärzte: Winzelbilder ihres Lebens und Wirkens*, Band 1, Berlin, Julius Springer, 1921.
JOURDAN, A. J. L. 'Notice historique sur Reil; *Journal Universel des Sciences Médicales*, 1817, **7**, 360–80.
MERTON, R. K. 'Science, Technology and Society in 17th Century England', In *Social Theory and Social Structure*, Glencoe, Free Press, 1949.
NEUBURGER, M. *Johann Christian Reil: Gedenkrede*, Stuttgart, Ferdinand Enke, 1913.
REIL, J. C. *Tractatus de Polycholia. Fragmenta Metaschematismi Polycholiae. Pars Posterior*, Halae, Sumtibus Orphanotrophei, 1783.
REIL, J. C. *Memorabilium Clinicorum Medio-Practicorum*, fasc. III, Halae, Impensis Curtianis; V. De Crisibus Morborum Nervosorum, 1792, p. 153.

REIL, J. C. *Rhapsodieen über die Anwendung der psychischen Curmethode auf Geisteszer-rüttungen*, Halle, In der Curtschen Buchhandlung, 1803.

REIL, J. C. *Ueber die Erkenntniss und Cur der Fieber. Besondere Fieberlehre*, vol. 4, *Nervenkrankheiten*, Zweite vermehrte rechtmässige Auflage, Halle, In der Curtschen Buchhandlung, 1805.

REIL, J. C. 'Fragmente über die Bildung des kleinen Gehirns im Menschen', *Arch. f. Physiologie*, 1807–8, **8**, 1–58, 273–304, 358–426; 1809, **9**, 129–35, 136–208, 485–524; 1812, **11**, 89–100.

REIL, J. C. *Kleine Schriften wissenschaftlichen und gemeinnützigen Inhalts*, Halle, Im Verlage der Curtschen Buchhandlung, 1817.

REIL, J. C. and HOFFBAUER, J. C. *Beiträge zur Beförderung einer curmethode auf psychischem Wege*, Band 1, Halle, In der Curtschen Buchhandlung, 1808.

REIL, J. C. and HOFFBAUER, J. C. *Beiträge zur Beförderung einer curmethode auf psychischem Wege*, Band 2, Halle, In der Curtschen Buchhandlung, 1812.

STEFFENS, H. *Johann Christian Reil: Eine Denkschrift*, Halle, In der Curtschen Buchhandlung, 1815.

TEMKIN, O. 'The Philosophical Background of Magendie's Physiology', *Bull. Hist. Med.*, 1946, **20**, 10–35.

4

HENRY MAUDSLEY: HIS WORK AND INFLUENCE

THE KEEN pleasure I felt when I was invited to deliver this lecture arose not only from the honour which it conferred, but also because it offered an opportunity to link again the lecture founded in Henry Maudsley's memory with the hospital which is the living witness to his wisdom and generosity. The first Maudsley Lecture was given by Sir James Crichton Browne, a contemporary and friend of Maudsley; the second was given at the Maudsley Hospital by Sir Frederick Mott, who had seen much of him during the last decade of his life. Since then very few of those called to give this lecture had had any personal contact with him, and it seems appropriate that now, a hundred years after Maudsley entered University College Hospital as an apprentice, when he has become for most of us a shadowy figure of the Victorian past, I should attempt to revive the memory of what he did during his life and consider how his work lives on after him—most of all in the hospital and school where I, and so many more, have the privilege of working. Before I do this I would like to recall that on the list of Maudsley lectures there is the name of Edward Mapother, a man singularly close to Maudsley in temperament and outlook, who carried forward the Maudsley Hospital in the spirit of its Founder's intention, and who would have been ideally fitted, in the 1939 lecture entrusted to him, to deal with the theme I am entering upon; unfortunately the war and his failing health came between, and Prof. Mapother never delivered the lecture. Sir James Crichton Browne compared Maudsley with Mercier; I compare Maudsley with Mapother, and recognize that in each generation there are men of rare gifts, severe in self-discipline, with strong and consistent purpose, who, in psychiatry as in other fields, accomplish much good and leave behind a lasting memorial.

Henry Maudsley was born in 1835. He grew up in a notable time; 'of all decades in our history, a wise man would choose the 1850's to be young in,' says Mr G. M. Young, The giants were on the scene: Faraday, Clerk Maxwell,

This paper was delivered as the twenty-fifth Maudsley Lecture to the Royal Medico-Psychological Association in November 1950. It is reprinted from the *Journal of Mental Science* (April 1951), **97**, 259–77.

Darwin, Lyell, Owen, Carlyle, Tennyson, Ruskin, Dickens, Matthew Arnold, Herbert Spencer, J. S. Mill, Lecky; and as many more. There was intense intellectual activity and material success, self-questioning also, and social and spiritual discontent. Maudsley, however, was not at first much exposed to this revolution of ideas. He was born on a farm in the West Riding of Yorkshire, not far from Settle in Ribblesdale, of a family of yeomen who had been settled there for two centuries and more. 'My father was a stolid Tory all his life, and quietly fixed to old ways of thinking and doing. He once told me, when I rebelled against traditional custom, that what was good enough for my forefathers was good enough for me,' he says in a fragment of autobiography, which the kindness of Dr Henry Maudsley of Melbourne has put at my disposal. Maudsley paints a drab picture of his childhood, after his mother had died; he attended the Giggleswick school, where 'we had to construe the Latin and then repeat the appropriate rule from the Eton Latin Grammar without in the least understanding what the words meant. Similarly, in the upper school, besides arithmetic I went through a part of the first-book of Euclid without any comprehension of the problems, learning the letters of the lines and angles by heart and repeating them offhand and instantly forgetting them. The little instruction which I obtained was probably not mainly due to the system there, but in part also the the fact that I was a day boy who had to walk over two miles to the school and back daily in summer and winter, in rain and snow. It was a hard time, but use and no experience of anything better made it tolerable, as it does everything else. Still it was a succession of sombre and dreary years, for my father was so profoundly afflicted by my mother's death, to whom he was ardently attached, that his natural silence was increased and hardly a word ever passed between us boys and him except when absolutely necessary.' There were, however, some enlivening people—his paternal uncle John, a wayward, philosophically minded, well-read man; and his maternal aunt, Elizabeth Bateson, a philanthropist of the true Victorian breed, who conducted schools, and after a quarrel with the vicar of Bolton set up her own dissenting chapel at Kellett. 'I owed more than I can reckon to her,' says Maudsley, 'for the poetry which she used to repeat to me, and I, having got it by heart, used to rush into the kitchen and declaim it to the servant. To that early and useful instruction I owe, I believe, any quality of style in my writings.' It was this aunt, Elizabeth Bateson, who had him sent, when he was 14, to be a private pupil in the house of the Rev. Alfred Newth at Oundle. There his world opened out. His teacher was a good classical and mathematical scholar, widely read in general literature, who took him through Homer and the great Greek tragedians and historians, and of course, the Latin writers: Thucydides and Tacitus made a lasting impression on the boy, and so did the *Prometheus Bound* of Aeschylus; no doubt the theme of man's futile struggle against necessity, which recurs so often in Maudsley's writings, got something of its imprint from that tragedy of rebellious pride.

To University College Hospital Maudsley went in 1850, after he had matriculated; he was apprenticed for five years to Clover, who was then the

Resident Medical Officer. He tells us that he was self-assertive and stubbornly rebellious against all control, 'as I have always been,' and that he did not avail himself of the opportunities the practice of the hospital afforded, so that Sharpey, the Professor of Physiology, remarked, 'Maudsley has great abilities, but he has chosen to throw them into the gutter.' Maudsley's terse comment is, 'Happily I managed to pick some of them up again before they entirely rotted.' His capacity for memorizing from books and for expressing himself well enabled him, he says, in spite of his wild courses, to gain a scholarship and a rouleau of gold medals. When he had his degree he designed to be a surgeon, but his lack of means and some trifling miscarriage of letters hindered him in this; so he decided to enter the East India Company's service. As they required their doctors to have spent six months in an asylum, he took a post as assistant medical officer at Wakefield, where he stayed nine months, and got on famously with his 'congenial Yorkshire countrymen.' From then there was no more talk of surgery or the East India Company; psychiatry had marked him for its own. A brief spell at Brentwood (where, I regret to say, he took a strong dislike to the people of Essex) was followed by a decisive event—his appointment as Medical Superintendent of Cheadle Royal.

He was only twenty-three, he had had no lengthy or formal training in psychiatry and no experience of administration, he had scamped his clinical studies, and he had vacillated in his career; his teachers did not think he was steady or tractable. What chance would he have had before a selection committee nowadays? What chance even of being 'short-listed'? Those hardheaded Victorian committeemen in Manchester gave over the conduct of their new Royal Hospital for the Insane to this clever, headstrong, handsome young Yorkshireman. His success in the post was outstanding, and their courage and judgment bore richer fruit than they could foresee, and in a wider field. I think it is worth pausing to consider whether we are not in danger nowadays of becoming hidebound in our demands upon every aspirant, whatever his talents and promise; no doubt our requirements are the safe and right ones for the majority of candidates, but we have no great cause to preen ourselves on our skill in selection or our readiness to back a winner when we make comparison with our staid forefathers of a hundred years ago. To go no further than neurology and psychiatry. Hughlings Jackson, born in the same year as Maudsley, was on the senior staff of the National Hospital by the time he was 27, and of the London Hospital at 28; Griesinger, Maudsley's nearest counterpart in Germany, had, like him, neglected his regular classes as a medical student, had been self-willed and impatient of control, and had no more than two years' mental hospital experience when he published, at 28, his great textbook which radically influenced German psychiatry and made him its accepted leader. The range and content of psychiatry have been much extended in the last hundred years; but it is still, I think, true that a man of exceptional powers can acquaint himself in a few years of concentrated observation, reading and reflection with all the current knowledge he needs and can use, while the rest of us work our way steadily through the appointed

31

stages of a lengthy training. If we force the Maudsleys and Griesingers of our day to delay their productive time until they have satisfied our normal and regular demands upon the would-be psychiatrist—and worse, until they have completed their 'analysis'—I think psychiatry may suffer. Our difficulty, obviously, lies in knowing how to distinguish between the slick, hasty smatterer claiming privilege, and the impatient man with an original mind, fertile, selective and independent.

I have called Maudsley's appointment to Cheadle Royal a decisive event. He stayed there only three years, but in that formative time he learnt to know his subject and himself in a way that had not been possible before. He set about the practical business of his charge with sense and energy, effecting many improvements and some enlargment; he thought deeply, read much and wrote profusely and experimentally, stretching his literary limbs. In these writings there is explicit statement of most of the ideas that were to occupy him for the rest of his life.

His three Annual Reports at Cheadle Royal (for access to which I am much indebted to Dr Roy) exhibit a mature and conscientious outlook. In the first he emphasizes the importance of treatment early in the illness, and points out that the supposed causes of insanity in each case are by no means definite efficient causes, that there are commonly many partial causes or conditions of the disease, some predisposing, some exciting, and that 'the bodily derangement which so commonly exists in cases of insanity cannot always be regarded in the light of a cause; it often partakes as much of the character of effect. The physical acts on the mental, and the mental back again on the physical, and vice versa—cause and effect acting and reacting, and mutually aggravating one another. The old rule that 'the cause having ceased, the effect ceases' is false almost as often as it is true; the effect often continues after the cause has ceased, and, thus abiding, becomes in its turn a cause. Disturbance of the emotions and morbid introspection are the most conspicuous features of insanity—'the insane walks along, in many cases, the embodiment of an exaggerated emotion. . . . There is no boundary line between sanity and insanity; and the slightly exaggerated feeling which renders a man "peculiar" in the world differs only in degree from that which places hundreds in an asylum. He who is eternally contemplating his own feelings can scarcely be pronounced to be perfectly sane'; exaggerated and distorted emotion leads to exaggerated and distorted ideas; if the ideas are lively and active, it is mania; if gloomy in character, it is melancholia. Hereditary predisposition is a most important cause, though often hidden by relatives who deny the facts: 'Where hereditary predisposition exists, a cause so slight as to be inappreciable to observers is often efficient to produce the disease.' As for treatment, he describes at length the many occupations and amusements which are arranged for the patients, and he denounces a 'system which permitted to the insane only the monotony of a lifelong incarceration, and the inestimable privilege of wishing, like Hafiz, "to break up the tiresome old vault of heaven into new forms".' In his report of the following year Maudsley

32

refuses to classify as 'recovered' those who were well when they left the hospital, but might not remain so, and he adds, as we might today, 'a candid experience in the treatment of insanity must teach the wisdom of a discreet scepticism with regard to very high percentages of so-called recoveries.' He remarks on the mild form of lifelong susceptibility to breakdown which makes the mental hospital a haven for some people; it might seem a painful thing to deprive of liberty persons who appear so little ailing, were it not that a repeated experience has shown it to be really a vain folly, if not a positive cruelty, to send them forth into the trials of life, when they are utterly unable to encounter them.' He deplores the 'strange, foolish, and unjust prejudice' about insanity: 'the slightest consideration would teach that an unavoidable affliction cannot be counted as a shame or disgrace'. Heredity, again, receives much notice: he deplores the dysgenic consequences of women leaving hospital to conceive more children who may inherit the disease; and à propos of the frequency of insanity in unmarried people, he refers to the harmful postponement of the age of marriage, because civilization multiplies tastes and causes luxuries to be regarded as essentials of life. A discussion of will and the power of emotion foreshadows his later writings on free will and responsibility. Degeneration, as Morel understood it, and the 'neuropathic taint' also begin to appear: 'inherited weakness of any kind, unless there has been the compensation of a good education and a happy collocation of circumstances, must be exhibited in some form of weakness or other, whether it be as drunkenness, crime, immorality or insanity. . . . Families, like trees, often grow till they have attained their greatest development, then begin to decay, and ultimately die out.' He reverts, in the tones of a preacher, to the theme 'that it is a grievous mistake to neglect the formation of character as an aim of existence'; when he dilates on this the future sceptic is out of sight, and the yeast of authentic Victorian earnestness is at work. In this report, as in the previous one, he shows a close acquaintance with the classical text-book of Esquirol. His last report, much briefer, in 1861, makes two cardinal points: First, that on no account should lies and stratagems be used to get the patient to hospital; secondly, that mental disorder is to be considered an illness, not a visitation—'truth has as much force with the insane as with the sane, and it would seem to be the simple right of those who are afflicted and need control, that they should have the truth spoken to them'; moreover, 'in place of the sufferer being sent to the hospital with the utmost secrecy as if some great disgrace were to be concealed, he is sent distinctly for the medical treatment of a disease, just as he would be placed under medical care for any other bodily disease.' You will notice that word 'other'—much of Maudsley's thought and writing was devoted to maintaining that insanity is a bodily disease.

I have dwelt upon these reports because they show us, so early in his life, Maudsley the psychiatrist, humane, practical, honest and outspoken, voicing in 1860 opinions which still in our day have to be asserted, which indeed many people suppose to have been unthought of until our generation asserted them.

Alongside Maudsley the psychiatrist there was then, and for the rest of his life, Maudsley the philosophic inquirer; Maudsley the positivist, to whom metaphysics was anathema. It is in the nature of our subject that every thoughtful psychiatrist can choose only between having his philosophic standpoint explicit or leaving it implicit; a philosophic standpoint of some sort he must have. Consequently the problems that troubled Maudsley are the perennial basic problems of us all. His views on them are inextricably woven into the fabric of his psychiatry, but his approach is that of his time and—need it be said—of his personality.

The first article of his that was published was on the 'Correlation of Mental and Physical Force, or, Man, a Part of Nature', which appeared in October 1859 in the *Journal of Mental Science*. It said substantially about metaphysics what he was still saying in 'Organic to Human' nearly sixty years later—that man's consciousness and moral nature and all his other psychological attributes are closely dependent on the physical structure of his brain. Much influenced by Grove's recent book on the correlation of physical forces, Maudsley argued, with skill and fervour, that the same continuity exists between mental and physical as between the various sorts of physical force; he inveighed against man's vanity in measuring himself against and apart from the rest of nature, his abuse of the power to see things in words, and his propensity 'to ignore himself as a material being and to speculate loosely and dilate rapturously on his mental being'. Metaphysics, says Maudsley, is the vanity of vanities, its study a vexation of spirit, because it concerns itself not with phenomena but with the hypothesis of essence. He regrets, moreover, that 'so eminent a philosopher as Auguste Comte should be one of those who have endeavoured to place science and religion in antagonism to one another'. Repudiating 'pure materialism', he glances at the universe in its gradual evolution, in which mind appears as one of the sequent effects in its due time and season, and he concludes that all forces are 'but modes of manifestation of one force—the Will of God—manifest in highest form and with least obscuration in the temple of man's body'.

This young philosopher and medical superintendent, who freely quotes Mill and Faraday, Spinoza and Leibnitz, St. Paul and Shakespeare, was the child of his time. In the late eighteen-fifties man's place in nature was a topic uppermost in the minds of thinking men. The conflict between the evolutionists and theologians like Bishop Wilberforce was already joined, though, of course, the *Origin of Species* had not yet been published and only a précis of Darwin's manuscript had been read before the Linnaean Society. Herbert Spencer had expressed in his *Principles of Psychology* a genetic and materialist view, rather loosely formulated, of the mind and its significance in evolutionary progress through differentiation, and he had objected to the hypothesis of special creation of species, just as Maudsley after him objected to the hypothesis of special creation of consciousness and moral feeling. Other influences producing the intellectual and spiritual turmoil of that generation were to be found among the philosophers—Sir William Hamilton, James and

John Stuart Mill, Bain, W. A. Carpenter, Mansel. The Germans Schelling and Herbart, and the French physiologist-philosophers like Cabanis and Bichat, also exerted indirect influence and were closely read by Maudsley.

There is little, I think, in that first essay of Maudsley's that is not to be found in other writings of the time; what is significant is that here was a young psychiatrist well versed in the great argument, bold and confident enough to take a stand which compelled the attention of philosophers, and evidently determined to carry these vigorous principles into his study of morbid as well as normal mental states and activities. He had not defined his position rigorously or consistently, as Croom Robertson and Stout sharply pointed out when examining his views some years later; his version of positivism (shorn of ritual and ethic) seems to have been, not philosophy acting in the service of natural science, to use R. G. Collingwood's phrase, but rather natural science acting in the service of psychology; and he attacks metaphysics with some of the metaphysician's own weapons—a dangerous venture, but the Maudsley of the *Physiology and Pathology of Mind*, of *Natural Causes and Supernatural Seemings*, of *Responsibility in Mental Disease*, was clearly presaged in the article by this audacious newcomer of 1859.

In 1860 he published two articles, both dealing with literary genius; one of these, much influenced in content and style by Carlyle, is about Edgar Allen Poe; the other examines discursively the insanity of many a famous man, and in one passage foreshadows Maudsley's treatise on psychiatry—'this must be the aim of a philosophical history of madness, should it ever come to pass that such a one is undertaken, a history which should aspire to establish some principle or principles but which, at any rate, should not be content to occupy itself with a catalogue of appearances. . . . In an account of insanity in any form there are thus two elements to be taken into consideration, one almost as important as the other; these are the subject and the environment, the man and his circumstances, subjective force and objective forces, both passive and active; and the problem for solution is, what there was in the one or in the other whereby harmonious co-operation between them became impossible and a discord was, of necessity, produced . . . materials (for a general history of insanity written in a philosophical spirit) lie in profusion around every one who has devoted himself to the care and treatment of the insane.' In this essay, testifying in its gusto and exuberance to its author's comparative youth, he expresses a young man's conclusion—that 'the act of dying is generally very agreeable.' It is noteworthy that shortly before his end, as a tired old man of 81, solitary and disillusioned, he repeated this belief in much the same language, in the characteristic essay on 'Death' that appeared in *Religion and Realities*. His account of various eccentrics in the 1860 essay is delightful in its tolerant enjoyment of absurdities; for example, his story of Thomas Wirgman, the philosophical goldsmith, who persuaded the Guardians of St Pancras to allow him to try out on the pauper children his system of metaphysics, which was to bring universal peace and virtue on earth by teaching a 'grammar of the five senses'.

In the next year Maudsley, no doubt stimulated by the fierce controversy between Owen and Huxley, wrote a learned and elaborate article on the 'Genesis of Mind', in which the problems of cerebral development are surveyed. It is notable for the plain indications of Herbert Spencer's influence and for its more than Tennysonian confidence in man's upward progress; as for the former, one can understand Herbert Spencer's petulance in his letter to Tyndal in 1868, wherein he complained at Maudsley's barely acknowledged but heavy indebtedness to him. Maudsley's confidence in man's future, expressed with a simple and—to our embittered view—naïve faith, is startling, coming from a man who is now remembered as a pessimist. In 1860 all is for the best in the evolutionary survival of the fittest; the degenerate and the primitive are being eliminated as 'humanity, in its progress upwards, fashions the supporting stem only by sacrificing the early branches. All observation proves that mankind is advancing. The beings of the present civilization are evidently superior to those of any past civilization, and the beings who now make barbarism appear to be disappearing from the earth.' 'When we reflect that moral principles are not merely intellectual speculations but actual laws of nature, as certain and uniform in their operations as are the physical laws there is every reason to anticipate that, as the recognition of the physical laws, has added so greatly to the power and comfort of mankind, so the practical realization of the moral laws in the conduct of life will increase the happiness, advance the mental development and perhaps, insure the stability of nations.' 'In place of degeneration and destruction from ignorance of, and disobedience to, the physical laws, there are development and salvation from knowledge of, and obedience to, them. . . . As soon as ever men have attained to a sincere, intellectual recognition of the causes and laws of events, there inevitably springs up the correlative moral cognition. . . . We have a certain guarantee of moral progress.' 'Love and virtue must replace cruelty and vice: that . . . simple scientific observation of the natural course of the development of mind compels us gladly and confidently to anticipate; it is the realization in general practice of those sublime principles which revelation has inculcated. And such, happily, will be the functional expression of the superior type of brain amongst modern civilized nations.' 'Advancing knowledge is becoming conscious of the love that there is in every apparent evil. In fact, the wider and deeper our insight becomes, the more clearly do we perceive love working in every event of nature, all-embracing, all-supporting, all-powerful.' These millenarian rhapsodies are strange; Maudsley was no Pangloss, nor was he writing a Bridgewater treatise, but he echoes the hopes of his time; and he was not the first to base his assurance of Utopia upon a pessimistic view of man's past state, from which a rational progress should henceforth redeem him. The development of this notion of progress in the nineteenth century, the confusion between the biological conception of progress through natural selection and the humanistic conception of it through the working of man's moral nature; the contrast, superficial but striking, between the optimists and the pessimists; the struggle to relate, if not to reconcile, religious with biological views of man's past and future—these are familiar to us in the pages of Ruskin and Carlyle, Herbert Spencer, Mill, and many more of the noted men of that time. Darwin himself wrote, at the conclusion of the *Origin of Species*: 'As natural selection works solely for the good of each being, all corporal and mental environment will tend to progress towards perfection.' I need not stress further the obvious similarity between Maudsley's views and those which agitated or comforted his generation, but his profession gave a special bias to his statement of these views, and later led him away from them. He wrote, when he was 60, 'a physician who had spent his life in ministering to diseased minds might be excused if, asking himself at the end of it whether he had spent his life well, he accused the fortune of an evil hour which threw him on that track of work. He could not well help feeling something of bitterness in the certitude that one half of the disease he had dealt with never could get well, and something of misgiving in the reflection whether he had done real service to his kind by restoring the other half to do reproductive work. Nor would the scientific interest of his studies compensate entirely for the practical uncertainties, since their revelation of the structure of human nature might inspire a doubt whether, notwithstanding impassioned aims, paeans of progress, endless pageants of self-illusions, its capacity of degeneration did not equal, and might some day exceed, its capacity of development.' That is a profoundly disillusioned, unhappy conclusion. It would be easy to read into it an unrelieved pessimism, but in later writings of his we find again qualified optimism, weighed against qualified pessimism; scepticism rather than despair. There were, as Maudsley himself maintained, two warring strains in him: 'I have always thought and said,' he wrote in his autobiography, 'that the paternal and maternal were never vitally *welded* in me, but only *riveted*.' He was, he tells us, in his youth self-assertive, but at the same time a tormenting critic of himself. His friends described his 'difficult personality, his tart replies and scathing judgments,' while they recall also his 'genial look and friendly interest.' He was, indeed, by no means a sociable, affable doctor, full of the team-spirit, who would demonstrate to the world that the psychiatrist is a good fellow; but he was not a Timon or Thersites either. He recognized the vigorous intrinsic animality in human beings, while he abhorred its manifestation in cruelty and deceit. As he grew older he took it more and more for granted, though he never quite reconciled the moral aspiration that had been so strong in his youth and was still quick in him as an old man, with the resigned, half-doubting meliorism that represented his final standpoint as philosopher-psychiatrist.

The warring strains in him, which he attributed to the intellectual tough-minded inheritance from his father and the emotional religious warmth from his mother, asserted themselves in other views that appear often in the writings that stretch over sixty years. He denounced introspection and metaphysics, yet he constantly returned to the metaphysical problem of the mind-body relationship, which fascinated him (as it has always fascinated psychiatrists); he inveighed against the tyranny and deceit of words, especially of newly-invented words, but he laboured to be eloquent and he proposed new coinages (such as 'paramorphic' and 'boulepsy'); he was a Positivist who rejected the ritual and religion which was the mainspring of Comte's teaching; he detested the brutishness, and worse than brutishness, men can display, yet he extolled war in language that shocks us: 'War in one shape or another, open or disguised, has plainly been the divinely appointed instrument of human progress, carnage the immoral-seeming means by which the slow incarnation of morality in mankind has been effected'—we have to remind ourselves that this also is the language of Tennyson's Maud, that it was commoner, and certainly easier, then than now for war to be misconceived as a heroic and beneficient instrument of natural selection. There are other contradictions evident in his writings, but these, so far from indicating weakness, bespeak, I believe, Maudsley's criticism of doctrines prevailing in his time—doctrines which he espoused, it is true, and which he enriched from his experience as a psychiatrist; but this very experience and the tenacity and candour of his mind compelled him to doubt their general application. In some matters on which he wrote he was no wiser than his generation, but his chief inconsistencies bring him closer to modern views than a consistent adhesion or opposition to the opinions of his time—I mean the period between 1860 and 1890—would have permitted. This is illustrated by his views about the pathology of mental disease, which I shall mention presently.

It is well, moreover, to remember that Maudsley was fond of contrasting the two types of creative mind; thus in 1866 he wrote that the men who influence mankind fall into two classes—'men of wide intellectual grasp, vast wisdom and serene energy; and the men of limited vision, intense feeling, and impetuous energy'; thirty years later he is more biting about the second class—'persons who are clever but flighty, talented but unstable, intense but narrow, earnest but fanatical; all sorts of persons who, plunging into new movements, good or bad, and pursuing them with intemperate, perhaps distempered, zeal, lack the just balance of the faculties, the calm equilibrium of a stable mental organization, the true proportion or mean of nature which is the highest sanity. In the end the result is some such misproportioned incongruity as the philanthropic zealot, reeking of self, whose testimony or character no prudent man of the world could trust, or the intensely neurotic investigator, aspiring to be scientific, who, seeing nothing else, is utterly untrustworthy as an observer.' In his latest book, written shortly before his death, he returned to the theme: 'The plain truth is that the pessimist observes sincerely, thinks fully and feels deeply. . . . Pessimism is alike the stern conclusion of thinking reason and the pious confession of reverent religion. . . . Optimism, on the other hand, is the practical expression of unthinking feeling.' There can be no doubt that he knew himself to belong to the more mournful company, though sometimes feeling the energy and often enjoying the faith and exultant vitality of the optimists.

The writers whom he most often quotes are significant: Goethe perhaps more than any other; Shakespeare, the Bible (especially Ecclesiastes and

Isaiah), Milton, Bacon, Pascal, Montaigne, Robert Burton, Sir Thomas Browne, Gibbon, Amiel; and of philosophers, Locke, Hobbes, Hume, Hamilton. These are lofty minds, often of a sombre and sceptical cast, like his own. Then there are the medical and scientific authors with whom he was evidently familiar: Darwin, Huxley, Carpenter, Laycock, Prichard, Brown-Séquard (but he never quotes Galton, and seldom Hughlings Jackson, though he and Jackson were both close to the thought of Herbert Spencer and had other things in common, including their Yorkshire origin; perhaps Hughlings Jackson's fear and contempt towards the mentally ill, which Savage noted, rather alienated Maudsley, who felt a close and sympathetic kinship with the insane). With the German and French writers of his middle life he was as familiar as with his English contemporaries; but he seems not to have kept up his psychiatric reading after the eighties and nineties as much as his general reading (which included Karl Marx's writings).

I come now to Maudsley as physician and psychiatrist. He had a high conception of what a doctor's life should be, and it would be hard to find a more outspoken panegyric of the value and opportunities of our profession than that contained in his introductory lecture delivered to the medical students at University College, London, in 1876, while he was Professor of Medical Jurisprudence there. Throughout his life he tried to keep abreast of clinical and scientific developments, as his 1905 British Medical Association Lecture in Medicine showed; indeed his familiarity with then recent developments in physics is startling to a reader today; he stresses, for example, the importance of the demonstration that matter can be resolved into moving electric charges, and he says, 'a living cell seems but a gross thing. Concencentrated within its little body are subtile and intense forces continuously and quietly working which, if let loose in large explosive display, might suffice to blow up the chemist and his whole laboratory.' It is his psychological rather than his general medical and scientific standpoint that is chiefly of interest to us.

Maudsley entered psychiatry at a time when the prestige of English and Scottish philosophers stood high throughout the learned world for their psychological speculations, and when British psychiatrists enjoyed very little regard outside these islands; Pinele's strictures upon them had not been lived down, and only J. C. Prichard's writings and Conolly's had attracted some attention or excited controversy abroad. When the young Maudsley in 1867 published his *Physiology and Pathology of Mind* it was promptly acclaimed by Westphal, in Griesinger's new journal, as the most important psychiatric work to appear in that year, one which he hoped might long exercise an influence on our science. Similarly, Ribot gave the book warm but discriminating praise a few years later, by which time it had been translated into German, Italian, French and Japanese. Henceforward, until well within this century, few of the most prominent psychiatrists of other countries failed to show some acquaintance with Maudsley's writings and views, either on psychiatry in general or on those special questions of psychosomatic relations, criminal responsibility in mental disease, and the psychology of 'supernatural seemings' to which he had devoted particular books. Although Bucknill, Daniel Hack Tuke, Clouston and some others later became known abroad, it was Maudsley that taught German and French psychiatrists that they could not safely disregard everything in our psychiatry except 'no restraint'. I think the same may be said of the Italian psychiatrists but I know too little of them, apart from Lugaro and Tanzi, to be sure. At all events, the publication of *Physiology and Pathology of Mind* was a turning point in English psychiatry; it presaged the end of the period in which psychiatry rested on a magma of empirical observations and windy philosophizing, and it embodied a critical synthesis of biological and other scientific advances so far as they had an evident bearing on mental activity, in health and disease. Moreover, it took account of what the French and Germans were then so vigorously contributing to psychiatric theory and observation. I would not like to give an impression that Maudsley appeared a giant among the English pygmies; I have been convinced in reading those early volumes of the *Journal of Mental Science* that in the Association of Medical Officers of Asylums and Hospitals for the Insane there was as much capacity and erudition as might be found now in a much larger circle of our members, and perhaps more vitality than is commonly exhibited in a professional association when it has become large and prudent. Only an arrogant and ill-informed psychiatrist in our day would look down on the men who contributed to the advance of our subject in the mid-Victorian period. But though these contemporaries of Maudsley were men of considerable stature, they had not the grasp, the acumen and the facility of expression which made his work outstanding and potent. He had something important to say on many topics that are fundamental for psychologists and psychiatrists, and he said it insistently, pointing to recent discoveries and, still more, to some recent and old absurdities which were, in his eyes, strangling progress.

On these matters he felt so strongly that he wrote intemperately. His attacks on introspection were violent, beyond what he could justify in his later writings; but he was battling less against introspection and metaphysics in psychology than against that irrational dualism which denied that mental activity could be studied by the scientific method on the ground that it was exempt from any laws of predictable succession. Hence his diatribes, and his vehement assertion that psychology was cerebral physiology. Hence also his lifelong concern with the problems of will in disease and crime. As early as 1863 he had shown his bitter indignation at the way popular clamour and legal pedantry could cause a manifestly insane murderer to be hanged, and he could never stomach the argument that man has a dual composition—body (including brain) acting in a way determined by its structure and history, and mind, which having free will, is to be judged and held accountable quite otherwise than as the body is.

This is the place to consider Maudsley's view about consciousness—obviously a crucial issue in his campaign against dualism. Briefly, he held that consciousness is the adjunct of mental function, merely lighting up a small part of the mental process; never preceding or dictating a mental occurrence, but only accompanying it or following it. The motives of behaviour 'are very mixed, and their main work is unconscious'. He was, of course, familiar with the views of von Hartmann, Schopenhauer, Beneke and other philosophers on this matter, and in his insistence from the beginning on a wholly physiological psychology he took account of the difficulties which the fact of consciousness had presented to these writers. He never succeeded in resolving the problem—who has?—but his standpoint about consciousness was, in essence, not different from that of, say, Lashley, allowing for the vast disparity in the relevant knowledge available to the two men. His constant stress upon the immense importance of the processes that occur unconsciously has led a psychoanalytic writer, Christoffel (to whose essay Dr Stengel directed my attention), to claim him as in some sort a forerunner of psychoanalysis. I do not think the claim can be sustained. 'Unconscious' was for Maudsley a negative psychological term of description; he applied it to cerebral happenings which in his view provided the whole dynamic of mental life, in contrast to the small segment of those cerebral happenings illuminated by consciousness, which the much-abhorred metaphysicians liked to study by introspection. As soon as some of his contemporaries attributed to 'subliminal consciousness' a mental force and quality of its own, he was up in arms; he called it a signal example of clever beguilement by words, and jeered at this 'subliminal consciousness which can do marvellous things—as well indeed it may, being a positive consciousness, created out of negation, . . . a something which is and is not at the same instant'. There can be no doubt that the Freudian conception of the Unconscious was alien to Maudsley's thought, though it should be said that in many respects he was in sympathy with the psychoanalytic attitude; he constantly stressed the animality of human beings, their control by forces which they denied or ignored, their inner conflicts, the power of unsuspected or curbed sexuality (especially in women) and the passionate urges of the child. On the last matter his words may be quoted: 'Whoever observes sincerely what a child's actual mind is, without being biased by preconceived notions of its primal purity, innocence and natural inclination to good, must see and own that its proclivities are not to good but to evil, and that the impulses which move it are the selfish impulses of passion. Give an infant in arms power in its limbs equal to its passions, and it would be more dangerous than any wild beast.'

It would be impossible in this lecture to set out the chief features of Maudsley's clinical and theoretical psychiatry. I can only say that I have compared his book with Kraepelin's, published at about the same time (Maudsley's third edition and Kraepelin's second), and Maudsley's does not suffer by the comparison, though there are very wide differences in style and method; Kraepelin's is a text-book, Maudsley's a treatise. It would be a most valuable formative experience even now for young psychiatrists of ability to read Maudsley's major works; there they would meet a powerful critical intellect,

41

versed in clinical practice, impatient of shams, and capable also of fertile synthesis. Maudsley's originality appears in his assertion of opinions, then heterodox, and even now fancied by many to be banners first inscribed and flown in our own enlightened day. I will mention a few of these. He maintained that the psychosomatic relation is a reciprocal one occurring within a complex but unified organism, 'each part of which calls the furthest brother, which acts upon the rest of it and is reacted on by it.' He emphasized that emotion affecting every part of the body is 'rooted in the unity of organic life', and he asserted that 'it is in the natural order of events that continuance of perverted function should lead to organic disease.' He required that treatment should be adapted to the particular patient—'always the rule of rules should be to treat an individual who is sick, not an abstract disease.' Narcotic drugs should be used with the greatest restraint. He rejected the claim of men like Schroeder van der Kolk to have discovered in the morbid anatomy of the brain the pathology of mental disease. 'The morbid anatomy of insanity,' he wrote, 'would take little room were speculation rigidly excluded and it limited to what is actually seen and known. Nor does that which is seen, it must be confessed, throw much light on the symptoms.... The intimate chemical and molecular changes which are presumably the conditions of mental disorder go on in a domain of nature the subtleties of which far exceed the subtleties of observation.' In another remarkable passage he suggests that it might be easier to conceive what nervous disorder means if, 'instead of thinking of the body as a material structure built up of so many organs, one were to abolish in imagination the gross matter, to think it clean away, and to conceive its organs as so many and divers complexes of very fine and active vibrations bound within the forms and shapes of the different organs and united by the most complete harmony of inter-nuncial vibrations, the whole organism being the formal unison of these multitudinous and various complexes of energies.' In all his writings on this theme, even where he falls (like every medical writer of his time who dealt with it) into 'brain mythology', he displays a prescient imagination; thus, in melancholia (for which no one had then suggested leucotomy) he speculated about the 'exorbitant and predominant, almost exclusive, activity of certain brain tracts charged with sad feeling'; and in mania he guessed that 'the functions of the most fine and special traceries of the cortical reflexes are suspended or effaced, being too delicate to lend themselves to the currents of turbulent energy which now pass along coarser channels'. Crude as these surmises are, they are perhaps no cruder than those will seem in fifty years which now, to us, represent the striking discoveries recently made in cerebral physiology, applied to the problems of mental disease. Still, these opinions of Maudsley's are at best speculations, unsupported by any evidence. Where he dealt with more substantial matters, Maudsley again strikes us as an anticipator of our practice. He even suggested, in his Goulstonian Lectures in 1870, that if we had the power to induce general convulsions in some cases of acute insanity, 'we might, for the time being at any rate, cure the insanity.' Not only in his precepts for treatment but in his general approach there is much that psychiatrists of our generation consider it important to reiterate. He emphasized the need for a full, searching life-history of the patient; causes are multiple, the notion of cause itself needing reconsideration and restatement; inherited predisposition is the most potent influence, but the actual outbreak of illness depends on whether circumstances of upbringing and subsequent life have been propitious or unpropitious; patients have often had the ill-fortune to be twice penalized, first in a bad inheritance, and secondly in a bad training given them by those who gave them that inheritance; there must therefore be 'close and diligent study of the particular qualities of individual character, mental and bodily, and an exact exposition of its relations to its circumstances ... a patient unfolding of (the person's) action on circumstances and of their action on him.' The effect of circumstances, acting on a suitable inheritance, may be not insanity, but a lesser mental deformity or nervous obliquity, or it may be crime; crime 'is clearly sometimes the result of an actual neurosis which has close relations of nature and descent to other neuroses'.

There is a further topic to be mentioned among the many which might be taken to illustrate Maudsley's expression of views now sometimes trumpeted as up-to-date corrections of the unwisdom of our predecessors—it is classification. I single it out because Dr Gregory Zilboorg, in his erudite *History of Medical Psychology*, has been severe upon Maudsley in this particular. He says that 'the classificatory effort of Maudsley appears unenlightened; were it not for his insistence on careful historical studies of each individual patient, one could not easily discern the human being behind the classificatory frame,' and he says that Maudsley was 'purely materialistic and purely descriptive'— a remark often made nowadays about Kraepelin too. As early as 1859 you will recall Maudsley had written that 'a philosophical history of insanity ... should not be content to occupy itself with a catalogue of appearances'. In his *Pathology of Mind* he followed at first, with patent misgivings, the classification of Esquirol; he was critical of Skae's ambitious scheme, though recognizing the practical if limited usefulness of singling out mental diseases regularly associated with a bodily disease; and he similarly appraised Morel's scheme of classification. The note on classification in the second edition, 1868, states his very reasonable position. In 1879, in the third edition, he gives a brief, clear explanation of his grounds for adhering, for the present, to a simple symptomatological classification; 'this necessity of calling up by a general term the conception of a certain co-existence and sequence of symptoms is a reason why the old classification holds its ground against classifications that are alleged to be more scientific; it is good as far as it goes, but it by no means goes to the root of the matter; whereas the classifications which pretend to go to the root of the matter go beyond what knowledge warrants and are radically faulty.' Finally in 1895 he says quite explicitly in the Preface, 'A leading aim through (the work) having been to clear the ground by endeavouring to think the subject into simplicity and to set forth the results in as plain language as possible, I have purposely avoided mention of the numerous and elaborate classifications which, in almost distracting succession, have been formally proposed as exhaustive and tacitly condemned as useless. For the same reason I have shunned the use of the many learned names—of Greek, Latin and Graeco-Latin derivation—which have been invented in appalling numbers often to denote simple things and sometimes, it may be feared, with the effect of confounding apprehension of them. Insanities are not really so different from sanities that they need a new and a special language to describe them; nor are they so separated from other nervous disorders by lines of demarcation as to render it wise to distinguish every feature of them by a special technical nomenclature.'

I have dealt a little more fully with this matter than its intrinsic importance warrants, but as Dr Zilboorg has been so damning in his main comment on Maudsley, largely on the score of his classificatory procedure, I thought it proper to clear the issue, in the hope that Dr Zilboorg in subsequent editions of his justly esteemed book will give due recognition to Maudsley's outstanding merits among nineteenth century psychiatrists.

So far Maudsley appears as the brilliant iconoclast, the erudite reasoner who could expound lucidly the principles of physiological psychology, the sage, the far-sighted writer on clinical psychiatry. His influence, in spite of his unsociable ways, was immense, and was not limited to the narrow circle of psychiatrists and psychologists; Darwin, for example, quoted Maudsley frequently in the *Descent of Man* and in the *Expression of the Emotions*. Professor Boring, of Harvard, the discriminating historian of experimental psychology, wrote in 1929 that the first edition of Maudsley's *Physiology and Pathology of Mind* was a 'very influential book which forms the background for the tradition for medical psychology in Great Britain'. I need not amplify such a judgment or look closely into the indirect means whereby Maudsley's influence extended beyond the range of those who knew him or read his books. It is clearly also difficult or impossible to separate his influence from that of precursors and contemporaries with whom he had much in common; still more difficult to separate or trace it in successors who have incorporated his views along with much knowledge which was not available to him and many opinions which would have astounded him. It might therefore be assumed that his influence, though great in his active period, became steadily less manifest and less potent as the decades passed. If his works had consisted solely of his writings and clinical activity, that would be so, and he would now be a fading, Victorian figure, no better known to the psychiatrists of a later day than, say, Hack Tuke, Magnan or Kahlbaum. But Maudsley, the sceptic, the childless pessimist, decided upon a constructive act which would project his intention further than books or talking could; he created a living organism to be his heir. The steps he took have been described by Sir Frederick Mott, who acted as go-between in the drawn-out negotiations between Maudsley and the London County Council that started in 1907, but the genesis of the project lay further back. While he was at Cheadle Royal, Maudsley had urged the need for early treatment. Then, in his early days as a rising consultant in London, he had evolved plans for such early treatment in concert with that earnest champion of family care, 'my friend Baron Mundy, M.D., of Moravia', and others of Maudsley's circle, who used to meet (as Crichton Browne tells us) at a Soho restaurant to discourse about the future of psychiatry and the betterment of mankind. I had supposed these plans of Maudsley's to be pioneer efforts until I chanced upon the paper in which Samuel Gaskell, in 1860, when he had become Commissioner in Lunacy, advocated voluntary treatment, free from legal forms, so that remedial measures might be instituted early and for a class of patient, with mild forms of disorder, who would not 'resort to asylums as at present constituted'. Maudsley must have read this paper with conviction, and still more he must have been impressed by the reiterated views of his father-in-law, Conolly, regarding the need for schools for clinical instruction in the nature and treatment of mental maladies. Thus Conolly, in 1862, four years before his death, told our predecessors in this Association that schools for psychiatric instruction were the 'great want of our profession, and a great impediment to any progress in it. . . . Until you have these schools, you will never be able to command men to take positions of great importance—not such as you would sometimes wish could be found'. It was not, however, until 1907 that Maudsley could begin to give practical effect to these ideas implanted so long before. Mott, who had been one of his pupils at University College and who was now Pathologist to the L.C.C. Mental Hospitals, wrote a proposal after visiting Kraepelin's Clinic at Munich, in which he urged the creation of a similar University psychiatric hospital in England which should be devoted to early treatment, research and postgraduate training. This accorded well with Maudsley's views; he got in touch with Mott and made his offer of £30,000 to the London County Council if they would build the hospital, subject to its association with the University of London; this offer, supported by A. J. Balfour and Arthur Rucker, the Principal of the University, was accepted by the London County Council in 1908, but there were delays; the site was not chosen until 1912, nor the building completed till the end of 1915. Before Maudsley died, he had seen the hospital, under Mott's energetic guidance, doing some of the teaching and pioneering work which he wanted, though, of course, it was not until 1923 that it was opened to fulfil all the purposes which Maudsley had outlined in the article he wrote for the *Archives of Neurology and Psychiatry* in 1909.

It is not for me to examine what effect the existence and activities of the Maudsley Hospital have had upon the advancement of psychiatry, but it is clear that the hospital has been the instrument whereby Maudsley, after his death, continues to be a potent force. If, however, its work were not carried out in his spirit and to further his aims, it would not be Maudsley's inheritor and agent, but his unfaithful steward, writing an ironical footnote on the vanity of human wishes. I have tried, therefore, with such knowledge of Maudsley's views and character as could be got by steeping myself in his writings, to picture him returning to the scene and judging us in the light of his purpose. Two things are certain: that what he saw and disliked he would condemn in good set phrase or scathing epigram; and that everything new or supported by new knowledge would be brought to the bar, not so much of his former opinions on the matter, as of his standards of truth and scientific method, and of his requirement that it should be relevant to the understanding of human nature in health and disease.

I think, when we were planning how to welcome this most worshipful and august of visitors, and thinking how we might fitly conduct our founder to show him to what uses his gift had been turned, we would decide to bring him first to Professor Meyer.* Not that neuropathology had been his concern—he was always a clinician who had no laboratory experience or any evident taste for experiment; but because the work done in that department, the outlook and method, the nexus with clinical problems and opportunity, are in the fullest accord with the beliefs he expressed in the *Physiology and Pathology of Mind*, in *Body and Mind*, in *Organic to Human*, and in many essays and addresses. He would even find kindred interests in what may be called the by-ways of Professor Meyer's department; I recall, for example, that he wrote, as long ago as 1867, 'It is deserving of remark that the different nervous centres of the body manifest elective affinities for particular poisons. . . . That medicinal substances do display these elective affinities is a proof, at any rate, that there are important though delicate differences in the constitution or composition of the different nervous centres, notwithstanding that we are unable to detect the nature of them. It may be also that there is shadowed out in these different effects of poisons on the nervous system a means which may ultimately be of use in the investigation of the constitution of the latter'—a prescient statement, ensuring his delight on finding how fully Dr Meyer had turned his prediction into fact.

Where we would wish to take him next I am not so sure; electroencephalography would surely fascinate and delight him, as a fresh disclosure of those delicate traceries and neural activities about which he constantly surmised; or biochemical studies, esoteric to him as to most of us, but in keeping with his faith in the importance for mental disorder of general metabolic and cell chemistry; these might be the most obvious activities to show him next. But if we delayed his entry into the clinical territories, it would probably be at the risk of a sardonic inquiry as to whether we treated any patients nowadays. We would therefore be brief in detaining him while we explained the subtleties of the relation between the Institute and the Hospital, and the closeness of our connexion with other medical schools of the University—a matter always near to his heart—and told him also of the auspicious union effected so lately between his Hospital and that ancient and notable hospital of which his friend Savage was the head, and which had had, long ago in the days of Henry the Seventh, a Thomas Maudsley as its Master and Warden. When in his visit he came to the wards he would find, I think, much being practised which he

* Professor Alfred Meyer occupied the Chair of Neuropathology at the Institute of Psychiatry in the Maudsley Hospital from 1949 till 1956.

had advocated and prized—the careful inquiry into history; the regard for physical examination; the concern with individual needs and constitution; the avoidance of liberal sedation; the dislike of rigidity and dogmatism, whether in diagnosis or treatment, theory or practice; the emphasis on the continuity or communality of healthy with morbid; the care for hereditary and eugenic considerations; the social approach to the study and treatment of childhood deviations, of occupational inadequacy, of neurotic deformity and suicidal despair. What he would say about our psychopathology and psychotherapy is a matter for wide conjecture; I think the Jungian doctrines would excite his warmest invective, and the Freudian perhaps his coldest approval—in parts; but seeing that at the hospital we are not all convinced of the rightness of the same theory of psychopathology or the same method of psychotherapy, he would, I imagine, concede that in matters such as these, admitting of legitimate differences of opinion and practice, it is fitting that a University School should allow teachers of proved capacity and experience to put their several standpoints *sine ira et studio*—or at any rate *sine ira*. Then, in the psychological department, he would certainly be pleased to find an animal laboratory and a child development unit, for he had said that the study of the plan of development of mind, as exhibited in animals and in infants, would furnish results of the greatest value and be essential to a true mental science. What he would make of the statistical methods and the study of personality through tests is a hard question, for he liked objective methods and rigorous logic, but had no taste for mathematics. It is significant that in his paper on 'The New Psychology' in 1900 he repudiated those psychological studies of animals and of children which used terms without definition and made observations without objectivity, and he extolled the experimental method, declaring that 'to express the results in arithmetical numbers or algebraic formulas is a method of demonstration which cannot fail ... to bring psychology into touch with realities and to put positive meaning into its language'. At the same time he castigated psychophysics for its aridity and neglect of individual differences, and said that though measurements might be 'multiplied and accumulated world without end, yet if they remain scattered, incoherent, fragmentary heaps, they will only be monuments of sterile industry—monumental mockeries of knowledge'. So it may be guessed that his judgment of our statistical labours in psychology would be favourable, but reluctantly so, since the bent of his mind was away from ready acceptance of such concepts as the statistical aggregate and uncertain inference, but this may be a hasty conclusion. It is well to remember what Maudsley said at the end of the soundly but rather destructively critical paper which I have just referred to: 'I conclude that man as a whole is a larger affair ... than any single method of minute inquiry—be it chemical, physical, pathological, microscopical, or psycho-physical—will ever unfold. . . . There is work enough for as many methods of study of mind as are rationally based: have the definite aim of a concrete mental organization to be studied, and work definitely and progressively for it by observation of facts, exclude not one

47

another, but know that in the end they must bring, and, knowing, strive to bring their results into harmony.'

I have said very little about Maudsley's personal life, partly, of course, because the data are meagre, but chiefly because he has plainly shown how he detested to see the trivial and private details of a man's life exposed after his death. Neither have I dwelt upon the themes, few but rather striking, on which the knowledge or the sentiments and experience of our later time would judge him to have been wholly mistaken. Each generation, as Maudsley himself often said, has a common heritage of ideas; each individual mind reflects the thought of its time; and the men of each generation are apt to look kindly but loftily upon the errors and defects of those who preceded them. Few, however, who had become familiar with his thought would feel disposed to condescend to Henry Maudsley, or to dwell, in extenuating advocacy, upon any mistakes into which he fell. He was, I have said it already, a man of incisive and tenacious intellect, a man gifted with unusual foresight, capable of planning and enforcing a great constructive design, such as I believe the inception of the Maudsley Hospital to have been. To his contemporaries at different phases of his long life he seemed other than this; there seem to have been times when they thought him a bitter recluse, given over to mordant nihilism. But they mistook the appearances. It is true, as he once scribbled on a blank page of the *Physiology of Mind*, that he never hated people, but often felt contempt; his contempt, however, was as free from bitterness as his social brusquerie was without malice or any unkindness. I may conclude with recalling the occasion when Maudsley delivered his Presidential Address to this Association; it was in 1871. When he had finished, Clouston took part in the discussion and said: 'Dr Maudsley's address has been one of utter and entire scepticism. He treated three subjects: the prevention of insanity; the sending of patients to asylums; and the treatment by sedatives. And he answered them (thus): 'Insanity cannot be prevented until we arrive at some future state of human existence in which we shall all live in the light of right reason: patients get much better out of asylums than in them; and do not give sedatives as you will probably poison your patients.' When Maudsley came to reply, he said: 'I think Dr Clouston accurately described my paper as one of scepticism, but in accepting this description of it I would use the word not in an ill sense, as Dr Clouston might do. I would remind him that scepticism was a very good word before it got an ill meaning: that fundamentally scepticism, and episcopacy, and bishop have the same root; that they all come from the Greek word σκοπεō which means to examine, to look to.' To examine, to look to—that is what Maudsley always did: he examined the knowledge of his time that had a bearing on psychology and mental disorder, and he looked well to it that out of his consideration of these things should come as much gain of truth, of benefit to the mentally ill, of continuing advancement of psychiatry, as his powers could compass. Such a sceptic we do well to honour.

5

SIGMUND FREUD: 1856–1939

THIS GENERATION, which recognizes Freud as a man of genius, is not disposed to belittle his abilities, nor to adopt without question his own modest appraisal of them: 'I have very restricted capacities or talents. None at all for the natural sciences; nothing for mathematics; nothing for anything quantitative. But what I have, of a very restricted nature, was probably very intensive.' With this modesty about his natural gifts, Freud combined a lofty estimate of his achievement; 'I have a high opinion of what I have discovered, but not of myself.' He ranked his discovery with those of Copernicus and Darwin; the passage in which he did so is notable. 'Humanity has in the course of time had to endure from the hands of science two great outrages upon its naïve self-love. The first was when it realized that our earth was not the centre of the universe, but only a tiny speck in a world-system of a magnitude hardly conceivable; this is associated in our minds with the name of Copernicus, although Alexandrian doctrines taught something very similar. The second was when biological research robbed man of his peculiar privilege of having been specially created, and relegated him to a descent from the animal world, implying an ineradicable animal nature in him: this transvaluation has been accomplished in our own time upon the instigation of Charles Darwin, Wallace and their predecessors, and not without the most violent opposition from their contemporaries. But man's craving for grandiosity is now suffering the third and most bitter blow from present-day psychological research which is endeavouring to prove to the "ego" of each one of us that he is not even master in his own house, but that he must remain content with the veriest scraps of information about what is going on unconsciously in his own mind. We psycho-analysts were neither the first nor the only ones to propose to mankind that they should look inward; but it appears to be our lot to advocate it most insistently and to support it by empirical evidence which touches every man closely. This is the kernel of the universal revolt against our science, of the total disregard of academic courtesy in dispute, and the liberation of opposition from all the constraints of impartial logic'.

Since those words were written, forty years ago, men have become more

This invited article is reprinted from *Discovery* (1956), **17**, 181–3.

ready to believe that they have an animal nature, impelling them to acts which they cannot consciously understand or wholly control. Virulent attacks on psycho-analysis, such as Freud sought to account for, are not in keeping with the temper of our day, and opposition to it has become courteous and for the most part logical. Opposition, however, there still is, on two counts: the status of psycho-analysis as a science, and its efficacy as a method of treating psychological illness.

It does not derogate from Freud's greatness as one of the most original and penetrating minds of the last hundred years, to admit that much of what he put forward is still in dispute, and that psycho-analysts have themselves modified and corrected some of his formulations. This he foresaw, since psycho-analysis was not for him a system but an ever-growing body of know-ledge, founded on observation of the facts of mental life, with its 'theoretical superstructure still incomplete and subject to constant alteration'. 'It may perhaps seem to you,' he wrote to Einstein, 'as though our theories are a kind of mythology and, in the present case, not even an agreeable one. But does not every science come in the end to a kind of mythology like this?'

MODERN ASSESSMENT OF FREUD

Because of the controversy which still surrounds the tenets of psycho-analysis, Freud is perhaps to be related to psychology and psychiatry more as Marx is related to economics and political theory than as Darwin is to biology or Einstein to physics. Many who deny neither the influence nor the greatness of his contribution contest its lasting truth. Others, observing its application—which covers many more fields than the medical ones of path-ology and treatment from which it arose—question the wider generalizations upon which such application rests. Doubts arise chiefly because of the great difficulty of testing the findings of psycho-analysis by methods customary in science.

Friendly critics (including some psycho-analysts) have often pointed out that psycho-analysts have paid too little regard to the duty of verifying, by methods found necessary in science, the observations and theoretical con-clusions of Freud and other pioneers. Freud expressed his hypotheses in the biological language of his time, with a plentiful use of metaphor and analogy. He had been influenced by men like Brentano, Hughlings Jackson, Brücke, John Stuart Mill, Meynert, Fechner and Breuer, men of the nineteenth century. It is inevitable that subsequent advances in many areas of knowledge will have compelled revision and restatement, such as indeed characterized Freud's own progress. Revision from within has sometimes led to divergence and defection—of which Adler and Jung were early instances, and Karen Horney a more recent one; in other cases, for example, Melanie Klein and W. R. D. Fairbairn, it has resulted in drastic changes of theory, vigorously rejected by some who regard these newer views as deviating from the funda-mental principles of psycho-analysis. In such a situation it is very plain that everything must be checked not on the basis of its accordance with accepted theory but on the basis of fact. Controlled observation and experiment are inordinately difficult to apply in this territory: but some work of the kind has been done. In many details confirmatory of psycho-analytic theory as stated by Freud, it usually bears on superficial aspects, however, and leaves the fundamental issues untouched. Until experimental and other methods of verification have been applied to these basic issues, psycho-analysis will lack the full status of a science. It must in any case rank as one of the social sciences, rather than as a physical science. Quantitative precision such as the physical sciences attain is a very remote goal for the study of man's motives and emotional development: but it is well within the scope of psychology to demand, and devise, surer methods of empirical substantiation for psycho-analytic theory than have hitherto been provided by psycho-analysts. It is, however, right to remember that until Freud opened the way, psychologists had been hardly at all concerned with forces that can be held to account for the irrational in human thought and behaviour. Motivation was ignored. Psychology was largely academic, in the pejorative meaning of the word. Freud brought life and stimulus into it; his theories will occupy it for many a day to come. E. G. Boring, the historian of experimental psychology (who has himself been psycho-analysed), holds that psycho-analysis has so far been prescientific, but he sums up its importance in a confident prediction of what posterity will think of it: 'It is not likely that the history of psychology can be written in the next three centuries without mention of Freud's name and still claim to be a general history of psychology.'

PSYCHOANALYSIS AND MEDICINE

It was psycho-analysis as a method of medical treatment that made it possible for Freud and those who followed him to make observations on which theory was constructed and modified. In that sense its therapeutic use was indispensable, and indeed continues to be so, for psycho-analytic inquiries into human nature. But important as psycho-analytic treatment may be to the individual patient and his doctor, it is not by its therapeutic success or failure that the true status of psycho-analysis is to be judged. This was evidently Freud's own view: 'The future will probably attribute far greater importance to psycho-analysis as the science of the unconscious than as a therapeutic procedure.' There is still room for honest doubt about the right indications for psycho-analytic treatment and its efficacy for particular forms of mental disorder: here, too, controlled studies are required to clarify the problem (which confronts every psychiatrist, and every citizen who believes that the National Health Service should provide every kind of treatment whose efficacy has been sufficiently proved); but the intrinsic obstacles in the way of a properly conducted assessment of these matters are so great as to have hitherto prevented any thorough and dependable inquiry.

The relation of psycho-analysis to medical practice has gone through some

51

vicissitudes. Freud was himself a well-trained physician; he had made important contributions to pharmacology and neurology before he devoted himself to the study of neuroses. His training in the laboratories of men such as Meynert and Brücke had a profound effect on his thought, as is very plain in the correspondence he had with Wilhelm Fliess between 1887 and 1902, and in the illuminating 'Project for a Scientific Psychology' which he drafted in 1895. But his mind ranged beyond the medical field to consider the motives of human behaviour in diverse forms and places: 'My interest, after making a lifelong detour through the natural sciences, medicine and psycho-therapy, returned to the cultural problem which had fascinated me long before, when I was a youth scarcely old enough for thinking. At the very climax of my psycho-analytic work, in 1912, I had already attempted in *Totem and Taboo* to make use of the newly discovered findings of analysis in order to investigate the origins of religion and morality. I now carried this work a stage further in two later essays, *The Future of an Illusion* (1927) and *Civilization and its Discontents* (1930). I perceived ever more clearly that the events of human history, the interactions between human nature, cultural development and the precipitates of primeval experiences (the most prominent example of which is religion) are no more than a reflection of the dynamic conflicts between the ego, the id and the superego, which psycho-analysis studies in the individual— are the very same processes repeated upon a wider stage.' This deflection of his interests was associated with a partial repudiation of medicine as the parent of psycho-analysis. In lively discussions concerning 'lay analysis' Freud went so far as to say (in 1927) that 'after forty-one years of medical activity, my self-knowledge tells me that I have never really been a doctor in the proper sense'; he required that doctors who wished to be psycho-analysts should 'overcome the one-sidedness that is fostered by instruction in medical schools and should resist the temptation to flirt with endocrinology and the autonomic nervous system'. Though this was his later view, perhaps the truer expression of his thought was in a letter to Ernest Jones in 1911, in which he wrote, 'We are to withstand the big temptation to settle down in our colonies, where we cannot but be strangers, distinguished visitors, and have to revert every time to our native country in Medicine, where we find the root of our powers.'

FREUD, THE MAN

Freud's personal life was so interwoven with his work that separate consideration of it is impossible: 'psycho-analysis came to be the whole content of my life ... no personal experiences of mine are of any interest in comparison to my relations with that science.' His personal qualities, set out by a faithful biographer, reveal a man of consummate integrity and courage, blameless in his domestic life, immensely industrious, and a leader who collected around him men of ability. He bore contumely, defections, painful disease, and exile with resolute dignity. Some of the distressing experiences of his earlier years probably influenced his outlook and character. Thus he attributed his firmness against opposition and his independence of judgment to the foundation laid when he entered the University of Vienna and found that he was expected to feel inferior and an alien because he was a Jew: 'at an early age I was made familiar with the fate of being in the Opposition and of being put under the ban of the compact majority.' There were complexities in his character and in his human relations: without them he could not have been the man he was. But transcending them was the overmastering passion to get at the truth about human nature: this passion went with a fundamental simplicity and directness, in paradoxical contrast to the intricacy and subtlety of the problems he grappled with all his life. No one conversant with his achievement and with the information Dr Ernest Jones has made available about him could withhold respect or deny greatness to this outstanding man.

6

JUNG'S EARLY WORK

A MAN'S early work is often so different from the achievements that bring him on the world's larger stage that we are amazed at the strange turns his road has taken. The difference may lie in subject-matter, or in method of approach, or in fundamental thought and philosophical framework. There may be an explicit denial at one time of life of a point of view which at another is stoutly maintained and brilliantly developed. In this sense his career is a paradox. But closer and truer scrutiny shows a historical and a psychological sequence, a continuous response to the impact of experience, observation, and fresh knowledge, which robs the paradox of its cruder contrasts.

Such an issue arises when we look at psychiatrists who have broken through the accustomed limits of their specialty, to range the larger territory of philosophy. They make a small but notable band—Theodor Ziehen, Sigmund Freud, Karl Jaspers, C. G. Jung. Their status as philosophers will be variously assessed, according as one is a professional philosopher hostile to invaders, or a psychiatrist with a particular bias. Ziehen, as you know, oscillated between psychiatry, psychology, and philosophy; Jaspers has long since deserted psychiatry, to which his orderly, comprehensive mind made a great contribution, unfortunately neglected in this country; and Freud's gradual passage from the comparative anatomist and neurologist to the student of civilization's discontents and the nature of man has been lately set out for us in his correspondence and in Dr Jones's absorbing biography.

The phase of Jung's work which I propose to consider stretches over a period of about five years, from 1902 to 1907, spent at Burghölzli Hospital. I do not know what occupied his interest before he went to Burghölzli in 1900—passing his medical examinations, I suppose. Burghölzli was the psychiatric clinic of the University of Zürich and at the same time a mental hospital for patients with acute and prognostically hopeful illnesses from the Canton: less hopeful patients were sent to Rheinau, a nearby mental hospital.

This paper was delivered as an invited address to the Society of Analytical Psychology in May 1956. It is reprinted from the *Journal of Analytical Psychology* (1957), **2**, 119–36.

Burghölzli was therefore a hospital set up with much the same aims as the Maudsley, but unable, as the Maudsley could, to keep free circulation through its wards: there was constant trouble from obstruction and over-crowding with chronic patients for whom there was no room in the other hospital. When Jung joined the staff, there were 391 beds, with an annual intake of 203 patients. There was no outpatient department, though some consultation of that kind had been organized by Forel, the director between 1879 and 1898. It was, in effect, a small, overburdened, under-staffed mental hospital: four doctors and seventy-six nurses carried out all the necessary duties. But it was a hospital with a fine tradition. Its directors had been Gudden, Hitzig, and Forel—men of academic distinction and great force of character. Forel in particular, had concerned himself scientifically not only with cerebral anatomy and the zoological study of ants—fields in which he was an outstanding figure—but also with psychology, psychopathology, and psychotherapy. His investigations into memory, instinct, hypnosis, and occupational therapy made a lasting impression upon the Zürich school of psychiatry; and so did his campaign for social betterment and the furtherance of mental health in the community, where alcoholism, sexual unrest, and crime stirred his humanitarian zeal. His successor was Eugen Bleuler. Bleuler had, after two and a half years in the psychiatric clinic at Berne, come to work under Forel in Burghölzli: then he had become superintendent of Rheinau. While he was at Rheinau, he lived among his patients and his nurses in such intimacy that he 'got to know the patients like members of his family, and himself experienced directly and intensively the way the bond between doctor and patient works' (Bleuler, M., 1951). When he came to Burghölzli as director, in 1898, he was resolved to study the human relationships which enter so closely into the texture of mental illness, and to continue Forel's work in advancing mental hygiene by combating social evils, especially alcoholism.

I have dwelt at some length on the situation at Burghölzli because there can be no doubt that in that hospital an intellectual atmosphere and *Weltanschauung* prevailed which powerfully influenced Jung and the other men who came to work there—such men as Ludwig Binswanger, Karl Abraham, Eugene Minkowski, Riklin, Frederick Peterson and, later on, Klaesi and Hermann Rorschach. The influence did not come only in Bleuler's time. It can be discerned clearly in Adolf Meyer, another minister's son from Switzerland, who left Zürich in 1892 but all his life showed the effects of Forel's teaching and example, so that in the United States he too worked for a psychological and psychotherapeutic approach to mental illnesses, on lines not far removed from those of the group that assembled around Bleuler a decade after Meyer had left for America.

The first product of Jung's work at Burghölzli was his study of so-called occult phenomena; then came several papers on simulation and hysteria, another on chronic mania, and the well-known series on word associations. The monographs on the psychology of dementia praecox closes the list of the publications I shall mention here.

There are, in effect, three subjects: hysteria; dementia praecox; and word association.

The associations between words and ideas had played a large part in the psychological speculations of nineteenth-century philosophers, especially in England. Indeed Locke had set the ball rolling, and before him Hobbes had drawn a distinction between free association and controlled or selective association (Hobbes, 1940, ch. 3). 'This Trayne of Thoughts, or Mentall Discourse, is of two sorts. The first is *Unguided, without Designe*, and inconstant; wherein there is no Passionate Thought, to govern and direct those that follow, to itself, as the end and scope of some desire, or other passion: In which case the thoughts are said to wander, and seem impertinent one to another, as in a Dream ... Their Thoughts are ... without harmony; as the sound which a lute out of tune would yield to any man; or in tune, to one that could not play. And yet in this wild ranging of the mind, a man may oft-times perceive the way of it, and the dependance of one thought upon another ... The second [sort of mental discourse] is more constant; as being regulated by some desire, and designe.'

Compare that passage from Hobbes with another, in which a nineteenth-century man of genius described his pioneer experiments in word association (Galton, 1879a, p. 149). 'The processes of thought fall into two main categories: in the first of these, ideas present themselves by association either with some object newly perceived by the senses or with previous ideas; in the second process, such of the associated ideas are fixed and vivified by the attention, as happen to be germane to the topic on which the mind is set. In this memoir I do not deal with the second process at all ... but I address myself wholly to the first ... My object is to show how the whole of these associated ideas, though they are for the most part exceedingly fleeting and obscure, and barely cross the threshold of our consciousness may be seized, dragged into daylight, and recorded.' And at the conclusion of the article, he summed it up: 'I have desired to show how whole strata of mental operations that have lapsed out of ordinary consciousness, admit of being dragged into light, recorded, and treated statistically, and how the obscurity that attends the initial steps of our thoughts can thus be pierced and dissipated. I then showed measurably the rate at which associations spring up, their character, the date of their first promotion, their tendency to recurrence, and their relative precedence. Also I gave an instance showing how the phenomenon of a long-forgotten scene, suddenly starting into consciousness, admitted in many cases of being explained. Perhaps the strongest of the impressions left by these experiments regards the multifariousness of the work done by the mind in a state of half-consciousness, and the valid reason they afford for believing in the existence of still deeper strata of mental operations, sunk wholly below the level of consciousness, which may account for such mental phenomena as cannot otherwise be explained.'

These quotations are from Francis Galton's article in *Brain*, which appeared in July 1879. The word-association studies which it reported had been described in less detail, but more vividly, in an article he wrote in the same year for the *Nineteenth Century*. I should like to quote the essential parts of that article (Galton, 1879*b*).

'There lies before every man by day and by night, at home and abroad, an immense field for curious investigations in the operations of his own mind.

No one can have a just idea, before he has carefully experimented upon himself, of the crowd of unheeded half-thoughts and faint imagery that flits through his brain, and of the influence they exert upon his conscious life. I will describe a few of the results of my own self-examination in respect to associated ideas.

It was after many minor trials that one afternoon I felt myself in a humour for the peculiar and somewhat severe mental effort that was required to carry through a sufficiently prolonged experiment as follows. I occupied myself during a walk from the Athenaeum Club, along Pall Mall to St James's Street, a distance of some 450 yards, in keeping a half-glance on what went on in my mind, as I looked with intent scrutiny at the successive objects that caught my eye. The instant each new idea arose, it was absolutely dismissed, and another was allowed to occupy its place. I never permitted my mind to ramble into any bye-paths, but strictly limited its work to the formation of nascent ideas in association with the several objects that I saw. The ideas were, therefore, too fleeting to leave more than vague impressions in my memory. Nevertheless, I retained enough of what had taken place to be amazed at the amount of work my brain had performed. I was aware that my mind had travelled during that brief walk, in the most discursive manner throughout the experiences of my whole life; that it had entered as an habitual guest into numberless localities that it had certainly never visited under the light of full consciousness for many years; and, in short, I inferred that my everyday brain work was incomparably more active, and that my ideas travelled far wider afield, than I had previously any distinct conception of.

My desire became intensely stimulated to try further experiments, and, as a first commencement of them, to repeat the walk under similar circumstances. I purposely allowed a few days to elapse before doing so, during which I resolutely refused to allow my thoughts to revert to what had taken place, in order that I might undergo the repetition of the trial with as fresh a mind as possible. Again I took the walk, and again I was aware of the vast number of extremely faint thoughts that had arisen; but I was surprised and somewhat humiliated to find that a large portion of them were identical with those that had occurred on the previous occasion. I was satisfied that their recurrence had in only a very few cases been due to mere recollection. They seemed for the most part to be founded on associations so long and firmly established, that their recurrence might be expected in a future trial, when these past experiments should have wholly disappeared from the memory.

It now became my object to seize upon these fleeting ideas before they had wholly escaped, to record and analyse them, and so to obtain a definite knowledge of their character and of the frequency of their recurrence, and such other collateral information as the experiments might afford.

The plan I adopted was to suddenly display a printed word, to allow about a couple of ideas to successively present themselves, and then, by a violent mental revulsion and sudden awakening of attention, to seize upon those ideas before they had faded, and to record them exactly as they were at the moment when they were surprised and grappled with. It was an attempt like that of Menelaus, in the *Odyssey*, to constrain the elusive form of Proteus. The experiment admits of being conducted with perfect fairness. The mind can be brought into a quiescent state, blank, but intent; the word can be displayed without disturbing that state; the ideas will present themselves naturally, and the sudden revulsion follows almost automatically. Though I say it is perfectly possible to do all this, I must in fairness add that it is the

57

most fatiguing and distasteful mental experience that I have ever undergone. Its irksomeness arises from several independent causes. The chief of these is the endeavour to vivify an impression that is only just felt, and to drag it out from obscurity into the full light of consciousness. The exertion is akin to that of trying to recall a name that just, and only just, escapes us; it sometimes seems as though the brain would break down if the effort were persevered in, and there is a sense of immense relief when we are content to abandon the search, and to await the chance of the name occurring to us of its own accord through some accidental association. Additional exertion and much resolution are required, in carrying on the experiments, to maintain the form of the ideas strictly unaltered while they are vivified, as they have a strong tendency to a rapid growth, both in definition and completeness.

It is important, in this as in all similar cases, to describe in detail the way in which the experiments were conducted. I procured a short vocabulary of words, and laid it open by my side . . . Before I began the experiment, I put myself into an easy position, with a pen in my right hand resting on a memorandum book, and with a watch that marked quarter seconds in my left hand, which was started by pressing on a stop, and continued going until the pressure was released. This was a little contrivance of my own appended to one of Benson's common chronographs. When I felt myself perfectly in repose, with my mind blank, but intent, I gently leant forward and read the word, simultaneously pressing the stop of the watch. Then I allowed about a couple of ideas to present themselves, and immediately afterwards released the stop and gave my utmost power of attention to appreciate with accuracy what had taken place, and this I recorded at once. Lastly, I wrote down at leisure the word that had been displayed, and the time shown by the chronograph to have been occupied by the experiment.

The number of words used in the experiments I am about to describe is seventy-five. I had intended it to be one hundred for the convenience of writing down percentages; but my original list became reduced by mislaying papers and other misadventures not necessary to explain. The result was that I procured a list of seventy-five words, which had been gone through as described, on four separate occasions, at intervals of about a month. Every precaution was used to prevent the recollection of what had taken place before from exercising any notable influence. It was not difficult to succeed in doing so, because the method of proceeding is permeated by the principle of completely discharging from the mind the topics on which it had previously been engaged.

. . . Now for the results. I found, after displaying each word, that some little time elapsed before I took it in, chiefly because the process had been performed so quietly. If the word had been flashed upon a dark background in large and brilliant letters, or if some one had spoken it in an abrupt, incisive tone, I am sure that period would have been considerably shortened. Again, whenever we read a single substantive without any context or qualifying adjective, its meaning is too general to admit of our forming quickly any appropriate conception of it. We have no practice in doing so in ordinary reading or conversation, where we deal with phrases in block, and not with separate words. Hence, the working of the mind is far less rapid in the experiments I am describing, than on common occasions, but not much less than it was in my walk along Pall Mall.

I found the average interval that elapsed between displaying the word, and the formation of two successive ideas associated with it, to be a little less than two and a quarter seconds—say at the rate of fifty in a minute or three thousand in an hour. These ideas, it must be recollected, are by no means atomic elements of thought; on the contrary, they are frequently glimpses over whole provinces of mental experiences and into the openings of far vistas of association, that we know to be familiar to us, though the mind does not at the moment consciously travel down any part of them . . .

The seventy-five words gone through on four successive occasions made a total of 300 separate trials, and gave rise between them to 505 ideas in the space of 660 seconds. There were, however, so many cases of recurrence that the number of different ideas proved to be only 279. Twenty-nine of the words gave rise to the same thought in every one of the four trials, thirty-six to the same thought in three out of the four trials, fifty-seven to two out of the four, and there were only one hundred and sixty-seven ideas that occurred no more than once . . .

I divided such part of the 279 different ideas as admitted of it into groups, according to the period of my life when the association that linked the idea to the word was first formed, and found that almost exactly the half of those that recurred either twice, thrice or four times, dated to the period when I had not yet left college, at the age of twenty-two . . .

The 279 different ideas fell into three groups. Those in the first and most numerous were characterized by a vague sense of acting a part. They might be compared to theatrical representations in which the actors were parts of myself, and of which I also was a spectator . . .

The second group of ideas consists of mere sense imagery, unaccompanied by any obscure feeling of muscular tension or action; such as mental landscapes, sounds, tastes, etc . . .

The third and last group consisted of purely verbal association, whether the mere names of persons or things, or bits of quotations in prose or verse.

. . . Experiments such as these allow an unexpected amount of illumination to enter into the deepest recesses of the character, which are opened and bared by them like the anatomy of an animal under the scalpel of a dissector in broad daylight. If we had records of the self-examination of many persons, and compared them, I think we should be much impressed by the differences between one mind and another, in the quality, wealth, and appropriateness of their associated ideas, and we should wonder that mutual misunderstandings were not more frequent even than they are.

I found the purely verbal associations to contrast forcibly in their rapid, medical precision with the tardy and imperfect elaboration of highly generalized ideas; the former depending on an elementary action of the brain, the latter upon an exceedingly complicated one.

It is a perfect marvel to me, when watching the working of my mind, to find how faintly I realize the meaning of the words I hear or read, utter or write. If our brain work had been limited to that part of it which lies well within our consciousness, I do not see how our intellectual performances would rise much above the level of those of idiots . . .

The more I have examined the workings of my own mind, whether in the walk along Pall Mall, or in the seventy-five words, or in any other of the numerous ways I have attempted but do not here describe, the less respect I feel for the part played by consciousness. I begin with others to doubt its use altogether as a helpful supervisor, and to think that my best brain work is wholly independent of it. The unconscious operations of the mind frequently far transcend the conscious ones in intellectual importance. Sudden inspirations and those flashings out of results which cost a great deal of conscious effort to ordinary people, but are the natural outcome of what is known as genius, are undoubted products of unconscious cerebration. Conscious actions are motivated, and motives can make themselves attended to, whether consciousness be present or not. Consciousness seems to do little more than attest the fact that the various organs of the brain do not work with perfect ease or cooperation. Its position appears to be that of a helpless spectator of but a minute fraction of a huge amount of automatic brain work. The unconscious operations of the mind may be likened to the inumerable waves that travel by night, unseen, and in silence, over the broad expanse of an ocean. Consciousness may bear some analogy to the sheen and roar of the breakers, where a single line of the waves is lashed into foam on the shores that obstruct their course.'

These inquiries of Galton's came quickly to the knowledge of Wundt, who had a strong interest in association, on theoretical grounds. Wundt and his pupils in Leipzig instituted experimental studies, with suitable apparatus; and a flow of papers ensued. The papers by J. McKeen Cattell, in particular, on controlled association in 1887, and on free association in 1889, were of classical importance: as he then stated, the association reactions 'lay bare the mental life in a way that is startling and not always gratifying', and he encouraged his pupils in turn, when he came back to Columbia University, to hoe this rewarding field. Hence came, at a later date (1910), the Kent-Rosanoff list of 'normal' associations to stimulus words. It was, however, in Germany, under Wundt's influence, that the seed planted by Galton grew into a many-stemmed shrub. From Trautscholdt (1883) onwards the experimentalists of the Leipzig school, and Ebbinghaus in Berlin, and the Würzburg group, notably Mayer and Orth (1901), had tended the growth of this plant, studying by it memory and thought. But for them association was predominantly a passive occurrence, mechanical and atomistic. It has indeed been urged against associationism, as they presented it, that it left out motive (Lewin, 1926, p. 294): 'The couplings caused by habit never supply as such the motor of a mental event ... Rather in all cases certain mental *energies* originating, as a rule, in the pressure of will or needs, i.e. mental systems *under stress* are the necessary conditions for mental events.' The criticism is very like that applied to the modern counterpart of associationism—the conditioned-reflex theory of mental action (cf. Russell, 1946).

Now this criticism, justified or not, cannot be made against Jung. It is in his search for individual motives for any particular association and its manner of production that he stood out from the other students of this popular subject of psychological inquiry.

It might be supposed that only psychologists had concerned themselves with word associations. But this was not the case. Able psychiatrists took up this promising method and applied it to their patients. Aschaffenburg, for example, who had in 1896 reported on experimental association studies in normal subjects, three years later published his findings in exhausted people, and a few years later his observations on manic patients who exhibited flight of ideas. The first systematic observations on the mentally ill had, however, been made by Kraepelin between 1888 and 1901. These investigations were, of course, well known to Jung and his collaborators, as numerous references in their papers testify.

It is not appropriate here to examine the six papers in which Jung put forward the results of his own work in this field, together with several papers by collaborators (Jung, 1906a and 1909). It is clear that in the major paper, by himself and his relative Riklin, he was particularly concerned with the influence of attention upon the process of association. He concluded from this elaborate study that 'emotionally-toned complexes' determine the personal response, and that distraction of attention accounts for the reactions of fatigued, intoxicated, and manic patients. In a successive chapter, on reaction-time, he stressed the value of long reaction-times (1906*a*, trans. p. 239): they 'would perhaps give us the means by a short and simple examination to discover things of personal import, especially the complexes which characterize the psychology of the individual. Pathology would get much help, for in this way we should get valuable sign-posts, say among hysterics, for the discovery of the complexes making for the disease of which the hysteric is not himself aware.' Another paper in that series was largely based on the earliest psycho-analytical notions concerning the effect of psychic trauma.

There can be no doubt that the Zürich investigators had very high hopes of what could be achieved by the method. Bleuler expressed these in his opening essay, where he claimed that in the mental process of association 'there is mirrored the whole psychical essence of the past and of the present, with all their experiences and desires. It thus becomes an index of all the psychical processes which we have but to decipher in order to understand the whole man' (Jung, 1906*a*, trans. pp. 4 f.). And, for practical purposes, the material accumulated by Jung 'serves not only for the presentation of psychological types among normal people, but also for the diagnosis and symptomatological understanding of a whole range of psychoses.

'From the associations we are now in a position in many cases to diagnose dementia praecox, epilepsy, various forms of imbecility, certain forms of hysteria, not to speak of [mania] with its well-known flight of ideas . . .

'Perhaps the most important result of all is that by the help of association experiments the mechanisms of . . . dementia praecox are laid bare.'

It soon became evident that these rosy conclusions were not warranted. The supposed diagnostic value of the method, which was responsible for the title of the original publication (*Diagnostische Assoziationsstudien*) proved illusory. The detection of 'complexes' needed more caution than these early investigators realized. Thus in 1921 Clark Hull and Lugoff (pp. 111 f.) using Jung's list of stimulus words, re-examined, with a stricter procedure, the correctness of Jung's finding that repetition of stimulus word, misunderstanding of stimulus word, long reaction-time, defective reproduction of response word, and repeated use of same response word, all pointed to a 'complex': but this they could not confirm with any great confidence by their method, and Hubbard, three years later (1924, pp. 342 f.), showed that factors which Jung had not considered might appreciably affect the interpretation of the mode and kind of response. There have been signs of its revival, but it is probably fair to say that as a method of applied psychology the word-association procedure has been dropped, after its limitations had been brought to light. But this is not to minimize its importance. If it had not been important, in the development of psychology and psychopathology, Wundt and Cattell and Scripture, Kraepelin and Aschaffenburg, Bleuler,

61

Jung, Claparède, Piéron, and many other very able men would not have given it so much attention. Jung's contribution demonstrated, by sustained and careful experiments, the truth of Galton's emphasis on the three essential features of such associations: that the responses are highly individual; that they provide indications of the deeper layers of the personality and especially of motivation; and that the psychological processes which determine the responses are in part unconscious. Jung's work was, in the clinical field, the prelude to the rich efflorescence of projective tests that has occurred in the last twenty years. It was, of course, another Zürich psychiatrist who introduced the most famous and popular of projective tests, but I cannot find any indication that Hermann Rorschach was closely acquainted with the association studies influenced by them directly.

The effects of these investigations on the development of Bleuler's and Jung's views, and, less directly, on certain aspects of psycho-analysis and psychiatry, was considerable. Peterson and Brill, who had collaborated in the work, especially in the psychogalvanic observations, carried news of it to the United States (and this was no doubt partly responsible for the invitation to attend the Worcester celebrations in 1909).

I said that the word-association procedure, as developed by the Zürich workers, has been dropped. Some might demur at this, recalling Rapaport's (1946, vol. 2) wartime study, the experiments of Luria (1932) and of Huston and Shakow (1934, pp. 65 f.), and Symond's evaluation (1931, ch. 10); others might remind me of its fairly recent use for screening purposes (as by Crown (1947, pp. 198 f.)) and for determining 'masculinity' and 'femininity'. But there is a world of difference between forced-option tests and free associations, and between group screening and study of the individual. There is, however, one odd field in which the word-association procedure is still employed, with some modifications, for a practical purpose which interested Jung. That is, the detection of crime.

In September 1905 Jung sent a note to the *Zentralblatt für Nervenheilkunde* (1905a, pp. 813 f.) in which he protested against an article, by Max Wertheimer and Julius Klein (1904, pp. 72 f.), which had just appeared in a criminological journal. (Max Wertheimer was later to become famous for his Gestalt psychology). These authors had written about the use of word associations for detecting the 'complex' arising from a crime. Jung emphasized that the concept of the emotionally-toned complex and the demonstration of its bearing on the association-response came from the workers in the Zürich clinic, who should have been acknowledged as the sources of the idea put forward by Wertheimer. 'Wertheimer's merit is, as yet, only that he has emphasized the special "complex" crime and the possibility of detecting it though word-associations.' Jung went on to report his own success in unmasking a suspected thief. In another paper in the same year Jung (1905b, pp. 653 f.) referred to the application of the method, for criminological purposes, by Hans Gross, A. Gross, and William Stern. He partly foresaw the subsequent development of the procedure in America, which came about through the stimulus of Münsterberg (a former pupil of Wundt, of course, and well acquainted with the Zürich studies). In the Clark Lecture which Jung delivered in America in 1909 he reported in detail another successful detection of an offender, rebutted the criticism that innocent persons may give a 'false positive' response, and concluded (p. 113) that 'we have here something that is not to be despised from a practical point of view, to wit, a culprit has been brought to light in a much easier and shorter way than is customary. What has been possible once or twice ought to be possible again, and it is well worth while to investigate some means of rendering the method increasingly capable of rapid and sure results'. Subsequent investigations had unfortunately the opposite result: they showed that unless the method were made elaborate and laborious it could yield very misleading results, though it can be used, as Jung in fact used it, as a lever for evoking a confession of guilt.

This interest in criminological problems was the outcome of a wider concern with hysteria, but owed much to the lively controversies then current about simulated mental disorder. Jung joined in the fray, and several of his 1902–1905 papers deal with various aspects of the problem. Ganser had in 1897 (pp. 633 f.) drawn attention to a curious state, in which patients (usually prisoners awaiting trial) gave grossly incorrect answers to questions, though evidently possessing the knowledge requisite for a correct answer: the patients showed a disturbance of consciousness, and of cutaneous sensation. Ganser regarded the condition as a hysterical twilight state. Then in 1902 Nissl wrote a vigorous attack on the correctness of the diagnosis in some of the cases reported by Raecke (1901) as examples of it. Nissl affirmed that the Ganser state was a form of catatonic negativism. Ganser replied to Nissl in an able paper read at Dresden the same year (1904, pp. 34 f.): in this paper he contested the Heidelberg view, championed by Kraepelin and Nissl, that if a person who turned out to have catatonic dementia praecox had previously shown what seemed hysterical traits and symptoms, these must have really been early signs of dementia praecox. He also elucidated some of the hysterical disturbance of consciousness in the Ganser state. Because of its theoretical and forensic implications, the controversy attracted much attention, and it was dead in the line of Jung's preoccupations at that time.

His first psychiatric contribution had been the thesis on occult phenomena (1902a). You will all be familiar with this, so there is no need for me to say more than that it covers the phenomena of dissociation—multiple personality, automatisms, sleepwalking, pathological lying—and that it shows close acquaintance with the rich French literature on this subject, especially by Janet, upon whom Jung draws heavily, and by the Geneva physician, Flournoy, whose famous and arresting report of a hysterical medium, *From India to the Planet Mars*, had just been published. The interest of this paper by Jung lies less in its intrinsic merit than in its presage of his subsequent concern with the symbolism of alchemy, gnostic myths, and other arcana: as he was

63

finishing the dissertation he added, almost parenthetically (p. 93), 'I naturally examined occultistic literature pertinent to the subject, and discovered a store of parallels with her gnostic system from different centuries scattered through all kinds of work. . . .'

This study of hysterical phenomena was continued, and narrowed, in his next publication, which also appeared in 1902 (Jung, 1902*b*). It was an explicit addition to the Ganser controversy, and described a complicated hysterical twilight state developing in a psychopathic woman who had been imprisoned on a false charge of theft. He examined the characteristic picture of hallucinatory excitement (which had been often described in prisoners) and turned to the psychopathology of the condition, with especial regard to the patient's state of consciousness and memory. She had an amnesia for the period of confusion. Jung tried to clear it up by means of hypnosis, employing two techniques derived from Janet and Forel. In the first of these, the patient was first hypnotized, and then, while in that state, rehypnotized; and the second, which Jung learnt from Forel, consisted in the now familiar procedure of suggesting to the hypnotized patient that she was in the required situation, whereupon hitherto inaccessible material surged up. He was able to demonstrate that the apparently severe disorientation, superficially like that of a delirium, was a superficial affair accompanied by some restriction of the field of consciousness. The disorder therefore, far from being part of a catatonic state, exemplified the mechanisms described by Breuer and Freud: the Ganser syndrome was (1902*b*, *Coll. Wks.*, p. 155) 'a pathologically exaggerated consequence of the unconscious urge to forget'.

In the following years Jung again showed that the interest in hysteria and hypnotism at the Zürich clinic had not waned since Forel's day, and that he was in close touch with current subjects of lively psychiatric discussion. The simulation of insanity by prisoners awaiting trial, which is another facet of the Ganser problem, had come very much to the fore. In 1902 Bolte in Bremen had read a paper describing how six criminals while in gaol developed mental disorders, mostly of the Ganser type, which presented difficulties in diagnosis: but he considered they raised problems of a theoretical rather than a practical nature (Bolte, 1903).

Jung (1903*b*) could not agree with this, and prompty said so in the *Journal für Psychologie und Neurologie* (of which Forel was an editor). The diagnostic problems were, he believed, very hard to settle. He then reviewed, in a discursive way, the relations between psychopathic predisposition (which in keeping with the notions of the time he called degeneration) and hysteria; he described three well-investigated patients (two of them mentally defective) who had come under his notice and on whom psychological observations, including word associations, had been carried out; he also reviewed the cases reported in the literature and made frequent reference to Janet's concepts and observations, as well as briefer allusions to Freud's views on hysteria. He concluded that some predisposed people develop 'emotional stupidity' after a severe shock, which may also favour the occurrence of psychic automatisms: consequently they may 'simulate' mental disorder, the Ganser syndrome being a very closely related phenomenon similarly evoked.

The subject of simulation continued to be much discussed, and Jung published further papers on it, until 1905. By this time he had become much better acquainted with Freud's work and now stressed his explanation of the psychopathology of such patients.

In 1903 Jung published a paper on manic 'distemper' (*manische Verstim-mung*) which reflected his current interest in psychopathic personality (or, as it was then called, 'inferiority') (1903*a*). It is not a good paper but gave him an opportunity to describe four patients who were extremely unstable people—three of them gross drunkards. He discusses the propriety of aligning these patients with those diagnosed as showing 'moral insanity', contrasts their intellectual with their conative level, and anticipates Ernest Jones in some remarks on the rationalizing work of the intellect (*Coll. Wks.*, p. 133). 'The role played by the intellect is mostly a subsidiary one, since all it does at best is to give the already existing characterological motive the appearance of a logically compelling sequence of ideas, and at worst (which is what usually happens) to construct intellectual motives afterwards. (Die Rolle die dabei der Intellekt spielt, ist meist eine ziemlich nebensächliche, indem er im besten Falle dem a priori vorhandenen characterologischen Motiv eine auscheinend logisch zwingende Begriffsreihe leiht, und im schlimmsten Falle (sehr oft dem gewöhnlichen) erst nachträglich intellektuelle Motive konstruirt.) ... Hence the prime motive for any abnormal action, provided that the intellect is fairly well preserved, should be sought in the realm of affect.' There are several other passages I should have liked to quote but unfortunately the soundness of the psychopathology in this paper is in inverse proportion to the clarity of its expression.

There remains for consideration the other notable production of this early period—*The Psychology of Dementia Praecox* (1906). It would be easy to assume that Bleuler was the moving spirit in this line of inquiry, and that Jung was falling in with the dominant interests of his chief. I doubt if this is so, not only, or mainly, because of the personalities of the two men but because there seems adequate evidence that Jung's studies in word association and in general psychopathology had led him to consider that familiar crux —the likeness, and the differences, between hysteria and dementia praecox. Thus he and Frederick Peterson, in their 'Psycho-physical Investigations with the Galvanometer and Pneumograph in Normal and Insane Individuals' (1907), mention that Jung had made 'innumerable analyses of dementia praecox', (p. 217) and (p. 179) they wish to 'call attention to the large number of undoubted katatonic processes which were formerly called "degenerative hysterical psychoses". There are many cases, too, of dementia praecox which for years are not to be distinguished from hysteria. We call attention to the similarity of the two disorders here in order to show that our hypothesis of the relation between "psychological adaptation to environment" and an emotional complex is an established fact in the matter of hysteria. If we find in dementia praecox similar conditions, we are justified in assuming that here, too, the general disturbances of mind may have a close causal relationship with an underlying complex. The complex is naturally not the only cause of dementia praecox, as little as it is of hysteria. Disposition is also a chief agency, and it is possible that in the disposition to dementia praecox affectivity brings about certain irreparable organic disturbances, as for instance metabolic toxins.

'The difference between dementia praecox and hysteria lies in certain irreparable sequelae and the more marked psychic disturbances from the former disorder . . . Hysteria is a caricature of the normal, and therefore shows distinct reactions to the stimuli of the environment. In dementia praecox, on the other hand, there is always defective reaction to external stimuli.'

It is pretty obvious that the association studies forced Jung to examine dementia praecox in the same light as he had examined hysteria—and to compare the two conditions. It is also plain that the specific disturbance— the 'weakening and loosening'—of associations was for Bleuler a fundamental characteristic of schizophrenia. Jung's word-association studies contributed powerfully to the conception of the disease which Bleuler advanced in the famous volume that he wrote for Aschaffenburg's *Handbuch*, and in some smaller monographs.

It would be going too far to attempt to traverse the ground covered in Jung's book on the *Psychology of Dementia Praecox*. A third of it was devoted to the detailed presentation of a carefully studied deteriorated schizophrenic woman; the rest reviewed the existing literature and put forward explanations and interpretations closely linked to Jung's earlier studies in hysteria and to Freud's views. I should, however, like to dwell briefly on the divergencies of view which now began to separate Bleuler from Jung.

Bleuler had developed his standpoint on the influence of affect. He published his *Affectivity, Suggestibility, Paranoia* in 1906 and therein stressed that affect-laden experiences, demonstrable as complexes, could determine a decisive change in a person's mental life, a 'false adaptation', which would thereafter follow a morbid, and often a deteriorating, course. Now Jung, while, of course, subscribing wholeheartedly to the opinions about the dynamic effect of complexes, which he had done so much to formulate, was reluctant to go the whole way in psychological explanation. He said, following a detailed comparison between hysteria and dementia praecox, 'whereas in hysteria there exists an unmistakable causal relation between the complex and the disease . . . we are not at all clear about this in dementia praecox. We do not know whether, in predisposed cases, it is the complex that causes or sets free the disease, or whether at the moment of the outbreak of the disease, a definite complex is present which then determines the symptoms. The more detailed and sharper the analysis, the more we see that in numerous cases, at the onset of the disease there was a strong affect from which the initial disturbance developed. In such cases one feels tempted to attribute

66

causal significance to the complex, but (perhaps) the complex, besides psy chological effects, produces also an X (toxin?) which helps along the process of destruction' (1906, trans. p. 88).

Again 'The greatest difficulty in these problems is the hypothetical X, the metabolic toxin (?) and its effects on the psyche ... The toxin (?) is to be considered as a highly developed body which adheres everywhere to the psychic processes, especially to those which are emotionally accentuated, reinforcing and automatizing them' (p. 89).

In considering this rather unexpected appeal to a hypothetical metabolic toxin, it is necessary to bear in mind that Kraepelin had from 1896 included dementia praecox among the metabolic disorders. The toxic origin of the disorder has of course been debated over and over: but what is startling is the suggestion that morbid affect is perhaps responsible for an 'endotoxin'. The theme was taken up by French psychopathologists: Hesnard, for example, in 1914 (when he was already much interested in psycho-analysis) put forward the assumption that an intense emotional shock may, by way of metabolic disturbances, liberate cytotoxins that act on the brain, liberating a psychosis to which the patient has been predisposed.

Jung was aware of Kraepelin's view, to which he alluded (1906, p. 32): 'In spite of an apparently uninterrupted causal chain of psychological events leading from the normal to the pathological, one can never disregard the possibility that in certain cases a change of metabolism (in the sense of Kraepelin) may be primary, whereby the accidental newest and last complex becomes "clotted" ... and thus determines the content of the symptoms ... The mechanisms of Freud are not comprehensive enough to explain why a dementia praecox originates rather than a hysteria; we must therefore postu late that in the case of dementia praecox there is a specific resultant of the affects (toxin?) which causes the definite fixation of the complex by injuring the sum total of the psychic functions. But one cannot, however, dispute the possibility that the "intoxication" might appear also as primary as a result of "somatic" causes and then seize the last complex which happened to be there and change it pathologically.'

This important monograph of Jung's provoked Ernst Meyer (1908, pp. 1312 f.), the Professor at Königsberg, to a critique attacking Jung's views on aetiology. Jung and Bleuler (1908) replied to this in a joint article which made clear the difference in their viewpoints. For Bleuler the toxic pathology of dementia praecox is 'a real autointoxication from internal secretions (Kraepelin), not mentally determined, or an infection (Bruce), or a glial proliferation': the complexes do not determine the underlying disease but they do determine much of its clinical picture. Hence his distinction between primary and secondary phenomena. Jung agreed with Bleuler about content—a subject to which he returned shortly after in *Der Inhalt der Psychose* (1908)—but is agnostic about the existence of primary, non-psycho genic symptoms; and he believes that the predisposition to dementia praecox can be activated and made manifest by psychological as well as by physical factors. The 'complex' can, in short, play a part in giving rise to the organic disease process of dementia praecox as the Zürich psychiatrists understand it. I think Adolf Meyer's strictures on this aspect of Jung's tenets were justified at the time they were made (1908): hypothetical toxins, of which there is no direct evidence, do not get us very far. Jung, however, was less certain than Bleuler that a physical process underlay schizophrenia.

The question is still an open one. I have dwelt on it at some length because it illustrates the perennial character of many cardinal problems of psychiatry. Dressed in a different language, tackled by different techniques of inquiry, they remain the same in essence for succeeding generations of psychiatrists. Until biochemical and biophysical methods reveal consistent and specific antecedents—or at least concomitants—of schizophrenia, or until psychological methods are more comprehensive and convincing in their explanatory force, the dispute of fifty years ago which we have just been considering will go on.

It may well be asked whether there is much profit in raking over these ashes. If indeed the problems recur, in different dress, would it not be better, one might suggest, to devote an hour to reviewing them in their modern form, rather than delving into volumes of extinct journals, reviewing musty statements and stale disputes. Well, it is arguable, but I think we gain something by seeing the steps that our predecessors were induced to take, the remarkable efforts of thought and inquiry made by notable men, the advances that depended on fortunate personal associations as well as on the ideas and knowledge of the time. As I see it, Jung made a powerful contribution to psychiatry in the work he did at Burghölzli during the five or six years we have been considering: and he was able to do so, because possessing great native ability and energy, he was exposed to the personal influence of Forel and Bleuler, the earnest climate of Swiss-German neurology and psychiatry at the turn of the century, the invigorating ideas of Freud, and, not least, the powerful aid to systematic and fertile inquiry which was afforded by the association method fathered by Galton and nurtured by the Leipzig psychologists and psychiatrists. Jung was fortunate in the time and place of his psychiatric apprenticeship, his *Lehrjahre*. The psychiatric products of that busy phase of his career call for recognition and appraisal in their historical setting: what he did in the ensuing half-century needs to be considered in another framework and judged by other standards.

REFERENCES

BLEULER, E., 1906. *Affektivität, Suggestibilität und Paranoia*, Halle, Marhold.
BLEULER, M., 1951. *Geschichte des Burghölzlis und der psychiatrischen Universitatsklinik*, Zürich.
BOLTE, A., 1903. 'Ueber einige Fälle von Simulation', *Allgemeine Zeitsch. f. Psychiat.*, 60, 1 and 2.
CROWN, S., 1947. 'A Controlled Association Test as a Measure of Neuroticism', *J. Personality*, 16, 2.

GALTON, F., 1879a. 'Psychometric Experiments', *Brain*, 2.

— 1879b. 'Psychometric Facts', *Nineteenth Century*, March.

GANSER, S. J., 1897. 'Ueber einen eigenartigen hysterischen Dämmerzustand', *Archiv. f. Psychiat.*, 30, 2.

————., 1904. 'Zur Lehre vom hysterischen Dämmerzustand', *Archiv. f. Psychiat.*, 38, 1.

HESNARD, A., 1914. 'Les Troubles nerveux et psychiques consecutifs aux Catastrophes navales', *Revue de Psychiat.*, 18, 139.

HOBBES, T., 1940. *Leviathan*, London, Odyssey.

HUBBARD, L. M., 1924. 'Complex Signs in Diagnostic Free Association', *J. exper. Psychol.*, 7.

HULL, C. L. and LUGOFF, L. S., 1921. 'Complex Signs in Diagnostic Free Association', *J. exper. Psychol.*, 4.

HUSTON, P. E., SHAKOW, D. and ERICKSON, M. H., 1934. 'A Study of Hypnotically Induced Complexes by Means of the Luria Technique', *J. Gen. Psychol.*, 11.

JUNG, C. G., 1902a. *Zur Psychologie und Pathologie sogenannter occulter Phänomena*, trans. 'On the Psychology and Pathology of so-called Occult Phenomena', *Coll. Wks.*, 1957, 1.

— 1902b. 'Ein Fall von hysterischem Stupor bei einer Untersuchungsgefangenen', *J. Psychol. u. Neurol.*, 1, 3, trans. 'Hysterical Stupor in a Prisoner in Detention'. *Coll. Wks.*, 1957, 1.

— 1903a. 'Über manische Verstimmung', *Allgemeine Zeitsch. f. Psychiat.*, 61, 1, trans. 'On Manic Mood Disorder', *Coll. Wks.*, 1957, 1.

— 1903b. 'Über Simulation von Geistesstörung', *J. Psychol. u. Neurol.*, 2, 5.

— 1905a. 'Experimentelle Beobachtungen über das Erinnerungsvermögen', *Zbl. Nervenhk.*, Sept., 28, 196.

— 1905b. 'Zur psychologischen Tatbestandsdiagnostik', *Zbl. Nervenhk*, Nov., 28.

— 1906. *Über die Psychologie der Dementia Praecox*. Halle, Marhold; trans. *The Psychology of Dementia Praecox*, by F. W. Peterson and A. A. Brill, New York, Nervous and Mental Disease Publishing Co., 1909.

— 1908. *Der Inhalt der Psychose*, Vienna, Deuticke; trans. 'The Content of the Psychoses', by M. D. Eder, *Collected Papers on Analytical Psychology*, London, Baillière, Tindall & Cox; New York, Moffat Yard, 1916.

— 1909. 'The Association Method', *Amer. J. Psychol*. Also in *Collected Papers on Analytical Psychology*, London, Baillière, Tindall & Cox, 1916.

JUNG, C. G. (ed.), 1906a and 1909. *Diagnostische Assoziationsstudien*, 2 vols., Leipzig, Barth; trans. *Studies in Word Association*, by M. D. Eder, London, Heinemann, 1918.

JUNG, C. G. and BLEULER, E., 1908. 'Komplexe und Krankheitsursachen bei Dementia Praecox', *Zbl. Nervenhk.*, 41, 2.

JUNG, C. G. and PETERSON, F., 1907. 'Psychophysical Investigations with the Galvanometer and Pneumograph in Normal and Insane Individuals', *Brain*, 3.

LEWIN, K., 1926. 'Untersuchungen zur Handlungs und Affekt-Psychologie', *Psychol. Forschung.*, 7.

LURIA, A. R., 1932. *The Nature of Human Conflicts*, New York, Liveright.

MEYER, A., 1908. 'The Problems of Mental Reaction-Types. Mental Causes and Diseases', *Psychol. Bull.*, 5.

MEYER, E., 1908. 'Bemerkungen zu Jung "Ueber die Psychologie der Dementia Praecox" ', *Archiv. f. Psychiat.*, 43, 3.

MÖNKEMÖLLER, O., 1904. 'Simulation oder Geistesstörung?' *Vierteljahrschrift fur gerichtliche Medizin*, 28.

NISSL, F., 1902. 'Hysterische Symptome bei einfachen Seelenstörungen', *Zentralbl. f. Nervenheilk. u. Psychiat.*, 25, 13.

RAECKE, J., 1901. 'Beitrag zur Kenntniss des hysterischen Dämmerzustandes', *Allgemeine Zeitschr. f. Psychiat.*, **58**, 1.

RAPAPORT, D., GILL, M. and SCHAFER, R., 1946. *Diagnostic Psychological Testing*, vol. 2, Chicago, Yearbook Publishers.

RUSSELL, B., 1946. *History of Western Philosophy*, London, Allen & Unwin.

SYMONDS, P. M., 1931. *Diagnosing Personality and Conduct*, New York, Century.

WERTHEIMER, M. and KLEIN, J., 1904. 'Psychologische Tatbestandsdiagnostik', *Archiv. f. Kriminalanthropologie*, **15**, 72.

7

MELANCHOLIA: A HISTORICAL REVIEW

MELANCHOLIA IS one of the great words of psychiatry. Suffering many mutations, at one time the tenacious guardian of outworn schemes or errant theories; presently misused, cavilled at, dispossessed, it has endured into our own times, a part of medical terminology no less than of common speech. It would seem profitable to consider the history of this word, and of the states of fear and distress with which it has from the beginning been associated.

THE ANCIENTS

The beginning was with Hippocrates [1]: 'If fear (phobos) or distress (dysthymia) last for a long time it is melancholia', he wrote, and so fixed the word. He insisted on the special temperament and constitution which tend to melancholia. His notion that black bile and phlegm altered the brain in its hotness and humidity, thus darkening the spirit and making melancholy, was to influence much subsequent speculation, and all classification was reared on his divisions—mania, melancholia, paranoia, phrenitis; but it is evident that for Hippocrates the atrabiliar conditions were numerous, and that the term 'melancholia' covered diverse states, now otherwise regarded. Furthermore, he considered epilepsy and melancholia to be closely related: 'melancholics ordinarily become epileptics, and epileptics, melancholics: of these two states, what determines the preference is the direction the malady takes; if it bears upon the body, epilepsy, if upon the intelligence, melancholy.' To the seasons he imputes much influence. However little now remains of these latter beliefs, once current in the School of Cos, there has been in recent times fresh interest in the doctrine of temperaments, most active and justified where depression and mania are in question; there has even been a revival in France of the long-rejected theory that black bile is the source of melancholy.

Aretaeus [2] of Cappadocia gives a detailed description of severe melancholia: 'If it (black bile) be determined upwards to the stomach and diaphragm, it forms melancholy, for it produces flatulence and eructations of a fetid and fishy nature, and it sends rumbling wind downwards, and disturbs

---

This paper is reprinted from the *Journal of Mental Science* (January 1934) **80**, 1–42.

the understanding. On this account, in former days, these were called melancholic and flatulent persons. And yet, in certain of these cases there is neither flatulence nor black bile, but mere anger and grief, and sad dejection of mind. . . . It is a lowness of spirits from a single phantasy without fever; and it appears to me that melancholy is the commencement and a part of mania. For in those who are mad, the understanding is turned sometimes to anger and sometimes to joy, but in the melancholics to sorrow and despondency only. But they who are mad are so for the greater part of life, becoming silly, and doing dreadful and disgraceful things; but those affected with melancholy are not every one of them affected according to one particular form; but they are either suspicious of poisoning or flee to the desert from misanthropy, or turn superstitious, or contract a hatred of life. Or if at any time a relaxation takes place, in most cases hilarity supervenes, but these persons go mad.'

He points out the recurrent character of the conditions, gives criteria of differential diagnosis, and concludes: 'The characteristic appearances, then, are not obscure; for the patients are dull or stern, dejected or unreasonably torpid, without any manifest cause: such is the commencement of melancholy. And they also become peevish, dispirited, sleepless and start up from a disturbed sleep. Unreasonable fear also seizes them, if the disease tend to increase, when their dreams are true, terrifying and clear; for whatever, when awake, they have an aversion to, as being an evil, rushes upon their visions in sleep. They are prone to change their mind readily; to become base, mean-spirited, illiberal, and in a little time, perhaps, simple, extravagant, munificent, not from any virtue of the soul, but from the changeableness of the disease. But if the illness become more urgent, hatred, avoidance of the haunts of men, vain lamentations; they complain of life and desire to die. In many, the understanding so leads to insensibility and fatuousness, that they become ignorant of all things or forgetful of themselves, and live the life of the inferior animals.'

Melancholia, like mania, Aretaeus would localize in the hypochondrium, and he would have it the fundamental form, from which other psychotic varieties develop—a doctrine that lasted until the end of the nineteenth century.

Asclepiades and his follower, Caelius Aurelianus [3], though important in the general history of psychiatry for their advocacy of rational therapy, have little to say about melancholia; the latter of them points out the distinction between the mood-disorders of mania and of melancholia. Celsus [4], another of that period, and greatly productive, includes many depressive states under the heading 'phrenitis'; he classifies partly according to duration, and speaks of 'another kind of madness which continues a longer time and goes no further than a sadness', and of a 'third kind of insanity, the longest of all, insomuch as it does not shorten life. There are two species of this. In some the deception arises from false images. . . . If imaginations mislead, first of all it must be observed whether they be melancholy or merry.' He classes melancholia among the partial deliria (general delirium being mania). His treatment is a curious mixture of very good and very bad.

Galen [5], living in the second century, developed the humoral pathology. Hippocrates [1] had insisted on the importance of the brain: 'Men ought to know,' he wrote, 'that from the brain, and from the brain only, arise our pleasures, joys, laughter and jests, as well as our sorrows, pains, griefs and tears. ... It is the same thing which makes us mad or delirious, inspires us with dread or fear. ... The corruption of the brain is caused not only by phlegm, but by bile. You may distinguish them thus. Those who are mad through phlegm are quiet and neither shout nor make a disturbance; those maddened through bile are noisy, evil-doers and restless, always doing something inopportune.' Galen agrees with this in general—'if we were well acquainted with the physiology of the brain, we should assuredly find in its pathological condition both the place and nature of the remedy'—but when he comes to speak about the humours and the part they play, he expresses not hopes and apodoses, but assured opinions. Melancholia depends on a superfluity of black bile 'in the very substance of the brain'; the melancholy humour is a condition of the blood, 'thickened and more like black bile, which, exhaling to the brain, causes melancholy symptoms to affect the mind.' He attacks Erasistratus for denying this. Under the designation 'melancholia' he describes indubitable schizophrenic pictures, and he agrees with Hippocrates as to the relation between epilepsy and melancholia.

There is in Plutarch an admirable description of one afflicted with religious melancholy, but it is proposed to abstain here from those citations out of non-medical writers and discussions about the madness of famous personages, from Hercules onwards, which are common in articles of this kind, but belong less to the history of psychiatry than to its *belles-lettres*.

THE MIDDLE AGES AND AFTER

From the time of Galen there is a long blank in occidental psychiatry. The influence of the Church was unfavourable. Demonology became the speculative foundation of thought about mental disorders. Exorcists continued through the Middle Ages the tradition of priestly intervention, long known among the peoples of antiquity. Religious value was placed on many of the signs of mental disturbance. In the East, and especially in Turkey, matters were better, but in Christendom, apart from a Greek survivor like Paulus Aegineta [6] and an occasional later voice like that of Jean le Charlier [7], belief in demoniacal possession, incubi and succubi, witchcraft, lycanthropy and such like usurp the place of medicine in this field. With the sixteenth century there is a gradual revival of empirical medicine in the study of insanity, characterized in part by a reversion to the teachings of Hippocrates and Galen, and by attempts at classification and a recognition of natural causes associated with the names of Paracelsus, Weyer and Plater.

In their views on melancholia, the majority of the writers of the first half of the sixteenth century repeat what Galen had said. Thus, Vallesius [8], in his *Tractatus Medicinalis* and his *Methodus Medendi* (1559–1589), compares and judges previous views about melancholia and gives as his own opinion 'the disease "melancholia" does not occur unless there be a melancholic tumour generated either in the brain itself (if it is primarily affected) or else-where (if it is affected consensually) . . . the disturbance causes black juices; these obscure the spirits, and hence come fear and sadness'. This is said with more to the same purpose also by Montanus [9], Cappivacci [10], Nicolas Piso [11], Walter Bruel [12], Gregory Horst [13] and others of note in their time, whose works the laborious Laehr has collected. Rondelet of Mont-pelier [14] (1507–1566) said that melancholia arose from a mere defect of the brain, or consensually from suffering of the whole body, or, finally, from the stomach as melancholia hypochondriaca, thus recalling Galen's [5] view, akin to that of Diocles of Carystus, that there is a melancholy that arises from the stomach. Similarly, Hieronymus Mercurialis [15] (1530–1606) emphasized the occurrence of disorders of digestion in all cases of melancholy, and said that there was also affection of the heart in them, which accounted for their special fears—a view developed forty years later by Daniel Sennert [16]. Among these writers, elimination of melancholic humours by purgation, clysters, blood-letting and baths, the use of hellebore, the specific from Anticyra, application of aromatic poultices, vesicants, leeches around the anus, cautery to the skull with long-maintained suppuration and finally working on the patient's imagination are the weapons for combating the *frigida intemperies cerebri, affectio tenebricosa.*

Felix Plater [17] (1536–1614), the Basle professor, is justly eminent for his attempt to build up an empirical psychiatry by classifying the diseases accord-ing to their nature and setting up empirically recognized varieties. Of his four divisions of insanity, the third, '*mentis alienatio*', includes melancholy and hypochondriasis among its subdivisions.

For the rest of the sixteenth and the seventeenth centuries there are Prosper Alpinus [18] (1553–1616), who gives a good description of melancholia and recommends warm baths for it, Riverius of Montpelier [19] (1589–1655), who says that there is a proximate cause, a poison generated in the body, which can be taken up and developed best in the atrabiliar constitution, Waldschmidt [20] (1644–1687), of the chemical school, who thinks melancholia arises from abnormal fermentation in the organism, Tozzi [21] (1638–1717), who reverts to Hippocrates's definition, Bellini [22] (1643–1704), who gives a good descrip-tion, especially of the aboulia and psychic inhibition, and Hoffman [23] (1662), who, like the Englishman, Sir George Ent [24] (1667) and others of the time, advised blood transfusion in melancholia, as in mental disorders generally. Of other Englishmen may be mentioned J. Johnston [25] (1603–1675), who follows Aretaeus in his views on melancholy, Sydenham [26] (who appears as an ardent phlebotomist, a Sangrado of the gloomy), and the illustrious Thomas Willis [27]. Willis has been described as the father of modern cerebral phsyiology; he regarded the 'animal spirits as the principle of sensation and movement—they are separated out in the brain from its blood; he sought to find the channels through which these animal spirits flowed during mental activity, and to defect or spoiling of them he attributed such disorders as melancholia. Sydenham appears to have adopted these views.

THE EIGHTEENTH CENTURY

A fresh period, in which the interaction of physical and mental factors is discussed and psychology brought nearer to practical medicine, begins with the influence of G. E. Stahl [28] (1660–1734), exercised through his animistic doctrine. Paracelsus [29] and, after him, van Helmont [30], had said that mental disorders sprang from anger, fright and other effects of the mystical Archaeus, the life-principle, *anima sensitiva*, the seat of which is in the stomach, and which builds up the organism and dominates all vital phenomena. Stahl, equally a vitalist, pointed to the influence of the psychic life on organic phenomena; these processes are united into one whole in the living organism by the *motus tonico-vitalis*; thereby all the single functions and organs express themselves in one animal economy as instinct in the healthy state, in morbid conditions as *vis medicatrix naturae*; mental disorders are an abnormal relationship of the soul, inhibited in its regular working by a strange motive (idea), which arises either from the senses, or from other bodily functions, or from the mood. It is not appropriate here to deal further with his views, essentially dualistic, on the genesis of mental disorder; they were carried into a later period by Zückert [31] (1737–78) and Unzer [32] (1727–99). The former described patients with strong 'imaginations' in whom all other senses and feelings are suppressed, thinking only of the subject which makes the imagination so lively; if this state be conjoined with lasting sadness, that is melancholia. Other currents in medical thought towards the end of this period are recalled with the names of Mesmer, Gall and Spurzheim, and Lavater, but they have no particular bearing on melancholia. The main features of European writings on psychiatry during this period (presently to be described, so far as they concern melancholia, under national headings) are new classifications, search after bodily changes, especially in the brain and crude attempts to apply psychological principles in treatment. There is also a large sediment of Galenical teaching in Friedrich Hoffman [33] (1660–1743), who considers the proximate cause of melancholia to consist in a rush of thick blood to the brain, its stagnation there and impeded return.

It will not be amiss to consider first the place of melancholia in the general nosological systems, more varied than in the last period. Vogel [34] (1724–74) divides the *morbi mentis* into six: *mania, melancholia, fatuitas, stupiditas, amentia* and *oblivio*. Boissier de Sauvages [35] (1706–67) divides insanity into three orders. The first is *morbi deliri*, and includes mania and melancholia; the cause of them is a material one, located in the brain, the sense-organs or the arrangement of the nerve-fibres. Melancholia is 'chronicum sine febre meditabundum paucis objectis affixum delirium' ('a chronic afebrile, brooding delirium fixed on a small number of objects'). Among his second order, the *morbi imaginarii*, is hypochondriasis; the third order is

75

morbi morosi. This is followed by Michael de Valenzi [36], in whose system the influence of Linnaeus may be discerned; Linnaeus had divided mental disorders on formal grounds into ideal, imaginary and pathetic, melancholy being one of the pathetic. Valenzi classes all the forms as vesaniae. Metzger [37], writing in 1793, separates feeble-mindedness (*mentis imbecillitas*) from insanity. True insanity is either febrile or chronic; if chronic, it is often ushered in by melancholia—a state of the mind in which it is occupied with sad pictures and thoughts. Sooner or later melancholia passes over into chronic insanity—a view that culminated long after in Kahlbaum's *vesania typica*. Kurt Sprengel [38], the medical historian, divides disorders of mood into melancholia, mania and fatuity. The essence of melancholy lies in an obstinate fixation of attention on one object and in mistaken judgment about it; from this one-sided activity result the feelings of inactivity and the sad mood; as proximate cause he assumes such an irregularity in the use of the brain's energy, that it becomes active only with one definite idea, all other having a weakened effect. Dreyssig's [39] classification (1770–1809) shows well the changes of meaning that the term 'melancholia' was undergoing. He collects all mental disorders into three forms—mania, melancholia, imbecility; melancholia is a partial insanity, or a partial failure of judgment and reasoning capacity, limited to one or a few subjects; it may be true or false; true melancholia is bound up with a lasting sad mood, false melancholia with indifference or cheerfulness; raging melancholy as the highest form approaches mania. This is clearly a very important distinction between 'true' and 'false' melancholia. The proximate cause of melancholia he took to be a disturbed balance between the power of judgment and the power of imagination. It is distinguished from hypochondria and hysteria on the ground that in the latter, irritability is specially increased in the abdominal viscera. As to the relation between mania and melancholia, just alluded to, the famous aphorisms of Herman Boerhaave [40] contain a similar opinion. Boerhaave regarded mania as a higher form of melancholia: 'si melancholia eousque increscit ut tanta accedat agitatio liquidi cerebrosi qua in furorem agantur saevum, mania vocatur' ('if melancholia go so far that the agitation of the cerebral fluid causes the patients to go raving mad, it is called mania'); he syncretized the prevailing nosological conception of melancholia in his definition of its as 'ille morbus in quo aeger delirat diu et pertinaciter, sine febre, eidem fere et uni cogitationi semper affixus' ('that disease in which the patient is long and obstinately delirious (deluded), nearly always dwelling on one and the same thought, but without having any fever')—almost identical with the earlier one of Johnston. The relation of mania and melancholia had been considered by Boerhaave; Morgagni [41], more akin to later writers, denied in his *De sedibus et causis Morborum* (1761) any complete distinction between the two: 'Melancholiae autem mania ut Willisii utar verbis in volumine eodem prolatis in tantum affinis est ut hi affectus saepe vices commutent et alter uter in alterum transeat; quin saepius dubitantes medicos videas hinc taciturnitate et metu, hinc loquacitate et audacia in eodem aegro subinde

76

alternatis, melancholicum an maniacum pronuntient' ('Mania, to use the words of Willis, is in so far akin to melancholia that these disorders often change from the one into the other, and so you may often see physicians doubting whether they should call a patient melancholic or maniac who alternates between talkative boldness and frightened silence'). This sounds a little like a reference to catatonic excitement, rather than mania. The Dutchman, Schim [42] (1779), went a step further and described periodic outbursts, and Philippe Pinel [43] described periodic insanity in more detail in 1798, concluding that the periodicity had no connection with the nature of the causes, and that the original site of this malady was in the region of the stomach, whence the attacks radiated. Fifty years later came Falret and Baillarger.

Before concluding these general considerations, a brief note on the therapy of melancholia as advocated by most writers of the eighteenth century may be added. Drugs were of all sorts, the most favourable being anagallis, arsenic, belladonna, datura, stramonium, phosphorus, tartar and other emetics and purges. Electricity was occasionally employed. Asses' blood was highly recommended, even regarded as a specific (Cardilucci [44]; Boenneken [45]). Boerhaave [40] recommended hydro-therapy: 'praecipitatio in mare, submersio in eo continuata, quamdiu ferri potest, princeps remedium est'. ('Plunging into the sea, immersion for as long as it can be borne, is the chief remedy.') Likewise John Ferriar [46] (1763–1815), who in his *Medical Histories and Reflections* advised warm baths to soothe mania, cold baths for melancholia. Some used immersion as a punitive or minatory remedy. Music was recommended as treatment for melancholia by French writers (Col de Villars [47], 1737, Buchoz [48], 1769); was there not King Saul in Holy Writ to attest its efficacy? Not all measures were so gentle. The barbarous methods of general management, including the whirling chair which Avicenna [49] long before had advised in melancholia to direct the blood into the proper parts, need no further mention here.

ENGLISH WRITERS OF THE PERIOD

It is convenient to consider separately and in some detail the contributions of English physicians of the eighteenth century to this subject of melancholy. The 'spleen', for long agreed to be a disorder peculiarly incident on the English—'*maladie Anglaise*'—was explored by Burton, by the essayists of the *Spectator* and Boswell's *Hypochondriac* with curious and familiar concern. Doctors were not behind in this. Cheyne (50) wrote a book, *The English Malady or a Treatise of Nervous Diseases of all kinds, as Spleen, Vapours, Lowness of Spirits, Hypochondriacal and Hysterical Distempers* (1733), and he discussed the great frequency of suicide among the English. Montesquieu, it may be mentioned here, was corrected by Philippe Pinel [43] for falling into this error of regarding suicide without evident motive as a malady peculiar to the English, though Pinel himself believed sufficiently in the national gloominess to write: 'On doit peut-être admirer la malheureuse fécondité des

Anglais en expressions énergiques et propres à exprimer les perplexités extrêmes, l'abattement et le désespoir des mélancoliques, même dans leurs ouvrages de médicine, et indépendamment de leurs romans et de leur poésie' ('One ought to admire perhaps the unfortunate richness of the English in vigorous expressions for the extreme perplexity, dejection and despair of the melancholic in their medical works, quite apart from their novels and poetry'). Benjamin Fawcett [51], though probably without medical training, published at Shrewsbury in 1780 his *Observations on the Nature, Causes and Cure of Melancholy; especially of that which is commonly called Religious Melancholy'*; he regarded it as a bodily illness, working on the mind, and he recommended, *inter alia*, rubbing the skin with a brush.

A more notable name is that of William Cullen [52], described by Kornfeld as 'the creator and founder of the theory and practice of psychiatry in England'. He classed vesaniae or 'lesions of the judging faculty' as one of the orders of neurosis, excluding from this order the hallucinations and the morositates—'the morositates, or erroneous passions, that accompany vesania, which as consequences of a false judgment, must be considered as arising from the same causes, and as symptoms only of the more general affection'. The vesaniae he subdivided into delirium (erroneous judgment, the meaning it still bears in France) and fatuity (weakness or imperfection of judgment). The nervous power or cerebral activity 'is, at different times, in different degrees of mobility and force. To these different states I beg leave to apply the terms of excitement and collapse. . . . To that state in which the mobility and force are not sufficient for the ordinary exercise of the functions, or when they are diminished from the state in which they had been before, I give the name of collapse'. He deplored the present incapacity to distinguish the several species of insanity according as they depend upon 'the different state and circumstances of the brain', and deprecated 'the ingenious Dr Arnold's' distinction of varieties: 'these varieties appear to me to be often combined together, and to be often changed into one another, in the same person: in whom we must therefore suppose a general cause of the disease . . .' Mania he believed to occur 'most frequently in persons of a melancholic or atra-bilarian temperament' as well as in the sanguine. The genus melancholia he described as a partial insanity, but speedily pointed out his doubts as to the justice of this 'I am inclined to conclude that the limits between general and partial insanity cannot always be so exactly assigned . . .' He considered it improper to distinguish melancholia by the character of partial insanity alone: 'If I mistake not, it must be chiefly distinguished by its occurring in persons of a melancholic temperament, and by its being always attended with some seemingly groundless, but very anxious fears.' He gave the differential points between it and hypochondriasis, which is one of the 'adynamiae'.

Another important figure is John Brown [53] (1735–1788), who declared insanity to be a disease, not of a single part, but of the whole body, mostly caused by excessive exertions of the mind—violent passions. His views on excitement, the sthenic and asthenic states, which reverted to the doctrine of Haller, had a considerable influence upon psychiatry in England and elsewhere, especially as to therapy; in this regard it was a most unhappy influence. He strove to excite the opposite passion in the patient to that which was evident and operative; thus he would rouse a melancholic from his torpor by the cruellest alarms.

Thomas Arnold [54], in his *Observations on Insanity*, published at Leicester in 1782 and 1786, shows himself an inveterate drawer up of schemes and categories, applied also to the analysis of melancholia, its forms, aetiology and prophylaxis. Linnaeus is his pattern. Richard Temple [55] (1792) defines melancholy as chronic disorder of the understanding in certain things, with sadness and rumination, the proximate cause being too great a dryness of the brain substance. W. Perfect [56] (1740–1789) was one of those who used electricity in treating melancholia; he gave careful descriptions of the somatic symptoms in his *Select Cases* (1787), and laid emphasis on inheritance. A. Harper [57], who confidently wrote *A Treatise on the Real Cause and Cure of Insanity, in which the Nature and Distinctions of the Disease are Fully Explained, and the Treatment Established on New Principles* (1789), considered there were two sorts of mental disorder besides insanity—melancholia and hypochondria. His bold claims as to treatment are not unjustified; he would have the body looked to as well as the mind; phlebotomy, diaphoretics, purges, diuretics, camphor, quinine, exercise, change of air, warm baths, music, sleep and moderate copulation shall be accompanied by the avoidance of all irritation and unnecessary restraint; isolation he declares especially harmful. One should try to discover the cause of distress, then remove it, give way to every sensible idea, avoid all exhausting activity of the mind, and prevent all unpleasant ideas and overstrung impressions. If these rules could be carried into practice early in the disorder, it would become exhausted and its progress stayed, he held. This was indeed admirable doctrine for the times. Faulkner [58], in his *Observations, etc.* (1790), is all for psychic treatment of the condition, and against the custom of immediately putting the patient into an asylum, since the sudden change of place and removal from all acquaintances may be harmful. Pargeter [59], writing in 1792, describes some cerebral changes in melancholia, but refrains from drawing any conclusion, remarking that it is uncertain whether these are cause or effect of the disease—a dilemma not unknown in later times. Among other remedies he liked snuff, which clears out unclean lymph from the respiratory passages and sinuses, and, especially in melancholia, shakes up the whole body through sneezing, and stimulates the nervous system. He recommended rubbing the belly with flannel for half an hour morning and evening—not unlike Fawcett, who used a brush instead of flannel. Pargeter, it may be mentioned, denied any influence of the moon in lunacy.

Better known than these is J. Haslam [60], one-time Apothecary to Bethlem Hospital. In his *Observations, etc.* (1798), he discussed the relationship of mania and melancholia: 'As the terms, mania and melancholia, are in general use, and serve to distinguish the forms under which insanity is exhibited.

there can be no objection to retain them; but I would strongly oppose their being considered as opposite diseases. In both, the association of ideas is equally incorrect, and they appear to differ only from the different passions which accompany them.' He objects to Ferriar's insistence of 'intensity of idea' in melancholia, and writes of the alternation of (schizophrenic) excitement and depression, 'when the furious state is succeeded by melancholy and after this shall have continued a short time, the violent paroxysm returns, the hope of recovery is very slight. Indeed, whenever these states of the disease frequently change, such alternation may be considered as unfavourable'. For melancholia he recommends blood-letting, but has little use for the other measures, such as emetics, camphor, opium, blisters to the head, and setons, then customary. Alexander Crichton's [61] *Inquiry, etc.* (1798), contains a psycho-pathological system unlike anyone else's, depending on a division of excitable parts, occasionally reminding one of Broussais' [62] *De l'Irritation*. The passions, according to Crichton, work on the nerves by means of the blood-vessels, and melancholia is the outcome of inhibition of vascular activity in the nervous system. Less fanciful and more intellectualistic were the views of James Sims [63] (1799), who considered melancholia to be a condition where imaginations of unpleasant experiences were mixed with correct recollections, the sufferer arriving from such faulty premises at formally correct conclusions. This was largely a restatement of John Locke's [64] view.

Of these English physicians, Philippe Pinel [43] wrote with severity: 'Un examen sévère et impartial n'y fait découvrir qu'une manière vague de disserter, des compilations répétées, des formes scolastiques, et quelques faits épars qui servent de temps en temps de points de ralliement, sans offrir un corps régulier de doctrine fondée sur les observations les plus multipliées' ('Severe and impartial examination discloses in them only a vague style of disquisition, repeated compilations, scholastic forms and some scattered facts which occasionally serve to hold the thing together, but do not make up a regular body of doctrine founded on many observations'). He is here talking of Arnold, Harper, Pargeter and Ferriar. For Perfect's *Annals of Insanity* he has high praise so far as it contains curious and valuable observations on different varieties of insanity, but he exclaims: 'Qu'il y a loin de ce recueil à un corps régulier de doctrine, à un traite général et approfondi sur l'aliénation mentale!' ('What a long way this collection is from being a regular body of doctrine, a general and thorough treatise on mental disorder!').

As to other countries, French and German writers are to be considered; the Italians are represented by Chiarugi [65], who supposes in melancholia a pre-occupation with one idea, presented by phantasy, the whole state being a product of sad passions; the patients should have their attention distracted.

PINEL AND OTHERS

In France there are Lorry [66] (1762), for whom 'melancholia' covers almost the whole range of mental disorders, including hysteria and epileptic convulsions, Le Camus [67], who denies psychic causes, J. F. Dufour [68] (1770), who follows Boerhaave's teaching, and the illustrious Philippe Pinel. In his *Traité Médico-philosophique sur l'Aliénation Mentale*, Pinel says: 'I have kept the name "melancholic delirium" for the variety that was directed exclusively upon one object or particular series of objects, with dejection, gloom and more or less tendency to despair, especially when it goes so far as to become incompatible with one's duties in society'. In the section of 'mélancolie ou délirie exclusif' he speaks first of melancholy as a habitual temperament (using it in the sense of Napoleon's remark 'cependant sans cette maudite bile on ne gagne pas de grandes batailles'); he then describes melancholy considered as a mental disorder, and includes quite exalted states (chiefly paranoiac) as well as depressive ones. He speaks of melancholia 'degenerating' into mania, but his illustrative case is of a paranoid schizophrenic. He speaks of the melancholy that leads to suicide and gives some vivid case-histories. He points out the danger of sending patients home too soon.

In Germany one picks out the names of Philipp Fischer [69] (1790), who asserts that to understand these cases properly one must get chronological data to permit of studying the whole psychological state of the patient—what is nowadays called 'the longitudinal section' of the case; and of M. A. Weickard [70], who makes the division of mental disorders into 'Geisteskrankheiten' and 'Gemütskrankheiten'. In the mood-diseases one will find lively affective qualities of mood or slow depressed retiring ones; among these latter are sleepiness, fatigue, sadness, depression, envy, shame, fearfulness, anxiety, despair, suicide. Simple depression and simple mania he thus regards as disorders of mood: while depression and excitement with delusions are included among the 'Geisteskrankheiten', subsection, 'Wahnsinn, Insania'. Where the patient is confused and deluded through preoccupation, sadness or other passion, it is melancholia; if he is raging, it is mania. The philosopher, Immanuel Kant [71], expressed general views about insanity in his *Anthropologie* (1798); he divided the 'Gemütskrankheiten' into mania and hypochondria. Melancholia is not quite a disorder of mood for him, but can lead to that: like hypochondria it may be a mere delusion of misery. J. G. Langerman [72], a follower of Stahl, advised that in diagnosis one should take carefully into consideration the somatic constitution and individual psychic character with especial emphasis on the tendency to phantasy. Finally, there is an interesting anonymous paper [73], *Beobachtungen und Erfahrungen über Melancholische*, by a gaol chaplain, in which melancholy is said to be that state of mood in which dark and confused ideas and sad and apprehensive feelings prevail.

ESQUIROL TO GRIESINGER

The next period starts with Esquirol [75] at the beginning of the century and ends with Griesinger, half-way through it. There is great preoccupation with methods of classifying the forms of insanity, and interest in their course and relations; description becomes more detailed.

Esquirol [75], following Pinel, assumed four varieties of mental disorder: mania, monomania or fixed delusion, dementia and idiocy. For depressive states, once called melancholic, he introduced the term 'lypemania', and instead of 'melancholia' in its current sense at that time, he substituted 'monomania'. The meaning of the word 'melancholia' had been much perverted and extended—the *'angor animi'* of Aretaeus had become insignificant, while the *'in una cogitationi defixus atque inhaerens'* of his definition was all important. The blame for this shift has been laid at the door of Reil and Hoffman, but it was much older; it is to be found in Daniel Sennert and very plainly in Boerhaave. By Esquirol's time it was the parent of confusion. Prichard [74], defending it, pointed out that in ordinary Greek writings, in Aristophanes, for example, μελαγχολᾶν meant simply to be mad, to be out of one's mind, without any lowness of spirits; but there was the special medical significance, given first by Hippocrates, and for long generally preserved, a usage firmly established, moreover, in popular speech. Esquirol did not get rid of the word, but through his criticism it was purged of accretions and returned to its proper use. Of lypemania Esquirol wrote: 'we believe that this a good definition: melancholia with delirium, or lypemania, is a chronic afebrile cerebral malady, with partial delirium, kept up by a sad debilitating or oppressive emotion.' He separates it from 'the habitual state of sadness in some individuals' and from monomania: 'It should not be confused with monomania, which is characterized by exclusive ideas with an expansive or cheerful emotion'. He also separated lypemania from dementia, and, with much emphasis, from hypochondria. As to the relation to mania, he wrote: 'Lypemania sometimes passes into mania; it is doubtless this change that has caused melancholia and mania to be confused.' In his lively description of the condition he surpasses his predecessors in accuracy and completeness. His influence upon English psychiatrists, as will presently be seen, was considerable. Prichard, for example, dedicated his treatise to Monsieur Esquirol, 'the most distinguished writer of his age on the subjects which I have endeavoured to investigate'.

Another writer in French was the Belgian, Joseph Guislain [76] (1797–1860), who assumed that every mental disorder was preceded by a more or less pronounced stage of depression—a view very generally adopted and later turned to the purposes of the *Einheitspsychose*. Among many opinions having a modern ring, Guislain advocated bed-treatment for melancholia.

English psychiatrists of this period devoted much attention to asylum arrangements and humanitarian principles in treatment; in theoretical psychiatry, discussions of classification and of pathological changes in the brain were in the forefront.

In his sober and admirable *Description of the Retreat* (1813), Samuel Tuke [77], though no doctor, gives a 'statement of cases and remarks' in which 'the cases are arranged under three classes, *viz.*, dementia, melancholia and mania. .... Under the class melancholia, all cases are included in which the disorder is chiefly marked by depression of mind, whether it is, or is not, attended by general false notions'.

In Philadelphia, on the other hand, Benjamin Rush [78] was advocating the opposed view. There are partial insanity and general insanity; melancholia is partial insanity in which the delusions apply to external objects. The melancholic patient may be sad or cheerful; so there are two varieties, tristimania (Esquirol's lypemania), and amenomania (monomania, paranoia).

Burrows [79], the maligned director of the Clapham Retreat, concluded, with Haslam, that 'mania and melancholia have one common physical origin, and are one and the same disease. All classification of mental disorders consequently appears to me worse than useless.' He discusses grief as a 'frequent moral cause of melancholia—often owing to an hereditary predisposition, or the person is of the melancholic temperament'. Schizophrenia and paranoia contribute to his array of the symptoms of melancholia, as with so many other writers. He follows Esquirol in the main, but disagrees with his substitution of monomania for melancholia.

Prichard [74], famous for his *Moral Insanity*—a term that has undergone a considerable change of meaning, but which, as he used it, included all affective disorders without delusions—says in *A Treatise on Insanity* (1835): 'A considerable proportion amongst the most striking instances of moral insanity are those in which a tendency to gloom or sorrow is the predominant feature,' and he gives a good clinical description of simple depressive states. Under the section 'Of Monomania' he explains how this term is synonymous with the 'melancholia' of earlier writers, and says, 'mental dejection or melancholy which extinguishes hope and gives the mind up to fear and the anticipation of evils, lays the foundation for many kinds or varieties of monomania', and he includes hypochondriasis as a form of monomania associated with fear and despondency.

M. Allen [80], in his apologia-born *Essay on Classification* (1837), regards mania and melancholia as 'effects of the same power being overactive in different directions', likely to be followed by 'a third stage, of exhaustion'. Neville [81] (1836) regards melancholy as a partial affective insanity; his views are manifestly coloured by phrenology, but do not otherwise differ from those of his contemporaries. Conolly [82], of Hanwell, the champion of 'no restraint', describes mania and melancholia as 'the two principal forms of mental malady' in his Croonian Lectures of 1849, but he casually differentiates apathy (? of early schizophrenia) from true melancholy in the following passage: 'Young persons not infrequently fall into a state somewhat resembling melancholia, without any discoverable cause of sorrow, and certainly without any specific grief; they become indolent, or pursue their usual occupations or recreations mechanically and without interest; the intellect, the affections, the passions, all seem inactive or deadened, and the patients become utterly apathetic; but the true melancholic patient is not apathetic. The mind sinks under some imaginary fault . . .' These are the chief writers early in the century. The thread of English psychiatry will be resumed with Maudsley.

In Germany the psychiatrists were especially concerned with general questions concerning the nature and causes of insanity, with systematic divisions, for example, according to the affection of will, mood, thought (Neumann [83]), or ideation, sensation, instinct (Hagen [84]), and predominantly with the question of psychic *versus* somatic, which was the great question for the first four decades of the century. The philosophical foundations of psychiatry were speculated on at length, and if it were not for the interest and enthusiasm of which these writings were indicative, one would find much pertinence in Burrows' [79] dictum: 'The best rule, however, for everybody to observe when attempting a judgment on any particular case of insanity is to take care and preserve his own faculties clear, and as free from the mysticism of speculative philosophy as from the trammels of nosology.' Of the numerous writers before Griesinger there are few who possess interest in the present connection; the different schools became known to English readers especially through the Sydenham Society's translation of Feuchtersleben's [85] *Medical Psychology.* Feuchtersleben included melancholy (lypemania, parathymia), in the restricted sense, in the general division 'fixed delusion', the monomania of Esquirol.

Flemming [86] divided the vesaniae into dysthymia (affective disorders), anoesia (where there are delusions with dysthymic phenomena that are of secondary significance) and mania. Zeller put forward an interesting division into two great groups; one characterized by the morbid origin, dominance and persistence of affective states with consequent modification of the whole psychic life; and another, where there are disorders of ideation and will, deriving not from dominance of an affective state, but representing an independent false thinking and willing without deeper excitation of mood, mostly with the character of psychic weakness. If the first of these groups be called affective disorders, and the second schizophrenia, with an allusion to Berze's [89] view about insufficiency of psychic activity in the latter, the differentiation seems modern. In Zeller's [87] *Berichte über die Irrenanstalt Winnenthal,* 1840, however, it is held that the states contained in the first group, in the majority of cases, precede the states of the second group; further, there is within the first group a certain definite succession of individual kinds of affective state, and so we come to regard insanity as showing in its different forms different stages of one disease process which may be modified, interrupted, changed by all sorts of intercurrent pathological happenings, but which, on the whole, keeps to a steady successive course which can go on to complete disintegration of psychic life—the Einheitspsychose.

The most important name in nineteenth century psychiatry, if one except Kraepelin, is that of Griesinger [88] (1817–1868). The general importance of Griesinger in the development of scientific psychiatry cannot be gone into here. As far as melancholia was concerned, he accepted Zeller's [87] view of 'two grand groups or fundamental states of mental anomalies, which represent the two most essential varieties of insanity'; he pointed out that in the first group were all the recoverable conditions: semeiology, psychological analysis and investigation of morbid anatomy all point towards recovery in these primitive affective mental anomalies. In this group are contained depression (Schwermut), mania, and delusional insanity. Among the forms of Schwermut are hypochondria, simple melancholia, melancholia with stupor (in which the schizophrenic form, regarded by Esquirol as dementia, is discussed also), melancholia with destructive tendencies (suicidal or homicidal), and melancholia with persistent excitement of the will (*folie raisonnante*, moral insanity, psychopathic character). Schizophrenia in its earlier stages was regarded by him as one of the affective disorders: 'Observation shows that in the great majority of cases those conditions which form the first leading group (emotions and emotional states) precede those of the second group; that the latter generally appear only as consequences and terminations of the first, when the cerebral affection has not been cured.' He agrees with Guislain [76] that most mental diseases commence with depression, and says he has no hesitation in speaking of the *stadium melancholicum* as the initiatory period of mental disease.

MAUDSLEY

The influence of Griesinger gradually made itself felt in England. His book was translated for the New Sydenham Society in 1867. In 1863 Dr Skae [90], of Morningside, had propounded a scheme of classification, with aetiological bias, containing twenty-five separate diseases, of which Blandford [91] wrote in 1871, 'The merits of this division are so great, and its superiority over all preceding so manifest, that it requires little or no comment'. It received, however, a great deal of comment, some of it critical, was modified by Batty Tuke [92], widely approved, and, with Bucknill's elaborate divisions, marks the height of classifying activity in England. But in 1868 one finds Henry Maudsley [94] putting forward a simpler view. The main changes of opinion in England during the rest of the century can in large measure be followed in the successive editions of his book, *The Pathology of Mind*. To trace these changes in some detail is at once relevant and pious in one who is writing from the Maudsley Hospital.

Following in the steps of Prichard [74], and influenced by Esquirol [75], Maudsley gives, in the edition of 1868, a symptomatological grouping into affective and ideational insanity which, in some of its implications, recalls Griesinger: 'If a broad division were made of insanity into two classes, namely, insanity without positive delusion and insanity with delusion—in other words, into affective insanity and ideational insanity; and if the subdivision of these into varieties were subsequently made—would not the classification, general as it may appear, and provisional as it should certainly be deemed, be for the present preferable to one which by postulating an exactness that does not exist, is a positive hindrance to an advance in knowledge?' 'The affective disorder is the fundamental fact; in the great majority of cases it precedes intellectual disorder; it co-exists with the latter during its course; and it frequently persists for a time after this has disappeared.' 'A third objection to an adherence to the present artificial classification is that it has unquestionably fettered observation, and hindered the faithful study of the natural history of insanity. The different forms of affective insanity have not been properly recognized and exactly studied because they did not fall under the time-honoured divisions; and the real manner of commencement of intellectual insanity in a disturbance of the affective life has frequently been overlooked.' He recalls Guislan's and Griesinger's observation that depression is often an initial stage in mental disorder, and adds that 'maniacal perversion of the affective life' may be equally a precursory stage. In his working out of this scheme, however, he is hampered by relics from the earlier writers. His affective insanity includes mania without delusions, melancholic depression without delusions, 'mental alienation proper' (moral insanity), and the insane temperament (neurosis spasmodica). Obsessions, compulsive disorders generally, phobias, etc., are included in it. As forms of ideational insanity there are acute and chronic mania and melancholia (which are called general forms), monomania and melancholia (partial forms), dementia, general paralysis of the insane, and idiocy. The significance of the relation of the delusions to the affective state, pointed out by Griesinger, is overlooked, hence the overlapping and the inclusion, in the clinical descriptions, of schizophrenic and true melancholic patients in the same grouping. Depressive states are actually described almost entirely under the heading 'ideational insanity'. There are adumbrations of a later adoption of Griesinger's view that there is but one disease, insanity: 'The different forms of insanity are not actual pathological entities, but different degrees or kinds of the degeneration of the mental organization—in other words, of deviation from healthy mental life.'

The third edition [95] of Maudsley's book appeared in 1879. Of this there is an interleaved copy, with his manuscript annotations, in the library of the Maudsley Hospital. There is here recognition of the occasional independence of the manifest affective state and the delusions. In regard to mania and melancholia with 'partial' delusions (monomania and lypemania) he writes: 'While the intellectual disorder is limited to a few ideas, the same thing can seldom, if ever, be said truly of the feelings; they are more deeply and generally affected, and yield a constant nourishment to the delusion which is rooted in and fed by them. Were our observer to reside long enough in the asylum to watch the course which these mental disorders went through, he would notice that there took place in some instances a gradually increasing failure of mental power with an increasing incoherence of ideas, the feeling that inspired the delusions waning in force, while the delusions themselves persisted and perhaps became more in number and more extravagant in character.' He puts forward the view that where there are delusions not explicable as arising out of the affective disturbance, strong hereditary predisposition may be assumed; this is summed up in a manuscript note, 'So calm and yet so deluded, he could never have developed that alone'; and in another such note he writes: 'Delusions not, as it were, the logical outcome of a predominant mood and coherent development, but independent, abrupt, of spontaneous outcome, as it were, have got themselves to be explained. The fact is, I take it, that it is with them as in dreaming, the supreme centres show their natural tendency to fashion or create, and to create according to their inbred form.' The pragmatic inadequacy of his grouping of mental disorders is explicitly admitted, but not on just grounds: 'when we have to think how a particular case has been caused, what course it will run, how will it end, and what sort of treatment should be used, we do not so much consider whether the symptoms are mania or melancholia as we do what constitutional diathesis underlies, or what bodily disturbance accompanies the derangement. It is certain that we get more help generally from the exact observation and appreciation of such bodily states than we do from the mental symptoms alone; for example, whether a mental disorder is maniacal or melancholic is not of much moment, but the recognition of a gouty disposition, of a syphilitic infection, of a commencing paralysis, of a puerperal cause, and the like, will help us much.' The clinical description of melancholia is full and admirable; though it is still included under 'ideational insanity', the essential unimportance of the mere presence of delusions is plainly stated: 'at the beginning of melancholia in most cases, and throughout the disease in some cases, there is no definite delusion, the person is simply morbidly melancholic'; the painful delusion 'has been precipitated, as it were, out of the vague feeling of unspeakable misery which is the medium in which its gestation or incubation has taken place; and it takes different forms according to the person's culture and habits of thought, and according to the prevailing social and religious opinions of the time'. In one place he describes the alternation of hypomania and mild depression as an example of moral insanity; elsewhere he alludes to Falret's *'folie circulaire'* as the succession of true mania upon true melancholia.

In the last edition [96], of 1895, classification is scarcely mentioned (though in this it was not wholly representative; the influence of Skae and the earlier classifiers was still working in Clouston and others). The emphasis is now all on the individual, his inheritance and make-up—an evidence of French influences. The physician 'will reflect if he is wise, that there is no such disease as insanity, that there are really so many insane individuals to be treated in the concrete'; in involutional melancholia 'here, as always, the right question is not whether the disease is one likely to end in recovery, but whether the particular sufferer from it, being what she is, is likely to recover'. The manuscript notes in the earlier edition are elaborated and polished. 'Moral or affective insanity' is thrown overboard; the importance of constitution (tinctured by Morel's [109] views on degeneracy) is underlined with fatalism; it is 'the inborn structure of the individual mind which determines whether disorder shall deepen into disorganization or shall pass away. . . . In this relation it is proper to remember and reflect that bad foundations of mental structure are laid, not by positive madness only in the parental stock, but by such wrong and unwholesome mental development in it. . . . Not that every degree and sort of neuropathic inheritance is fraught with so serious a risk. It is a question of kind and degree of degeneracy. . . . The heritage may amount to no more than an unstable equilibrium, prone to be over-thrown suddenly and perhaps as suddenly restored. This is especially the case where there was an external cause of mental disturbance in some physical or moral shock, some stress or strain, not apparently adequate in itself, but adequate in the case, and where the disorder was acute.' He is speaking here of mania, but has similar views as to melancholia and the alternating recurrent form, 'Janus-faced'. All depressive states, including hypochon-driacal melancholy, are described together, with more stylistic effort and less detail than in the earlier books; the general features of the disorder replace or subsume the catalogue of individual symptoms. There is a striking account of the selfish and exacting claims which many melancholics, professing lowliness, make upon their relatives or nurses—an observation made again by Sigmund Freud. Maudsley, interpreting it, introduces speculations from neurology: 'But is all this self-indulgence the selfishness which it looks? It is the indulg-ence of a partial, maimed and morbid self. . . . The probable pathological condition of things is an exorbitant and predominant, almost exclusive, activity of certain brain-tracts charged with sad feeling . . . entailing a molecu-lar sluggishness and, according to its degree, a lessened or suspended function of other tracts.' Hughlings Jackson [97] had speculated in a more tentative and unprecise way about the nature and factors of insanity (1894), but this audacious playing with unsuitable physiological and neurological conceptions, an aberration in Maudsley, was a dominant vice in other English psychiatrists and, more soberly applied, was the characteristic in Germany of Wernicke [98] and his school.

OTHER NINETEENTH CENTURY WRITERS

After this detailed examination of the manner in which Henry Maudsley considered the problem, there is little need to write further at length on English psychiatrists during the latter half of the nineteenth century. The influence of Prichard [74] and Skae [90], and less immediately of Esquirol [75] and Griesinger [88], was considerable among the earlier of them, such as Blandford [91], Bucknill and Tuke [92], and Dickson [99]; then come Sankey [100] and Savage [101], the latter notably simple in his classification and clear in his pictures of types of disorder; he describes simple melancholia, active and passive melancholia, and melancholia with stupor; he notices the relationships of melancholy with periods of life and with bodily disorders, such as gout, cardiac and renal disease. He speculates very little, and re-marks in one place that 'wise men investigate while fools explain'. Bevan Lewis [102] devotes nearly half of his work on *Mental Disorders* to anatomy and structural pathology; in his clinical description of states of depression there is much psychologizing. He insists, however, as did Falret [104], on the indivisibility of the mind; speaking of 'purely emotional or affective insanity' he remarks: 'So interblended are all the mental faculties in their mutual co-operation, that no such division can be drawn, in a strictly scientific sense, between the purely emotional and the intellectual states. When we speak of emotional states, we must ever bear in mind that the term connotes more or less of the intellectual element of mind . . . feeling, memory, reason, volition; or rather that these are but different aspects of the same state'. The section (by Rayner [103]) on Melancholia in Allbutt's *System of Medicine* covers no new ground and abounds in technical terms.

In France Jean Pierre Falret [104], in 1851, drew attention to the differences between ordinary melancholia and the periodic variety. Then, in 1854, Baillarger [105] described to the Academy of Medicine his 'folie à double forme'; there was a brief controversy as to priority, and Falret at the following session read his paper, *De la Folie Circulaire*. In this he points out the frequency and intensity of remissions and paroxysms in the course of mental disorder, and says that many grave errors have been the consequence of not considering this: 'It is also one of the causes for the persistence in regard to partial insanities of the scientifically erroneous doctrine of the single delusion, of monomania'. Intermittent disorders 'have most commonly a sudden onset, a more uniformly continuous less paroxysmal course during the attack'. Moreover, it resembles in all points precedent attacks, and, as against the opinion of earlier and of contemporary authors, 'The duration of each attack can be and often is longer with advancing years, but it is a mistake to believe that intermittent insanity always ends as continuous insanity. On the contrary, that is very rare.' Most curable in its attacks, it is incurable in its essence, though one may be able to delay and even abort the attacks. It is intermittent, not periodic. Exciting causes can precipitate an outburst. The intermittency may be prolonged, or brief (eight days to a month). *Folie circulaire* is characterized 'by the regular sequence of maniacal state, melancholic state and lucid interval of varying duration'. He considers it . . . 'a genuine form of mental illness, because it consists in a group of constant physical, intellectual and affective or total behaviour symptoms'. He gives further grounds for regarding it as a natural form; describes its clinical features: 'There is no limited impairment of intelligence and predominance of certain well-defined delusions as in ordinary melancholia, but a physical and mental depression, even to the point sometimes of complete suspension of the intellectual and affective faculties.' He says that it is strongly hereditary, and commoner among women than men. And, finally, a classification based on 'a collection of characteristics related together and following a definite course' is in his judgment most likely to lead to sound prognosis and rational treatment. His reasons for this view and objections to the older classification are expounded with great clarity. His influence on Kraepelin in regard to the manic-depressive psychosis may be safely assumed.

Just as Falret demolished monomania, so Brierre de Boismont [106] (1867) showed that *folie raisonnante* was only a symptom of widely different forms of insanity (later Krafft-Ebing (107) designated very chronic and constitutionally conditioned melancholia as 'melancholic *folie raisonnante*'). Lasègue [108], in 1852, pointed out that the '*délire de persecution*' was not part of lypemania. Morel [109] (1860), whose insistence on inheritance and the make-up of the individual was of great service, proved less happy in applying his principles to the actual distinction and painting of pictures of mental disorder. Cotard [110] (in 1880) described the syndrome known by his name, in which *délire des négations* is conspicuous; he recognized its unfavourable prognostic significance, which he took to be invariable.

Magnan [111] (1882), accepting Morel's general group of hereditary insanities, distinguishes true melancholia from melancholic states occurring among these '*dégénerés*', and he describes as a special group '*folies inter-mittentes*'. In his general description of them he follows Falret and Baillarger, but says, 'the recurrence of the attacks, *whatever their form* (melancholia or mania), is the most important phenomenon from the prognostic point of view', and says that the form of the attack is very variable—'one finds the most unexpected combinations of mania and melancholia in the same patient'.

It will have been observed that the distinction between psychoses and neuroses (excepting hysteria) was in some measure a product of the nineteenth century; at first grouped under the 'moral or affective insanities', as by Prichard and Maudsley, more carefully separated by French psychiatrists, beginning with Morel, and regarded as evidences of hereditary alienation or 'degeneration', the disorders in which compulsion or anxiety is the chief clinical feature were gradually delimited, but it was not until the present century that the 'neuroses' attained a nosological independence that is nowadays unduly insisted on in some quarters. In the main tide of psychiatry the occurrence of fear, doubt, obtrusive thoughts and more precisely defined 'neurotic' symptoms in the course of melancholia has long been clearly recognized. Burrows [79], though in his terminology 'neurosis' was the general term for disease of the nervous system, pointed out from the genetic standpoint the close relationship between insanity and certain neuroses in the modern sense. Trélat and Legrand du Saulle [112] developed and modified Morel's views on the same matter. Kahlbaum [113], somewhat later, discussed the interrelation between neuroses and psychoses. In the present century Lange [149], Kahn and Abraham [175, 176] have made notable contributions to the subject, so far as melancholia is concerned.

PART II

With Kahlbaum [113] one stands on the threshold of the modern period in psychiatry. His contributions towards the delimiting of 'dementia praecox' have been often stressed. Here it is only necessary to recall that for him general paralysis of the insane (*vesania paralytica*) was the paradigm to which *vesania catatonica* was to be approximated; mania, melancholia, moria and dementia are 'not the appearances of different kinds of mental disorder ... but the appearances of their different stages, or, better still, the appearances of the different symptom-complexes which they can assume at different periods of their course'. Here he follows Griesinger and Neumann. The difficulties of this, when considered with regard to actual cases, and especially to *folie circulaire*, are acknowledged. In 'stable' melancholia, he remarks, all the psychic symptoms can be derived from the morbid affect, not so in 'primary dementia'. He would reserve 'melancholia' as a designation for initial or transitory melancholy, a stage in *vesania typica*, but for stable or definitive melancholy (melancholia in the modern sense) he suggests 'dysthymia'—a term already borrowed from Hippocrates by Flemming and Griesinger. This dysthymia he regards as a variety of mental disease (a special, or partial, mental disorder), while the other is only a morbid state. *Folie circulaire* he includes as a modification of *vesania typica*, destined to end in dementia. The relation of melancholia to *vesania typica* is compared by his pupil, Hecker [114], to that between coryza and measles—the former may be an initial stage of the latter, or an independent disorder. Hecker incidentally emphasizes the frequency with which anxiety attacks, often referred to the praecordium (*Precordialangst*), may occur in 'genuine melancholia'. Hecker further describes the features of the 'melancholia' that usher in *vesania catatonica*—the rigidity, stereotypy, etc.

KRAEPELIN

With Kraepelin [116, 117], the door of the modern period is opened. Prominent in his work may be recognized the nosological principles of Kahlbaum, the insistence on identity of causal factors (*Entstehungsbedingungen*), course and outcome as the criteria of a mental disease. The *Einheitspsychose* is forsaken. Manic-depressive insanity and dementia praecox take the field; and in the successive editions of his textbook Kraepelin defines more and more clearly the features of the 'disease'—*manisch-depressives Irresein*. In the fourth edition the most diverse terminations are ascribed to mania and melancholia, and essentially different states are included as sub-groups of melancholia. In his 1896 edition [116] (the fifth), which he describes as betokening 'the last decisive step from the symptomatic to the clinical approach to insanity', he divides all insanity into acquired disorders and those arising from morbid predisposition; among the former 'melancholia' figures as an insanity of the involution period; among the latter, periodic insanity is given as one of the constitutional mental disorders, and constitutional mood-disorder (*constitutionelle Verstimmung*) as one of the psychopathic conditions (insanity of degeneration). In 'periodic insanity' he describes manic, circular and depressive forms.

In the following years controversy centred mainly about the independence of 'melancholia' of the period of involution, which Kraepelin had given as a separate disease. Thalbitzer [118] began an attack on the Kraepelinian view in 1902, and in later writings pointed out the grounds on which he would include this variety of agitated depression within the manic-depressive psychosis, of which it is in clinical form, if not in course, a mixed state. It was only, however, after Dreyfus's [119] monograph in 1907 that Kraepelin ceased to denominate as 'melancholia' the depressive anxiety of the presenium and accepted it as one of his *Mischzustände*. Dreyfus, unlike Thalbitzer, used Kraepelin's own criteria. In spite of Kraepelin's attitude, the point continued to be hotly contested; among Germans, Westphal [120], Ziehen [121, 122], Specht [123], Rehm [124] and Forster [125]; among the French, Régis [126], Masselon [127], Ducoste [128], Dény and Camus [129] contributed to the discussion, and in 1910 '*die Melancholiefrage*' was still being debated when Hoche's [131] famous Referat with this title cut the ground from under the feet of the disputants. His pupil Bumke [133] the year before had published a trenchant criticism of the whole Kraepelinian position. Hoche [131], following it up, pointed out that in the eighth edition (1909) Kraepelin had relegated 'melancholia' (involutional depression) from '*Krankheitenseinheit*' to a '*Zustandsbild*'—from a disease to a clinical picture— and that it no longer mattered whether there was mania or melancholia, occurrence once in life, or many times, at irregular or at regular intervals, whether late or early, with predominance of these symptoms or those—it was still manic-depressive insanity. This standpoint Hoche attacked on theoretical and practical grounds, and proceeded to his general thesis—that clinically distinguishable *Krankheitseinheiten* do not exist. With incisive sarcasm he derided the systematizing efforts of his contemporaries, 'who give the impression of a great number of diligent workmen, most energetically engaged in clarifying a turbid fluid by pouring it busily from one vessel into another'. Typical cases are the exception: 'It is here that a kind of thought-compulsion, a logical and aesthetic necessity, insists that we seek for well-defined, self-contained disease-entities, but here as elsewhere, unfortunately, our subjective need is no proof of the reality of that which we desire, no proof that these pure types do, in point of fact, actually occur'. He cited the great variety of clinical pictures seen in structural disease of the brain, toxic disorders, etc., and proposed to substitute for diseases 'symptom complexes' or syndromes: 'Now I believe that we will make more progress if we make an attempt to find entities of a secondary order, certain constantly-recurring accumulations of symptoms which we shall learn to recognize when once our attention is directed to them.' Hypochondria, neurasthenia and hysteria were given as examples of this. He declared that for practical and didactic purposes labelling with names of diseases is unnecessary: 'That we can predict the patient's behaviour; that, from certain features, in themselves insignificant, we can yet, as a rule, soon obtain a picture of an individual's inner psychic activity; these facts surely depend, not on the existence of disease-types, but on experiences of a much more general nature, which are quite independent of the question of the labelling of these states.' There are certain regularly recurring symptom-complexes which account for the similarity of utterance and behaviour in countless madmen of all times and countries. Certain of these syndromes lie pre-formed and ready in normal psychic life—the melancholic is one of them. There are in the individual case endless possibilities as to form and course. 'If the term "manic-depressive" is meant as a theoretical expression of the close internal relationship of the two opposite poles of affectivity, then there are no objections to raise against it. But the name is to be rejected as a disease-entity and consequently as a designation of diagnostic and prognostic value.' 'Just because of its close relationship with normal psychic events, melancholia, more than other mental disorders, takes its stamp from the subject's age, sex and personal temperament, and so, too, presents quite special characters when it occurs in the involutionary period.'

The influence of these views upon German psychiatry was great, and Kraepelin himself in 1920 made considerable concessions in his *Erscheinungs-formen des Irreseins* [117]. In this he recognized Bonhoeffer's [145] '*Exogene Reaktionsformen*', and went on to remark how significant it is 'that numerous manifestations of insanity are laid down once and for all by previously established dispositions of the human organism, and therefore run their course in the same way in all cases, given the same conditions.' We are thus obliged to limit to the utmost the assumption that this or that disorder is characteristic of a definite disease-process ('Krankheitsvorgang').

EARLY TWENTIETH CENTURY

There has been an independent movement along the same lines in America. Adolf Meyer [134], working at first with the Kraepelin groupings, gradually between 1902 and 1905 developed out of his dynamic-genetic interpretation a concept of reaction types, clearly expressed in his paper of 1908. These views are given more at length below; but it may be mentioned here that in 1904, in a discussion [135] on melancholia at the New York Neurological Society, he said that 'for practical reasons he would rather favour a different classification. On the whole he was desirous of eliminating the term melancholia, which implied a knowledge of something that we did not possess, and which had been employed in different specific ways by different writers. If, instead of melancholia, we applied the term depression to the whole class, it would designate in an unassuming way exactly what was meant by the common use of the term melancholia; and nobody would doubt that for medical purposes the term would have to be amplified so as to denote the kind of depression. In the large group of depressions we would naturally distinguish our cases according to aetiology, the symptom-complex, the course of the disease and the results. . . . The distinction had best be made according to the intrinsic nature of the depression. From that point of view we might distinguish the pronounced types from the simple insufficiently differentiated depressions. Besides the manic-depressive depressions, the anxiety psychosis, the depressive deliria and depressive hallucinations, the depressive episodes of dementia praecox, the symptomatic depressions, non-differentiated depressions will occur.' The further development of this will be described later.

At about the same time the subject of cyclothymia received much attention, especially in France. Under this name Kahlbaum [113] had collected the mildest forms of circular insanity; his pupil Hecker [115] treated the subject in a special paper [1898], as did Hoche [132] in 1897; Wilmanns [136] pointed out the features which have since come to be associated with 'psychogenic' depression, and Römheld [137] wrote on similar lines. Ziehen described periodic menstrual melancholia with depersonalization or excitement, and Kraepelin eventually grouped all these conditions together as 'Grundzu-stände.' In France, Deny [130] and Kahn [138] somewhat earlier (1909) extended the term 'cyclothymia' to cover not only mild forms of manic depressive insanity, but also a special morbid predisposition, highly inherit-able—an attitude in keeping with the general trend of French psychiatry. Friedmann's [139] 'neurasthenic melancholia' was regarded in a similar way, though the word 'cyclothymia' was eschewed. The importance of the constitutional factors was recognized by Reiss [140] in his paper on 'Kon-stitutionelle Verstimmung'; he found fluid transitions between the various types of depressions, genuinely endogenous circular forms at one end of the scale and clear reactions to an environmental situation at the other. Alz-heimer [141] wrote a paper on 'diagnostic difficulties in psychiatry' which likewise paid due regard to the constitutional factors—still viewed in the light of 'degeneration'. Other writers dealt at this time with 'hysteromelancholia', 'pseudomelancholia' and similar newly-named groupings. At the same time psychological experiments along Wundtian lines were carried out chiefly by Rehm [142], Isserlin [143] and Aschaffenburg [144]. Clinical studies were published in great numbers, but were largely occupied with statistics and quarrelling.

NOSOLOGICAL PROBLEMS

The brilliant work of Bonhoeffer [154] in describing the exogenous types of reaction served to emphasize the difficulties of an aetiological classification. It was clear that the same cause might produce widely different clinical pic-tures, and the reverse, and that constitutional metabolic, genetic and biological factors generally called for consideration, together with careful analysis of the clinical features, from a phenomenological point of view. Some, presently to be considered, thought that salvation lay rather in minute psychological analysis—a different thing entirely, and open to epistemological objections, as they practised it.

Kraepelin had made concessions to Hoche's view, but it was not surrender. Manic-depressive insanity remained for him, as for his followers, a disease to be differentiated and delimited. He held, as shown above, that the individual brain reacts to the trauma of the disease in the manner determined by its own constitution; among these *Erscheinungsformen* he included delirious, paranoid, emotional, instinctual, schizophrenic, verbal hallucinatory, encephalopathic, oligophrenic and spasmodic kinds. But the fundamental diseases remained. His pupil, Johannes Lange [147], examined in accordance with these principles catatonic phenomena occurring 'in the frame' of manic-depressive insanity. The bold claims of Urstein were disposed of. The difficult problem of the interpretation of schizophrenic features occurring in the course of a predominantly affective disorder was gone into by Lange in the light of the exogenous and genetic factors, as well as the time of life. Bonhoeffer [146] showed that periodic confusional states were special variants of manic-depressive insanity, and pointed out the frequency with which compulsive phenomena occur in depressive states—a subject with which Stocker [150] also concerned himself. Lange [148] also made a study of depressive states, following in the footsteps of Reiss [140], but making more use of the somatic and genetic criteria in accordance with the tenets of Kretschmer [166] and others. The psychogenic forms of depression were dealt with by Kurt Schneider [151], who emphasized the 'vital' elements in endogenous depression, in accordance with the philosophic doctrine of Scheler; Westermann [152] followed suit.

Among those who did not support the Kraepelinian views were Rittershaus [153], who, like Hoche [131], saw in manic-depressive insanity only a symptom-complex, and Schröder [154], who would accept pure cases of it as a special disease-group, but would include all the complicated forms (*Mischzustände, Grenzzustände*) in a new group, the degeneration-psychoses or metabolic disorders, in which there might also be put impure psychotic pictures, odds and ends from dementia praecox, epilepsy, etc. Kleist [155], the disciple of Wernicke [98] and inheritor of his 'motility-psychoses', which he was at first inclined to allot back to the manic-depressive disorder, came to the conclusion that one may delimit the pure manic-depressive psychosis and set alongside it as of equal value motility-psychoses, periodic hallucinoses, periodic paranoid pictures, expansive and depressive autopsychoses, periodic confusional states, etc.—all linked together by their autochthonous development and cyclic course; the whole collection, including mania and melancholia, he denominated 'the autochthonous degeneration-psychoses'. Later, under the influence of biological tendencies, he separated pure cases of manic-depressive insanity from the degeneration-psychoses, therein agreeing with Schröder [154], and prosecuted his very individual 'localizing' method of study. Gaupp and Mauz [156] have arrived at similar conclusions, calling their rubbish-heap '*Mischpsychosen*'. A failure to consider the individual and pathological elements in the symptom-picture may be suspected to be the basis of their problem. The word 'pathoplastic' was used by Birnbaum [157], in contradistinction to 'pathogenetic', when discussing the causal factors in the building-up of a psychosis; its implications as to structural analysis were the same as those of Kretschmer's [166, 167] 'pluridimensional diagnosis'— the necessity, in brief, for considering the individual upbringing, experience, environment, setting, when assigning its value to any symptom or group of symptoms. This has been emphasized also by Adolf Meyer [134] and, of course, by those with psycho-analytic convictions or bias.

Ewald [158], in a paper dealing with this subject of degeneration psychoses, expressed the view that, like Thalbitzer [118], he regarded manic-depressive psychoses as endogenous 'quantitative diseases', while the other members of the group could be qualified with various combinations of the epithets, 'qualitative' and 'quantitative', 'exogenous' and 'endogenous'. (It is curious to set alongside his 'quantitative' a passage written by Bernard Hart [160] (1912): 'In another variety of general mental change observed in cases of insanity, the alteration is qualitative rather than quantitative. It may be regarded as a change in the general attitude of the mind towards its experience, either transitory or more or less permanent. Under this heading are included excitement, depression and apathy.')

The work of Kleist has met with little acceptance so far, outside Frankfurt. An isolated and independent attempt with, in this respect, not entirely dissimilar results, has been that of Shaw Bolton [161] in England to discover a structural basis for the symptoms of mental disorder. Under the group heading 'amentia' he was led to include a great variety of disorders—feeble-mindedness, paranoia, manic-depressive types, and psychopathic personality; his other division, 'dementia', ranged from dementia praecox to dementia senilis. In the 'amentia' groups, he concluded from his clinical and minute histological studies, there is evidence of subevolution of the brain without structural lesions. The choice of the term 'amentia' was unfortunate, since among German and American writers it is used, after Meynert, to designate confusional states.

BIOLOGICAL STUDIES

Efforts, with strong dualistic bias, were made to find the somatic basis or 'essence' of the disorder. Attention at first centred on the ductless glands and the vegetative nervous system. Stransky [162] put forward the theory of endocrine pathogenesis for manic-depressive insanity in 1911; many workers have dealt with it since, but most inconclusively. The accent has shifted somewhat; it is now rather the bodily concomitants than the somatic basis of the disorder that are the object of countless investigations into chemical and physical changes in metabolism. To enumerate the investigators would be idle, nor are there as yet any definite and specific conclusions concerning depressive states of the manic-depressive group. It is of interest to mention here the revival of ancient views about the role of the liver. Jacobi [163] has concluded from interferometric studies, and Ewald [159] from another, admittedly inadequate series of investigations, that in mania the thyroid gland, in melancholia the liver play a certain part. Büchler [164] found the bilirubin value in the blood to be raised in 90 per cent of melancholic patients. Chiray has in many articles described an atony of the gall-bladder with biliary stasis; in his and Zitzermann's paper [165] (1930) there is a reference to Pécholier (who showed that veratrine, the active principle of white helle-bore, is a powerful cholagogue, thus efficacious in melancholia) and to many other French writers who have thought the liver and melancholy to be causally connected, as the common people suppose, and puns aver. Chiray and Zitzer-mann give their X-ray findings of atony of the gall-bladder, together with detailed accounts of their procedure for collecting the thick, black, stagnant bile from depressed people, most of them with digestive symptoms; they raise and reject the possibility of the biliary phenomena being secondary to 'vago-tonic imbalance', and report how the parasympathetic and other symptoms of the depressive attack are ameliorated if the biliary atony be dealt with by daily duodenal lavage, the use of olive oil, etc. These observations are given at length here for their historical interest. There have been few opinions on mental disorder expressed in past times for which one cannot find a counter-part in the writings of the present century, often couched in such terms as to suggest a revival rather than a modern analogue. To illustrate this further would be otiose; the above example is a sufficient warning against neglect of the ancients, or supposing them wholly in oblivion.

It is necessary to speak particularly of the investigations into the relation of character to physique that are usually associated with the name of Kretsch-mer [166, 167], their most active and brilliant representative. His correlation of the cyclothymic or manic-depressive psychic constitution with a pyknic habit of body has been the most fruitful and acceptable of a number of bold assumptions, qualified by statistical data. There has been much criticism of Kretschmer's claims, now greatly reduced. The methods of examination and criteria of particular body-types have been shown to be open to objection, but it seems plain that a higher proportion of manic-depressive patients show pure pyknic build than may be found in schizophrenic patients or in the aver-age population. Less popular, but equally or more valuable, has been Kretsch-mer's [167] work on temperaments. In this field he has prosecuted inquiries that may be compared with the work of August Hoch and Adolf Meyer in the United States. It is the restatement, with fresh knowledge, of the older doctrines. Kretschmer pointed out a 'diathetic proportion', a relation between hypomanic and depressive qualities, characteristic of 'cycloid' people, and described the characteristics of the depressive temperament, among others. The value of these studies of constitution has been less in their accepted conclusions or results than in the stimulus they have given to the study of the pre-morbid personality, the total make-up of the individual.

Alongside these biological studies others on inheritance have been prose-cuted, chiefly by a small group directed by Rüdin [168]. At first it appeared that manic-depressive insanity represented a dominant character, but the matter proved less simple. Kleist [155] thought that separate genes should be assumed for mania and for melancholia, but this is generally thought to be unsound. Kahn [169] has published reports on the children of manic-de-pressive parents; of 50 children only 10 were manic-depressive. Lange [149] sums up his own conclusions as follows: manic-depressive insanity is un-questionably a hereditary disease; not only are the manic-depressive disorders determined, but also in many cases the time of occurrence, and occasionally even the course of the disorder; the genetic factors are complicated, and constellative external influences which cause changes in metabolism or in the brain are also important in deciding the time of occurrence of an attack. The work of Mott [170] in England has also to be mentioned in connexion with studies in heredity.

PSYCHOLOGICAL AND PSYCHO-ANALYTICAL WORK

Before passing to the American school of thought dominated by Meyer, there remains for consideration one important method of studying the depres-sive psychoses—the psychological. Kraepelin and his followers paid attention to this in some measure, especially as regards inhibition (*Hemmung*, retarda-tion) but the application of Wundt's experimental or physiological psychology to the problems of psychiatry did not prove particularly happy. Janet [171] in France has made some notable contributions. Other investigators of the disorders of thinking and related matters in depressed patients have been influenced by philosophical teachings, as von Domarus [172] by Husserl's phenomenology, Kant [173] by Klages, K. Schneider [151] by Scheler, and Mayer-Gross [174] by Jaspers. The application of Rorschach's ink-blot experimental method to the differentiation of cycloid personalities seems of limited or doubtful value. But much more important than these has been the advent of Freud's psycho-analysis. To present in detail the conclusions reached about melancholia by Freud [177], Abraham [175, 176] and some less notable writers would be impossible here, and a critical examination of them, as of much other detailed work in the field of depressive states, is reserved for another place. It is idle to gainsay their importance. The psycho-analytic concern with melancholia may be said to begin with Abraham's [175] paper of 1911; it is carried on with Freud's [177] 'Trauer und Melancholia' (1916–18), and is presented with clarity in Abraham's 'Short Study of the Development of the Libido, Viewed in the Light of Mental Disorders' [176] (1924). Maeder [178], Brill [179] and Nunberg [180] are other writers on the subject.

Abraham's first paper [175] was based on the analysis of six patients; the structural likeness to obsessional neurosis impressed him, and he discovered striking points; whereas, for example, in the obsessional, substitutive aims take the place of unattainable sexual ones, in the depressive patient sadistic impulses towards the 'love-object' are repressed; projection occurs, the patient feels hated by his environment; there arise guilt, self-reproach, anxiety; masochistic tendencies are reinforced.

Freud's illuminating paper [177] assumes that the loss of a 'love-object' is the precipitating cause of an attack. The differences between the mourning or grief of the healthy person and the morbid depressive state lie chiefly in the withdrawal of love into the patient's self (giving up of 'object-cathexis') and identification of the abandoned object with the self; it is thus a narcissistic regression; the desire to incorporate, i.e., devour, the loved object is fixed at the oral stage, hence the difficulties about taking food. There is essential ambivalence in the love relationships, which makes itself felt when the loved object is lost. 'The melancholic's erotic cathexis of his object undergoes a twofold fate: part of it regresses to identification, but the other part, under the influence of the conflict of ambivalence, is reduced to the stage of sadism which is nearer to the conflict.' 'It is this sadism, and only this, that solves the riddle of the tendency to suicide.' The complex of melancholia can withstand the desire for sleep (on the part of the ego): 'the complex of melancholia behaves like an open wound, drawing to itself cathectic energy from all sides and draining the ego till it is utterly depleted.' He recognizes constitutional factors, and says of the improvement that occurs towards evening that it is probably due to a somatic factor, and not explicable psychologically—a noteworthy recognition of possible somatic elements. Some unanswered problems, especially as to the economics of the situation (energy) are posited by Freud, who deals with the subject incidentally in his *Group Psychology and the Analysis of the Ego*.

Abraham's lengthy and candid paper of 1924 [176] can only with difficulty be summarized. The conclusions as to depression are bound up with his views on the fixation points in the development of the libido. In the melancholic, as in the 'obsessional' patient, there is a common relation to the anal sadistic organization: the former regresses to the ontogenetically earlier of its two levels, at which hostile tendencies of destroying and losing the object predominate, the latter only to the later conserving and controlling level. In melancholia there may be regression further to the oral phase, where also there are two levels, on the higher of which only can an ambivalent attitude of the ego emerge. There are a number of aetiological factors in the 'choice of neurosis': first, a constitutional factor, though he thinks that what is inherited is not a manic-depressive tendency as such, but an over-accentuation of oral erotism; this predisposition helps to bring into operation the second factor—special fixation of the libido on the oral level; thirdly, a severe injury to juvenile narcissism; fourthly, a disappointment in love before the oedipus wishes have been surmounted; and finally, a repetition in later life of this primary disappointment. It is against the original 'love-object' that all the patient's anger is directed, though a substitute has provoked the immediate attack. With time and gradual appeasing of the sadistic desires, the introjected 'love-object' is again safe and, for the patient, becomes again part of the outer world, ceasing to be part of himself: this is, for his unconscious, an act of evacuation.

The re-statement of these views in terms of ego, id and super-ego has received relatively little attention; Rickman [181], accepting Abraham's and Freud's conclusions, remarks that the difference between mania and melancholia consists in the relation of the ego to the super-ego: in melancholia there is pathological separation of function, with cathexis transferred from the ego to the super-ego; in mania, fusion; this is, of course, a translation into psycho-analytic terms of the obvious situation. These psycho-analytic investigations, conjectures and conclusions, extended also into the field of therapy, offer at least an explanation, however speculative in places, of many of the obscure manifestations of melancholia: even though unaccepted, they are exerting influence on psychiatrists who approach the problems with other methods of a familiar and on the whole more trustworthy kind.

ADOLF MEYER'S INFLUENCE

It is not possible to end this *résumé* without some further remarks on the work of American psychiatrists, among whom the psycho-biological view of Adolf Meyer [134] has chiefly prevailed. His work in the field of dementia praecox has made more stir, as it has been more actively put forward, than that on the affective disorders, but his general formulation of a psycho-biologically integrated organism reacting to situations covers the whole of the phenomena, emancipated from any dogmatic nosological scheme: 'We work with a reasonably limited number of reaction-sets, that is, groups of facts that have a specific meaning for us. These may be of the nature of part-disorders—the irritable weakness type, the anxiety-reaction, the hypo-chondriacal, the dysmnesic-hysterical, the obsessive-ruminative and the simple defect type of facts; or we consider the more sweeping reaction sets, the thymergastic or affective, the parergastic or twist, the dysergastic or toxic and the anergastic or organic defect complexes, always remembering that any one patient can present more than one of these sets of facts. We study the factors entering into the disorders, the poisons and infections (exogenic), the metabolic (organogenic) components, and then the constitutional and the more definitely modifiable and adjustable psychogenic experience-determined factors and special function-tendencies.' Ergasia, being the term used for performance or psycho-biologically integrated activity in general, there are, among others, the thymergastic reactions, in which depressive states may appear as reactions (projective at any rate in intention, designed to withdraw the individual from an ill-adjusted situation), with concomitant phenomena on various levels—vegetative, kinetic, and topical mental, characterized chiefly by diffuse general inhibition. There may be sadness, with feelings of difficulty and dearth of ideas and activity, or actual retardation; catathymic reaction, with harping on one set depressive topic; or the dominant affect may not be sadness but anxiety. Neurasthenia, hypochondriasis, anxiety attacks and obsessive-ruminative states of tension are, together with hysteria, denominated 'merergastic reactions', by which is meant a substitutive disorder not involving the whole personality and behaviour. In these and other reaction sets it is not a disease or even a diagnosis that is set forth, but a suggestion of fairly definite situations, reactions and kind of personality, all of which need evaluation in any particular case. The insistence is not primarily on outcome, but on the possibilities of therapeutic modification.

The full working out of these doctrines cannot be given here; their influence as far as affective disorders are concerned may be traced in the work of Meyer's colleague, August Hoch, on benign (depressive) stupor [182], states of perplexity [184], and (in common with McCurdy) the so-called involutional melancholia [183]; McCurdy's [185] analytical and descriptive studies of emotional reaction, including the depressive; Greenacre's [186] investigation of schizophrenic characteristics occurring in affective disorders, with which Kirby also dealt; and Hohman's [187] discussion of thymergastic reactions may also be mentioned.

OTHER RECENT VIEWS

The influence of Meyer's teaching has been considerable in England also during the last lustrum. So far as depressive states are concerned, the English position was stated in a discussion on manic-depressive disorder in 1926, when Mapother [188] gave a critical presentation of the whole problem, in which he incidentally laid stress on the impossibility of sharp or fundamental distinction between psychotic depressive states and the related 'neurotic' states, especially of anxiety; this view, based by Mapother on clinical observation, but receiving independent support from Abraham's psycho-analytical work referred to above, has been contested by many English psychiatrists, who put forward therapeutic accessibility as the chief point at issue; their views were expressed in the discussion on Mapother's paper and at the Royal Society of Medicine (April, 1930) [189]. Gillespie [190], a thorough-going believer in the essential difference between 'cyclothymic' and 'psycho-neurotic' depression, has in several papers accepted in effect Lange's differentiation of the types of depression, as laid down in the latter's 1926 paper on melancholia. Kraepelinian influences of an older date are still occasionally evident in England, alongside bold psycho-analytical advances; as regards depression, the main currents are those alluded to above. Much work on metabolic changes has also been prosecuted, but so far with no special bearing on depression. In France the vegetative changes have received much attention, as may be seen in the following quotation from Laignel-Lavastine's [191] book: 'La mélancolie est un syndrome, caracterisé par un sentiment de tristesse et d'impuissance, expression psychique d'un état cénesthésique pénible, l'inertie motrice et le ralentissement de l'activité vitale, surtout visible dans le domaine des idées et de la parole' ('Melancholia is a syndrome, characterized by a feeling of sadness and weakness (the mental expression of a painful state of coenaesthesia), motor inertia and slowing of vital activity, especially evident in ideas and speech'). Von Monakow, of Zürich [192], recently, in collaboration with R. Mourgue, put forward a comprehensive biological theory covering the psychoses, in which the role of the instincts and 'the time-factor receive much attention. Erwin Straus [193] in Germany has likewise emphasized the importance of the time-factor, especially in depressive states, in two recent publications.

There has been very little written in this review as to therapeutics. Notable as have been the changes in the general care of the insane, there is little to be said about the particular treatment of depressive states. To hinder suicide, to prevent irritation, and to provide for nutrition, sleep or rest and, in due course, occupation and interests, have long been the objects of judicious treatment, conscious that of the factors potent to heal, time is more important than any kind of interference so far attempted. Only psycho-analysts have of late challenged this; their hardy claims are as yet unconfirmed. The differentiation of psychogenic from endogenous depressions, already alluded to, with the consequent adoption of active psychotherapy for the former as against resignation in the latter, has been urged recently, with scarcely enough consideration for the frequent difficulties that attend any such attempt at discrimination. The advocates of mental hygiene are hopeful as regards prophylaxis, but their optimism has so far more of an affective than of a demonstrable scientific foundation.

It has been difficult to avoid turning a history of melancholia into a history of psychiatry. It has been also difficult to set forth the interplay between different countries and different schools, the submission in every age to current philosophical and medical conceptions—a constant intermingling of streams which could better be set down, as it seemed, in a straightforward chronological account, than if one should attempt to follow the parallel development of discrepant modes of thought. There are still many modes of thought in psychiatry, many methods of research, not wholly discrepant nor unsusceptible of co-ordination, if not fusion; among them the biological conception is now chief, and likely to be unifying.

HISTORICAL WORKS CONSULTED.

Birnbaum, K., 'Geschichte der psychiatrischen Wissenschaft', in Bumke's *Handbuch der Geisteskrankheiten*, vol 1, Berlin, 1928. Bumke, O., *Die gegenwärtigen Strömungen in der Psychiatrie*, Berlin, 1928. Del Greco, 'Aperçu Critique sur l'Histoire de la Médecine Mentale', in Marie's *Traité International de Psychologie Pathologique*, vol. 1, Paris, 1910. Farrar, 'Some Origins in Psychiatry', *Amer. Journ. of Insanity*, **64, 65, 66,** 1908–1909. Farredin, Kocim and Schükry, 'Geschichte der Psychiatrie in der Türkei', *Allg. Zeitschrift fur Psychiatrie.* **84.** Friedreich, J. B., *Versuch einer Literärgeschichte der Pathologie und Therapie der psychischen Krankheiten*, Würzburg, 1830; *Systematische Literatur der Ärztlichen und gerichtlichen Psychologie*, Berlin, 1833. Homburger, A., 'Die Literatur des manisch-depressiven Irreseins, 1906–1910', *Zeitschr. f. d. ges. Neur. u. Psychiat.*, Ref. und Ergeb. 2, 1911. Jelliffe, S. E., 'The Psychiaters and Psychiatry of the Augustan Era', *Johns Hopkins Hosp. Bull.*, **19,** 1908. Kornfeld, 'Geschichte der Psychiatrie', *Handbuch der Geschichte der Medizin: Neuburger-Pagel*, Jena, 1905. Kraepelin *Hundert Jahre Psychiatrie*, Berlin, 1918. Morel, 'Exposé des doctrines qui ont régné en aliénation dans l'antiquité, le moyen âge et les temps modernes',

Traité des maladies mentales, livre 1, Paris, 1860. Muller, H., 'Manisch-depressives Irresein und Dementia Præcox. Bericht über die Literatur der Jahre 1910–1920', *Zentralbl. f. d. ges. Neur. u. Psychiat.,* **28.** Pilcz, *Die periodischen Geistesstörungen,* Jena, 1901. Sprengel, Kurt, *Histoire de la Médecine,* Traduit de l'allemand, Paris, 1815. Tuke, Hack, 'Historical Sketch of the Insane', *Dictionary of Psychological Medicine,* London, 1892.

REFERENCES

1 *Hippocratis et AliorumMedicorum Veterum Reliquiae,* edidit Franciscus Zacharias Ermerins, Trajecti ad Rhenum, 1862. Aphor. vi, 23, 56, i, pp. 442, 446; Epidem. Lib. vi, sectio 8, 31, i, p. 613; Praenotion, 76 *et seq.,* 313, pp. 44, 75. Also *Hippocrates,* with an English translation by W. H. S. Jones, Loeb Classical Library, iii, pp. 175–6; 'De Morbo Sacro', xvii, xviii.

2 ARETAEUS. *Aretaei Cappadocis Quae Supersunt,* recensuit F. Z. Ermerins, Traj. ad Rhen., 1847. 'Peri Aitiôn Kai Semeiôn Chroniôn Pathôn.,' Bibl. 1, Keph. 3, pp. 66–8, 320; *The Extant Works of Aretaeus, the Cappadocian.* Edited and translated by Francis Adams, LL.D. 'On the Causes and Symptoms of Chronic Diseases', Book 1, ch. v, p. 298. London: The Sydenham Society, 1856.

3 CAELIUS AURELIANUS SICCENSIS. *De Morb. Acut. et Chron.,* Amstelaedami, 1722. 'De Morb Acut.,'' Lib. Prim., cap. v, vi, pp. 327, 339, 340.

4 CORNELII. *CELSI Quae Supersunt,* recensuit F. Marx. Corpus Med. Lat. Lipsiae et Berol, 1915. Medic., lib. iii, xviii, pp. 125, 126 *et al.*

5 GALEN. *Opera Hippocratis Coi et Galeni Pergameni,* ed. Renatus Charterius. Lutetiae Parisiorum 1679. De Loc. Affect. lib. iii, cap. vi, vii, x. Hippoc. Praedict. Lib. Duo et Galeni in Prim. Lib. Comment. Tres. 1, 4, 10, t. vii, 41, pp. 432, 439 *et seq.,* t. 8, pp. 700, 706.

6 PAULUS AEGINETA, translated by Francis Adams. The Sydenham Society, London, 1844. Book 3, sect. 14, i, p. 383.

7 JEAN LE CHARLIER, DIT GERSON. Quoted in Birnbaum, and Huizinga, *Herbst des Mittelalters,* and Quercy, *L'Hallucination.*

8 FRANCISCUS VALLESIUS. *Controversiarum Medicarum et Philosophicarum,* Libri Decim. Lugduni, 1625. Lib. v, cap. xiv, p. 349.

9 JOANNES BAPTISTA MONTANUS. 'De Uterinis Affectibus', in *Gynaec. Phys. et Chir.,* Basileae, 1586. Tom. 2, p. 212.

10 HIERONYMUS CAPIVACCEUS. *Opera Omnia,* Venet., 1617. Sectio quarta, 11, Cap. Pract. Med. Lib. Prim., cap. ix, pp. 429–30.

11 NICOLAUS PISO. *De Cognosc. et Curand. Praecip. Intern. Humani Corp. Morbis,* Lugduni, 1736. Lib. i, cap. xxiii, pp. 161–2.

12 WALTER BRUEL. *Praxis Medicinae,* or *The Physician's Practice.* Written by that famous and worthy Physician Walter Bruel, London, 1632, pp. 24–6.

13 GREGORIUS HORSTIUS SENIOR. *Opera Medica Omnia,* Norimb., 1660. Lib. ii, observ. 18, 19, 27; t. 2, pp. 81 *et seq.;* t. 1, pp. 62, 293.

14 GULIELMUS RONDELETIUS. *Opera Omnia Medica,* Genevae, 1628. 'Meth. Curand, Morb.', lib. i, cap. xli, xlii, pp. 200, 208, 217.

15 HIERONYMUS MERCURIALIS. *Med. Pract.,* Lugduni, 1623. Lib. i, cap. x, pp. 41–2, and *Praelect. Patav.,* Lugduni, 1621. In *Sext. Lib. Aphor.,* xxiii, p. 596.

16 DANIEL SENNERT. *Opera Omnia,* Lugduni, 1656. *Med. Pract.,* lib. i, pars 2, cap. xi, t. 3, p. 97.

17 FELIX PLATER. *Prax. Med.*, Basileae, 1656. De Funct. Laes., cap. iii, t. 1, pp. 83-4.

18 PROSPERUS ALPINUS. *De Med. Meth.*, Patav., 1611. Lib. x, cap. xi, p. 340.

19 LAZARUS RIVERIUS. *Observ. Med. et Curat. Insig.*, Londini, 1646. Cent. Prim. Observ. lxxiv, p. 88; also *Praxis Medica*, Hagae Comitis, 1658. Lib. i, |cap. i, xiv, pp. 3, 93 *et seq.*

20 JOANNES JACOBUS WALDSCHMIDT. *Prax. Med. Ration. Succinc.*, Parisiis, 1691. Colleg. Med. Pract. ad cas. med. Tim. v. Guldenklee, lib. i, cas xv, pp. 535 *et seq.*

21 LUCAS TOZZI. *Opera Omnia*, Venetiis, 1728. Med. Pars Prior. De Delir. Melanch., t. 1, pp., 119-20.

22 LAURENTIUS BELLINI. *De Urinis et Pulsibus*, etc., Francofurti et Lips., 1685. De Morb. cap., p. 521.

23 MICHAEL ETTMÜLLER. *Dissertatio de Chirurgia Transfusoria*, Communicata anno 1682. Opera Medica Theoretico-practica, Francofurti et Amstel., 1697, t. 2, pars. 11, pp. 1618 *et seq.*, 1634.

24 BIRCH. *History of the Royal Society*, vol. 2, p. 202, and *The Philosophical Transations*, 1667-8-9, 2, pp. 489, 560, 617; 3, pp. 679, 710; 4, p. 1075.

25 JOHNSTON, J. *The Idea of Practical Physics*, written in Latin by John Johnston, Professor of Physic in the famous City of Francfort, and Englished by Nich. Culpeper, Gent., London, 1657. Book viii, ch. iv, article iv, pp. 20–21. (Friedreich says Johnston was a Pole.)

26 THOMAS SYDENHAM. *Opera Medica.*, Genevae, 1723. Febr. Intermit., t. 1, p. 61. Dissert. Epistol. ad G. Cole, p. 419.

27 THOMAS WILLIS. *Opera Omnia*, Genevae, 1676. 'De Anima Brutorum', pars. 2, cap. xi, pp. 266 *et seq.*; pars. 1, cap. x, pp. 82 *et passim.*

28 GEORGIUS ERNESTUS STAHL. *Theoria Medica Vera*, Halae, 1708, pp. 154, 1420 *et passim.*

29 PARACELSUS. *Opera Omnia*, Genevae, 1658, vol. 1: 'Opus Paramirum', lib. iv, p. 97, and 'Paradoxorum', t. 4, lib. iv, p. 605.

30 JOANNES BAPTISTA VAN HELMONT. *Opera Omnia*, Francofurti, 1707. Tract. Novus. Post. De Virt. Mag. Verb. ac Rer., pp. 754 *et passim.*

31 ZÜCKERT, K. *Medizinische und Moralische Abhandlungen*, Von den Leidenschaften, Berlin, 1764, §55.

32 JOHANN AUGUST UNZER. In Willing's *Kurze Zusammenstellung*, etc., *Allg. Zeitschr. für Psychiatrie*, 1857, **14**, p. 346. Also in *Deutsche Irrenärzte*, von Theodor Kirchhoff, vol. 1, 1921, p. 13.

33 FRIDERICUS HOFFMAN. *Opera Omnia Physico-medica*, Genevae, 1740. Med. Rational Syst., t. 4, pars. 3, sect. i, cap. vi; t. 3, p. 67.

34 R. A. VOGEL. *Academicae Praelectiones*, Göttingen, 1772. Quoted in Kornfeld, p. 619, and Cullen, Bk. iv, ch. 1.

35 BOISSIER DE SAUVAGES, F. *Pathologia Methodica, seu de Cognoscendis Morbis*, Lugduni, 1759. Nosol Pathol., sect. 1, class 8, p. 338.

36 DE VALENZI, M. *Completum Systema Morborum*. Brunn, 1796. In Kornfeld, p. 620.

37 METZGER, J. D. *Kurzgefasstes System der Arzneiwissenschaft*, Königsberg und Leipzig, 1793, §406 *et seq.*

38 SPRENGEL, K. *Handbuch der Pathologie*, Leipzig, 1797. In Kornfeld.

39 DREYSSIG, W. F. *Handbuch der Pathologie der sog. Chronischen Krankheiten*, Leipzig, 1799. Quoted in Friedreich.

40 BOERHAAVE, H. *Aphorismi de Cognoscendis et Curandis Morbis*, Lugduni Batav., 1728. Aph. 1089, p. 257; aph. 118, p. 268.

41 JOHANNES BAPTISTA MORGAGNI. *De Sedibus et Causis Morborum per Anatomen indagatis*, Venetiis, 1761. Epistola Anatomica-Medica, viii, Tomus Primus, p. 54.

42 SCHIM, K. *Genees-Natuuren Huishoudkundig Kabinett*, etc., Leyd, 1779. In Kornfeld, pp. 624–5.

43 PINEL, P. *Traité Médico-philosophique sur l'Aliénation Mentale*, Paris, 1809, §166, p. 168, pp. xix, xxii; §144, p. 138. Sect. iii, part 2, §162 *et seq.*; part 12, §251 *et seq.* p. 303.

44 CARDILUCIUS, J. H. *Officina Sanitatis a J. Hartmanno conscripta, nunc locupletata*, Norimb, 1677, p. 84.

45 BOENNEKEN. *Biga casu. med.*, Werth, 1744. De Mania. In Friedreich and Kornfeld.

46 FERRIAR, J. *Medical Histories and Reflections*, London, 1810, vol. 2, pp. 115, 137.

47 COL DE VILLARS, E. *Cours de Chirurgie: Dicté aux Écoles de Médecine de Paris*, Paris, 1741, Tome 3. Des Plaies, livre 2, chap. vi, p. 194.

48 BUCHOZ. *Mémoire sur la manière de guérir la melancholie par la musique, etc.*, Paris, 1769. In Friedreich.

49 AVICENNA. *Liber Canonis, de Med. Cordial. et Cantica*, Venetiis, 1555. Lib Canon 3, Fen. 1, Tract. iv, v, pp. 207–8.

50 CHEYNE, G. *The English Malady*, London, 1733. Preface, p. 111 *et passim*.

51 FAWCETT, B. *Observations on the Nature, Causes and Cure of Melancholy, etc.*, Shrewsbury, 1780, pp. 14, 15.

52 CULLEN, W. *First Lines of the Practice of Physic*, Edinburgh, 1829, vol. 2, bk. iv, ch. 1, pp. 165, 170, 176; ch. 2, p. 186; ch. 3, *passim*.

53 BROWN, J. *The Elements of Medicine*. Translated from the Latin, with comments and illustrations by the Author. London, 1795, vol. 1, part 2, ch. 1, cxlii, p. 131; ii, part iv, cap. i, dcxxiii, pp. 266 *et al.*

54 ARNOLD, T. *Observations on the Nature, Kinds, Causes and Prevention of Insanity*, Leicester, vol. 1, 1782; vol. 2, 1786.

55 TEMPLE, R. *Practice of Physic*, London, 1792, Bk. iv, ch. i, pp. 272–3.

56 PERFECT, W. *Select Cases in the Different Species of Insanity*. Rochester, 1787. Case xlii, pp. 227–8; Case lix, p. 315, and elsewhere.

57 HARPER, A. *A Treatise on the Real Cause and Cure of Insanity*. London, 1789. Pp. 20, 47, 60–3.

58 FAULKNER, B. *Observations on the General and Improper Treatment of Insanity, etc.*, London, 1790.

59 PARGETER, W. *Observations on Maniacal Disorders*, Reading, 1792, pp. 14, 92, 101–3, 133.

60 HASLAM, J. *Observations on Insanity*, London, 1798, pp. 12, 119, 136 *et seq.*

61 CRICHTON, A. *An Inquiry into the Nature and Origin of Mental Derangement*, London, 1798, vol. 1, bk. 1, ch. v, p. 174; vol. 2, bk. 3, ch. iii, iv, pp. 178, 261; conclusion, pp. 344, 345.

62 BROUSSAIS, F. *De l'Irritation et de la Folie*, Bruxelles et Paris, 1828.

63 SIMS, J. 'Pathological Remarks upon Various Kinds of Alienation of Mind', *Memoirs of the Medical Society of London*, 1799, **5**, article xxxvii, p. 372.

64 LOCKE, J. *An Essay Concerning Human Understanding*, bk. 2, ch. xi, sect. 12. Bohn's edition, 1854, vol. 1, p. 276.

65 CHIARUGI, V. *Della Pazzia in Genere e in Spezie*, Flor., 1793–4. In Guislain and Schüle's *Handbuch der Geisteskrankheiten*. (Ziemssen, xvi, p. 356).

66 ANNAEUS CAROLUS LORRY. *De Melancholia et Morbis Melancholicis*, Lutet, Paris, 1765. Pars. 1, cap. vii, pp. 159–60 *et passim*.

67 LE CAMUS, A. *Médecine de l'Esprit*, Paris, 1769. vol. 1.

68 DUFOUR, J. F. *Essai sur les Opérations de l'Entendement Humain, et sur les Maladies qui les derangent*, Amsterd. et Paris, 1770. In Kornfeld, p. 644.

69 FISCHER, P. *Von den Gebrechlichkeiten des menschlichen Verstandes, eine Rede, etc.*, München, 1790. In Kornfeld, p. 650.

70 WEICKARD, M. *Der Philosophische Arzt.*, Frankfurt, 1790. Kornfeld, p. 650, and Kirchhoff's *Deutsche Irrenarzte*, vol. 1, p. 17.

71 KANT, I. *Anthropologie*, Königsberg, 1798, p. 140.

72 LANGERMANN, J. *De Methodo Cognoscendi Currandique Animi Morbos, Stabilienda*, Jena, 1797. In Friedriech and Kornfeld, and Ideler in *Allg. Zeitschr. für Psychiatrie*, 1895, **51**, Heft. 5, p. 854.

73 ANON. *Beobachtungen und Erfahrungen über Melancholische, besonders über die religiöse Melancholie, von einem Prediger*, Leipzig, 1799. Kornfleld, p. 657.

74 PRICHARD, J. *A Treatise on Insanity and other Disorders Affecting the Mind*, London, 1835, ch. ii, pp. 18, 27, 30.

75 ESQUIROL, E. *Des Maladies Mentales*, Bruxelles, 1838, première partie, chap. viii, t. 1, pp. 201, 218.

76 GUISLAIN, J. *Leçons orales sur les Phrénopathies*, Gand., 1852, leçon 22, t. 2, p. 158; leçon 27, t. 2, p. 22.

77 TUKE, S. *Description of the Retreat*, York, 1813, ch. vi, pp. 215–16.

78 RUSH, B. *Medical Inquiries and Observations upon the Diseases of the Mind*, Philadelphia, 1812. (Quoted in Esquirol, Friedreich and others.)

79 BURROWS, G. *Commentaries on the Causes, Forms, Symptoms and Treatment, Moral and Medical of Insanity*, 1828, part 2, comment 1, 5, pp. 252, 258, 352.

80 ALLEN, M. *Essay on the Classification of the Insane*, London, 1837.

81 NEVILLE, W. *On Insanity, its Nature, Causes and Cure*, London, 1836, ch. vi, p. 103.

82 CONOLLY, J. *On Some of the Forms of Insanity*, Croonian Lectures, London, 1849, lect. ii, pp. 24, 29.

83 NEUMANN, K. G. *Die Krankheiten des Vorstellungsvermögens, Systematisch bearbeitet*, Leipzig, 1822.

84 HAGEN, F. *Psychologie und Psychiatrie.* (Wagner's *Handwörterbuch der Physiologie*.) Braunschweig, 1844, vol. 2, p. 698.

85 V. FEUCHTERSLEBEN, E. *The Principles of Medical Psychology*, The Sydenham Society, London, 1847, ch. v, p. 276.

86 FLEMMING, C. 'Über Classification der Seelenstörungen', *Allg. Zeitschr. für Psych.*, 1844, **1**, p. 113.

87 ZELLER, A. 'Bericht über die Wirksamkeit der Heilanstalt Winnenthal,' *Allg. Zeitschr. für Psych.*, 1840, **1**, pp. 26 *et seq.*

88 GRIESINGER, W. *Mental Pathology and Therapeutics*, The New Sydenham Society, London, 1867, book 3, pp. 207, 210, etc.

89 BERZE, J. *Die Primäre Insuffizienz der psychischen Aktivität*, Leipzig und Wien, 1914.

90 SKAE, D. *Of the Classification of the Various Forms of Insanity on a Rational and Practical Basis*, 1863. (Tracts in Royal Society of Medicine Collection, 1864–5, lii.)

91 BLANDFORD, G. FIELDING. *Insanityand its Treatment*, Edinburgh, 1871, lect. 3, pp. 48, 186.

92 BATTY TUKE, J. 'A Pathological Classification of Mental Disease', *Journ. Ment. Sci.*, 1871, **16**, p. 195.

93 BUCKNILL, J. *On Classification.* Reprinted in Bucknill and Tuke's *Manual of Psychological Medicine*, London, 1874, p. 801.

94 MAUDSLEY, H. *The Physiology and Pathology of Mind*, London, 1868, part II, ch. iii, pp. 366 *et seq.*

95 *Idem. The Pathology of Mind*, 3rd ed., London, 1879, ch. vii, pp. 326, 412; ch. ix, p. 432; ch. viii, p. 358.

96 *Idem. Ibid.*, London, 1895, part III, ch. i, p. 363; part II, ch. iii, pp. 256–7; ch. ii, pp. 194–5.

97 HUGHLINGS JACKSON, J. 'The Factors of Insanities', *The Medical Press and Circular*, 13 June, 1894.

98 WERNICKE, C. *Grundriss der Psychiatrie*, Leipzig, 1894.
99 THOMPSON DICKSON, J. *The Science and Practice of Medicine in Relation to Mind*, London, 1874, pp. 176, 410.
100 SANKEY, W. *Lectures on Mental Disease*, London, 1884, pp. 107 *et seq.*, p. 441.
101 SAVAGE, G. *Insanity and Allied Neuroses*, London, 1884, ch. ii, vii.
102 BEVAN LEWIS, W. *A Text-book of Mental Diseases*, London, 1899, pp. 167, etc.
103 RAYNER, H. 'Melancholia and Hypochondriasis', in Allbutt's *System of Medicine*, London, 1899, vol. 8, p. 361.
104 FALRET, J. P. 'De la Folie Circulaire', *Bulletin de l'Académie*, t. 19, p. 382 *et suiv.* (Reprinted in *Des Maladies Mentales*, by J. P. Falret, Paris, 1864, p. 456.)
105 BAILLARGER, J. G. 'Note sur un genre de folie, etc', *Gazette Hebdomadaire*, 3 February, 1854. Quoted in Morel.
106 DE BOISMONT, A. B. *De la Folie Raisonnante*, Paris, 1867. Abstrated in *Journ. Ment. Sci.*, 13, p. 341, 1867.
107 KRAFFT-EBING, R. *Lehrbuch der Psychiatrie*, Stuttgart, 1888.
108 LASÈGUE. 'Le délire de persécution', *Arch. Gen. de Med.*, February 1852.
109 MOREL, B. R. *Traité des dégénérescences humaines*, Paris, 1857.
110 COTARD. 'Du délire hypochondriaque dans une forme grave de la mélancolie anxieuse', *Ann Médico-psychologiques*, année 38, t. 4, 1880, p. 168. Also 'Du délire des négations', *Arch. de Neurol.*, 1882, pp. 152, 282.
111 MAGANAN, V. *Leçons Cliniques sur les Maladies Mentales*, Paris, 1893, p. 201.
112 LEGRAND DU SAULLE. *Die erbliche Geistesstörung* aus dem Franzosischen übersetzt von Dr Stark, Stuttgart, 1874.
113 KAHLBAUM, K. 'Die klinisch—diagnostischen Gesichtspunkte der Psychopathologie', *Klin. Vorträge 126, Innere Medicin*, no. 45, 1876, p. 1138 (12).
114 HECKER, E. 'Die Ursachen und Anfangssymptome der psychischen Krankheiten', *Klin. Vorträge 108, Innere Medicin*, no. 38, pp. 928, *et seq.*
115 HECKER, E. 'Die Zyklothymie', *Zeitschr. f. prakt. Ärzte*, 1898, no. 1.
116 KRAEPELIN, E. *Psychiatrie*, 5th ed., Leipzig, 1896, 'Vorwort. Formen des Irreseins', pp. 561, 621, 757.
117 *Idem.*—'Die Erscheinungsformen des Irreseins', *Zeitschr. f. d. ges. Neur. u. Psych.*, 1920, 62, p. 1.
118 THALBITZER, S. 'Melancholie und Depression', *Allg. Zeitschr. f. Psych.*, 1905, p. 775, Also 'Die Manio-depressive Psychose', *Arch. f. Psych.*, 1908, p. 1071.
119 DREYFUS, G. L. *Die Melancholie, ein Zustandsbild des Manisch-depressiven Irreseins*, Jena, 1907.
120 WESTPHAL, K. 'Bemerkungen zu dem Aufsatz von Specht', *Centralbl. f. Nervenheilk.*, 1907, p. 246.
121 ZIEHEN, T. 'Über die klinische Stellung der Angstpyschose', *Allg. Zeitschr. f. Psych.*, 1907, 64, p. 1010.
122 *Idem.*—'Seltenere Fälle des periodischen und zirkulären Irreseins', *ibid.*, 1906, 63, p. 760.
123 SPECHT, G. 'Über die Struktur und klinische Stellung der Melancholia Agitata', *Centralbl. f. Nervenheilk.*, 1908, p. 449.
124 REHM. 'Verlaufsformen des manisch-depressiven Irreseins', *Allg. Zeitschr. f. Psych.*, 1907, 64, p. 490.
125 FORSTER, O. *Die klinische Stellung der Angstpyschosen*, Berlin, 1910.
126 RÉGIS. *Précis de Psychiatrie*, Paris, 1909.
127 MASSELON. *La Mélancolie*, Paris, 1906.
128 DUCOSTÉ. 'De l'involution présenile dans la folie maniaque-dépressive', *Ann. med-psych.*, 1907, p. 299.
129 DÉNY ET CAMUS. *La Psychose maniaque-depressive*, Paris, 1907.
130 DÉNY. 'La Cyclothymie', *Semana Méd.*, 8/4, 1908.

131 HOCHE, A. 'Die Melancholiefrage', *Centralbl. f. Nervenheilk.*, 1910, p. 193.

132 *Idem. Über die leichteren Formen des periodischen Irreseins*, Halle, 1897 (ref.).

133 BUMKE, O. 'Über die Umgrenzung des manisch-depressiven Irreseins', *Centralbl. f. Nervenheilk.*, 1909, p. 381.

134 MEYER, A. 'Inter-relations of the Domain of Neuro-Psychiatry', *Arch. Neur. and Psych.*, 1922, 15; 'The Aims and Meaning of Psychiatric Diagnosis', *Proc. Amer. Med.-Psych. Assoc.*, May, 1917; also 'Objective Psychology or Psychobiology, etc.,' *Journ. Amer. Med. Assoc.*, 4 September, 1915, and numerous papers and lectures.

135 *Idem.* 'A Discussion on the Classification of the Melancholics', *Journ. of Nerv. and Ment. Dis.*, 1905, 32, p. 114.

136 WILMANNS, K. 'Die leichten Fälle des manisch-depressiven Irreseins, etc.', *Volkmann's Sammlung*, no. 434, 1906 (ref.).

137 RÖMHELD. 'Über die leichten Formen der periodischen Störungen, etc.', *Klin. f. Psych. u. Nerv. Krankheiten*, 1907, p. 449 (ref.).

138 KAHN, E. 'La Cyclothymie', *These de Paris*, 1909.

139 FRIEDMANN, M. 'Über neurasthenische Melancholie', *Monats. f. Psych. u. Neurol.*, 1904, 15.

140 REISS, E. 'Konstitutionelle Verstimmung', *Zeitschr. f. d. ges. Neur. u. Psych.*, 1910, 2, p. 347.

141 ALZHEIMER, A. 'Die Diagnostischen Schwierigkeiten in der Psychiatrie', *ibid.*, 1910, 1, p. 1.

142 REHM. 'Psychologische Versuche bei manisch-depressivem Irresein,' *Allg. Zeitschr. f. Psych.*, 1906, 63, p. 905.

143 ISSERLIN, M. 'Psychologische Untersuchungen an Manisch-Depressiven', *Monats. f. Psych. u. Neurol.*, 1907, 22.

144 ASCHAFFENBURG, G. 'Experimentelle Studien über Assoziationen', *Kraepelin's Psychologische Arbeiten*, 1904, 4.

145 BONHOEFFER, K. 'Zur Frage der exogenen Psychosen', *Centralbl. f. Nervenheilk. u. Psych.*, 1909, 32, p. 500, and numerous other papers and books.

146 *Ibem.* 'Über die Beziehungen der Zwangsvorstellungen zum manisch-depressiven Irresein', *Monats. f. Psych. u. Neurol.*, 1913, 33, p. 354.

147 LANGE, J. *Katatonische Ercheinungen im Rahmen manischer Erkrankungen*, Berlin, 1922.

148 *Idem.* 'Uber Melancholie', *Zeitschr. f. d. ges. Neur. u. Psych.*, 1926, 101, p. 293.

149 *Idem.* 'Die endogenen und reaktiven Gemütskrankheiten', in Bumke's *Handbuch der Geisteskrankheiten*, Berlin, 1928, spez teil ii, p. 33.

150 STOCKER. 'Über Genese und klinische Stellung der Zwangsvorstellungen', *Zeitschr. f. d. ges. Neur. u. Psych.*, 1914, 23, p. 121.

151 SCHNEIDER, K. 'Die Schichtung des emotionalen Lebens und der Aufbau der Depressionszustände', *ibid.*, 1920, 59, p. 281.

152 WESTERMANN, J. 'Über die vitale Depression', *ibid.*, 1922, 77, p. 391.

153 RITTERSHAUS, H. F. 'Die klinische Stellung des manisch-depressiven Irreseins', *ibid.*, 1920, 56, p. 10, and 1921, 62, p. 320.

154 SCHRÖDER, J. L. 'Über Degenerationspyschosen', *ibid.*, 1926, 105, p. 539.

155 KLEIST, K. 'Die klinische Stellung der Motilitätspsychose', *ibid.*, Ref. 1912, 3. Also 'Autochthone Degenerationspsychosen', *ibid.*, 1921, 69, p. 1.

156 GAUPP, R. 'Krankheitseinheit und Mischpsychosen', *ibid.*, 1926, 101, p. 1.

157 BIRNBAUM, K. H. *Der Aufbau der Psychose*, Berlin, 1923.

158 EWALD, G. 'Das Verhältnis der Degenerationspsychosen zu den grossen Formenkreisen des Irreseins', *Klin. Wochenschr.*, 1927, jg. v, no. xix.

159 *Idem. Die Abderhaldensche, etc.*, Berlin, 1920.

160 HART, B. *The Psychology of Insanity*, Cambridge University Press, 1912.

161 SHAW BOLTON, J. *The Brain and Health in Disease*, London, 1914, ch. xi. Also 'The Rôle of Mental Confusion in Prognosis', *Mott Memorial Volume*, London, 1929, p. 67.

162 STRANSKY, E. 'Das manisch-depressive Irresein', *Aschaffenburg's Handbuch der Psychiatrie*, Leipzig und Wien, 1911.

163 JACOBI, M. 'Psychiatrisch-interferometrische Studien', *Zeitschr. f. d. ges. Neur. u. Psych.*, 1923, **83**, p. 153.

164 BÜCHLER, K. 'Über das Verhalten des Blutbilirubins bei Geistes- und Nerven-kranken', *Monats. f. Psych. u. Neur.*, 1925, **58**, p. 141.

165 CHIRAY and ZITZERMANN. 'États mélancoliques, atonie vésiculaire et stase biliaire', *Presse Méd.*, January 1930, **38**, no. vi.

166 KRETSCHMER, E. *Körperbau und Charakter*, Berlin, 1921.

167 *Idem*. 'Störungen des Gefühlslebens, Temperamente', in Bumke's *Handbuch der Geisteskrankheiten*, Berlin, 1928, allg. teil i.

168 RÜDIN, E. Praktische Ergebnisse der Psychiatrischen Erblichkeitsforschung, *Die Naturwissenschaften*, 1930, jg. xviii, heft xiii, p. 273.

169 KAHN, E. 'Über Ehepaare mit affektiven Psychosen und ihre Kinder', *Zeitschr. f. d. ges. Neur. u. Psych.*, 1926, **101**, p. 248.

170 MOTT, F. W. 'Heredity in Relation to Mental Disease', Harveian Oration, 1925.

171 JANET, P. 'Les sentiments du vide', *Journ. de Psychol.*, 1927, **24**, no. x. Also *Fear of Action as an Essential Element in the Sentiment of Melancholia*, Worcester, 1928.

172 DOMARUS, E. V. 'Über das Denken der Manischen und Depressiven', *Zeitschr. f. d. ges. Neur. u. Psych.*, 1928, **112**, heft iii.

173 KANT, O. 'Über die Psychologie der Depression', *ibid.*, 1928, **118**, p. 255.

174 MAYER-GROSS, W. *Die oneiroide Erlebnisform*, Berlin, 1924.

175 ABRAHAM, K. 'Notes on the Psycho-analytical Investigation and Treatment of Manic-depressive Insanity and Allied Conditions (1911)', *Selected Papers*, London, 1927.

176 *Idem*. 'A Short Study of the Development of the Libido, Viewed in the Light of Mental Disorders (1924)', *ibid.*, London, 1927.

177 FREUD, S. 'Trauer und Melancholie', *Intern. Zeitschr. f. ärztliche Psychoanalyse*, 1916–18, **4**. Reprinted in Sammlung, 4te Folge. Engl. transl.

178 MAEDER. 'Psychoanalyse bei einer melancholischen Depression', *Jahrb. f. psychoanalyt. Forsch.*, 1911, **3**, p. 479.

179 BRILL, A. A. 'Ein Fall von periodischer Depression psychogenen Ursprungs', *Zentralbl. f. Psychoanalyse*, 1912, **1**, p. 158.

180 NUNBERG. 'The Sense of Guilt and the Need for Punishment', *Intern. Journ. of psycho-anal.*, 1926, **7**, p. 420.

181 RICKMAN. *The Development of the Psycho-analytical Theory of the Psychoses*, London, 1926.

182 HOCH, A. *Benign Stupors*, New York, 1921.

183 HOCH, A. 'Prognosis of Involution Melancholia', *Amer. Journ. of Insanity* (now *Amer. Journ. of Psychiatry*) 1922, **1**, p. 432.

184 HOCH, A. 'A Clinical Study of Psychoses Characterized by Distressed Perplexity', *Arch. of Neur. and Psych.*, 1919, **1**, p. 415.

185 MCCURDY. *The Psychology of Emotion*, London, 1925.

186 GREENACRE. 'The Content of the Schizophrenic Characteristics Occuring in Affective Disorders', *Amer. Journ. of Insanity*, 1918, **75**.

187 HOHMAN. 'Thymergastic Reactions and a Consideration of Certain Types of Hypochondriacal Hypothymergasias' (abstract and discussion), *Journ. of Nerv. and Ment. Dis.*, 1937, **66**, pp. 393–401.

188 MAPOTHER, E. 'Manic-depressive Psychosis', *Brit. Med. Journ.*, November, 1926.

189 BUZZARD and Others. 'Discussion on Diagnosis and Treatment of the Milder Forms of the Manic-depressive Psychosis', *Proc. Roy. Soc. Med.*, 1930, **23**.

190 GILLESPIE, R. D. 'The Clinical Differentiation of Types of Depression', *Guy's Hosp. Reports*, 1929, **79**. Also *Medical World*, 1930, **32**.

191 LAIGNEL-LAVASTINE, J. *La Pratique Psychiatrique*, Paris, 1929.

192 V. MONAKOW, C. *Introduction biologique à l'étude de la neurologie et de la psychopathologie*, Paris, 1928.

193 STRAUS, E. 'Das Zeiterlebnis in der endogenen Depression und der psychopathischen Verstimmung', *Monats. f. Psych.*, 1928, **68**. Also *Geschehnis und Erlebnis*, Berlin, 1930.

EDUCATION

8

PSYCHIATRIC EDUCATION :
BACKGROUND AND HISTORY

THE HISTORY of psychiatry is full of paradoxes. One of them is the change in the attitude of clinical teachers towards the psychological element in illness during the nineteenth century. As Charles Newman put it, at the beginning of that century the important thing for the doctor and for his students was not the pathology or the physical signs of the illness but the symptoms and what the patient thought about the illness. This

'put the patient's mind and concerns into the principal place in those days, in contrast to the later tendency, born of physical signs, to ignore what the patient complained of, feared, or thought about his illness, in favour of the doctor's finding of what was "really" there; this meant that in those days the mind, the psychological factors in causation, and their influence on the progress of the disease, were stressed, while the importance of physical changes was hardly appreciated and their nature only guessed at. By the end of the century mental or emotional factors in disease tended to be considered as nonsense, or imagination, and only physical changes were taken seriously. Such ignorance of the physical used to lead to unbelievable horrors in treatment, but in a hundred years' time people will probably look back on our incredible cruelty, resulting from the ignoring today of the psychological aspects of disease by materialist doctors. The different attitude in 1800 affected medical education fundamentally.'

A hasty conclusion from this might be that the teaching of psychiatry was far better at the beginning of the nineteenth century than it became later. But it was not so. The more or less intuitive concern with the patient's state of mind which Newman stresses as characterizing the earlier period was not accompanied by any satisfactory attempt at systematic teaching either of undergraduates or of the doctors who worked in mental hospitals and were otherwise particularly concerned with mental disorder.

The changes in psychiatric education that occurred during the last century and in the first half of this century have been gradual, sometimes almost

First delivered as part of a symposium on *Psychiatric Education* held at the Institute of Psychiatry, London, in March 1963. It is reprinted from a book of a similar title published by Pitman Medical Publishing Co. Limited, in 1964 under the editorship of Dr D. L. Davies and Dr M. Shepherd, pp. 6–25.

imperceptible, and never dramatic. There is, it is true, some drama in the heated discussions that took place in the Medico-Psychological Association; but unless one has a particular interest in the assertive men who dominated these discussions, the story can be a somewhat tedious record of intermittently large aims and meagre achievements. It has, of course, to be judged in relation to the social conditions which affected the education of doctors. These were so different in some other countries that it is necessary in this very brief survey to keep within national limits.

The most convenient date at which to begin the history of psychiatric education in this country is 1753, when the Governors of St Luke's Hospital authorized the Physician to the Hospital to take pupils. It is true that this permission was rescinded fifty years later, but it was a straw in the wind. By the time the Governors of St Luke's authorized the resumption of teaching in 1843, other places had instituted something of the kind. In 1823 Alexander Morison began to give lectures on psychiatry in Edinburgh, which continued in various guises for the next twenty years. At Hanwell clinical teaching was commenced by John Conolly in 1842. His account of it years later indicates how much it was linked in his mind with the reforms for which he is now chiefly known:

'It appears to me that then only (i.e. after the abolition of mechanical restraint) could the proper study of insanity begin; the removal of restraints and of all violent and irritating methods of control thus first permitting the students to contemplate disorders of the mind in their simplicity, and no longer modified by exasperating treatment. Patients could then be presented to their observation as subjects of study and reflection ... and regarded as persons to be cured of illness, or relieved from distress, and not as beings to be tortured by confinement of the limbs or mortified by punishments.'

The year after Conolly started his lectures, Bethlem admitted a few pupils and from 1848 onwards there were regular courses there lasting for four months and held twice a year.

The development at Edinburgh which Morison had instituted was later taken under Laycock's wing—Laycock was the Professor of Medicine—and in 1864, at the conclusion of his optional course of lectures he emphasized the progress made in this branch of medicine in the last quarter of a century:

'the visits of a class of students to an asylum are much more beneficial than injurious, if injurious at all; and ... it would greatly conduce to the better knowledge of insanity, and the better treatment of the insane, if the practical study of mental disorders and defects was not limited to the medical profession, but was included in the course of training of other professions.'

The examination which he conducted jointly with the Commissioners in Lunacy for Scotland had yielded creditable answers. It is of interest to read the questions that were asked:

'Give a synopsis and brief description of the different forms of Mania.
State the physiognomical aspect, symptoms and methods of treatment of Acute Melancholia.

114

Discriminate between illusions, hallucinations and delusions, and illustrate by examples the leading varieties of each of these.

What are the common cerebral lesions found after death from general paralysis?

When may insanity be regarded as incurable?

Under what conditions would you feed the insane artificially? Describe the process followed, and state the reasons for preferring any particular process.

What results may be expected from the efforts now being made for the education of imbeciles and idiots?

State how a practitioner should proceed in diagnosing the mental condition of a person presumed to be insane and what precautions are needed in forming and expressing an opinion.

The practical examination consisted in an examination of a patient in an asylum by the candidate, and a written commentary.'

From this time on, i.e. from the 'sixties, one comes across papers by psychiatrists working in mental hospitals, in which they deplore the fact that most of those practising this branch have had no special instruction, and they urge that psychiatric patients should be admitted to acute wards of general hospitals so that students can become acquainted with the sort of emergency they may encounter in practice. Then, and long after, the stress was, of course, entirely on the various forms of insanity: the neuroses were dealt with by general physicians.

In 1885 a prominent Irish psychiatrist (Edward Moore) in an address to the Medico-Psychological Association coped with some familiar objections. He considered, for example, the fear that another subject might be piled on to the already lengthy medical curriculum: his rejoinder was 'omit a subject of less importance'. He believed that there was already a change of public opinion which would compel psychiatrists to be better trained in their speciality.

In the same year the Medico-Psychological Association decided to institute a postgraduate Certificate in Psychological Medicine. Among the requirements for sitting the examination were three months residence in a mental hospital and attendance at lectures on insanity. However, nobody took the examination; so the requirements were made still easier. Thirteen people then took the examination.

In the meanwhile Edinburgh, London and Dublin had agreed that mental diseases might form part of the M.D. examination, and in 1893 the General Medical Council said that mental disorders must be a part of every medical student's education—a notable decision. Whether this should be tested by examination was left open. Clouston in Edinburgh regarded formal questions and a written examination as of limited importance. He put the chief emphasis upon regular attendance at clinics, and a clinical test in this branch in the Final examination.

The postgraduate Certificate of the Medico-Psychological Association survived precariously till 1911, but it was unpopular because it was obtained on vocational rather than academic grounds, was narrow in its scope, and took no account of basic sciences. Clouston therefore suggested the establishment in Edinburgh of a postgraduate Diploma which would deal with the anatomy, physiology and pathology of the brain, psychology, neurology and mental diseases.

The next step forward was taken in 1908. Henry Maudsley had just written to the L.C.C. his historic letter proposing that there should be created a hospital providing early treatment, research and teaching in association with the University. Dr Thomson, a superintendent from Norfolk, seized on this and in an impassioned address declared that

'I am absolutely convinced that the success of any scheme of reform in the medical aspect of asylum or rather lunacy work depends entirely upon the provision of definite post-graduate training of our future alienists, and this post-graduate training can only be organised and rendered effective if it is instituted by the universities or other teaching bodies as suggested by Dr Maudsley and a diploma in mental medicine can be granted, without which no one can aspire to lunacy work or appointments.'

His outline of desirable training included one of two years study of the anatomy and physiology of the nervous system, neuropathology, experimental psychology normal and morbid ('such as that done by Dr Sherrington and Dr Rivers and one or two others'), and of course systematic and clinical psychiatry.

'All those subjects could be taught in wards and laboratories of a mental hospital, such as Dr Maudsley proposes in London, and afterwards in similar institutions in the great teaching centres Edinburgh, Dublin etc., and would provide the "good" instruction he refers to in his letter. Dr Maudsley does not write loose English: he must have had some comparative idea in his mind as between what is in vogue in the way of psychiatric instruction at present, and what psychiatric instruction ought to be in his use of the word "good" before the word "instruction".'

In the ensuing debate Dr Savage said that for teaching it would be helpful to have wards for the insane in general hospitals, while Dr Mercier said that views like Dr Thomson's were more widely held outside the specialty than inside it: and then in his usual tart way Mercier went on to arraign teachers and students alike for a rather unexpected crime; as an examiner he had found that candidates for the certificate had 'read German, Italian and American books quite unnecessarily, because the knowledge they got from them was, for the most part, secondhand knowledge derived from this country'. Further in this patriotic view he declared that study of psychiatry was not backward in this country, but the teaching of it was. He had no sanguine hopes about experimental psychology being of any great importance.

However, ensuing on this debate Mercier in 1910 wrote soberly, as President of the Association, to all the examining bodies in Great Britain and Ireland, i.e. the universities and the colleges:

'It has long been felt by those most intimate with the subject that there is in this country no adequate systematic instruction in psychiatry. The evils of this neglect become year by year more and more manifest. This Association is impressed with the urgent necessity for post-graduate teaching in psychiatry in medical schools; and for the granting of a special diploma to candidates after examination, as has already been done with such conspicuous success in public health and tropical medicine. The position of psychiatry as a branch of medicine is unsatisfactory; it is not properly affiliated to other departments of medicine, to their mutual detriment; and under present conditions cannot make full use of those modern methods of research which have resulted in such advances in general medicine.

Young medical men, on their appointment as medical officers to asylums find themselves face to face with work and problems of which they have had no previous knowledge, and in preparation for which they can obtain no systematic and scientific training or teaching. As is well known, lectures on psychological medicine and pathological laboratories have been established here and there, and in one or two universities chairs of experimental psychology have been founded; but there is no systematic course of instruction and no recognised diploma at the end of such course. It is submitted that the time has now arrived when such a course and diploma should be established in the principal medical schools of this country, and a diploma in the subject should be instituted by the examining bodies. My Association is of the opinion that the institution of a diploma would impose a high standard of acquirement in the officer of asylums, would stimulate the scientific study of insanity, and would have an effect of widening and deepening our knowledge of the subject, comparable with the effect produced in public health and tropical diseases by the institution of diplomas in these subjects.

In this letter it is unnecessary to enter into details as to the time required for the post-graduate work and the subjects to be studied; probably each university and examining body will form its own views on these points. I may say, however, that my Association considers that the minimum period should be one year; that provisionally the subjects be divided into (a) compulsory and (b) optional; that in the former should be included: (1) anatomy, physiology and pathology of the nervous system; (2) psychology, normal and morbid; (3) clinical pathology; (4) clinical neurology; (5) psychiatry, systematic, clinical and medico-legal. The optional subjects suggested are (1) experimental psychology; (2) biochemistry; (3) bacteriology; (4) comparative anatomy and physiology of the nervous system; (5) eugenics. It is suggested that only one optional subject be required of candidates. The Council of my Association respectfully asks that its proposals may receive earnest consideration, so that in the near future it may be possible to place the teaching of psychiatry on a sound, scientific basis, and so bring it into line with other special departments of medicine in this country.'

A number of universities responded to the stimulus by authorizing courses of instruction and an examination leading to the Diploma. Paeans of praise and hope were then sung by several psychiatrists, who expected that the new scheme would 'keep medical officers' minds keen and on a higher level, raise the ethical standard, dignity and importance of psychiatry, and foster the enthusiasm and joy of making discoveries', as it was phrased. Other were less starry-eyed. Dr Bernard Hart, for example, said that at the beginning of the nineteenth century the main forces which moved the great reforms (in which England took a very prominent part) were the progress of science on the one hand, and the progress of humanitarianism on the other: they worked hand in hand. 'But now, at the beginning of the twentieth century, these two forces seem to have been divorced. Humanitarianism and the reforms which flow from it are very much in evidence in England, but science seems to have gone elsewhere.' He went on to stress the need for teaching clinics.

By 1913 a review of the facilities for teaching psychiatry in the various

117

medical schools showed some advance, not so much in regard to the under-graduates as in the provision of courses for those doctors who wished to take the Diploma. But even so it consisted mainly of lectures, and postgraduate instruction in the sense in which we now know it does not appear to have been available in more than one or two places (Edinburgh, Cambridge).

In 1914 a detailed review by Bedford Pierce disclosed a rather gloomy situation. Summarily stated there was very little organized teaching, few asylums had laboratories, no scientific career was available in this branch, and disparaging comparison was made between arrangements for post-graduate study in this country and those available at Johns Hopkins under Adolf Meyer and Munich under Kraepelin. Dr Rows of Lancaster, who had visited Munich noted the disconcerting comparison and strongly advocated the creation of a psychiatric clinic attached to each university, where those entering the asylum service and those already in it might go on study leave and acquire an interest not only in the clinical aspect of their work but also in research. The gloomy concluding remark of the President of the Association was to the effect that the real difficulty lay in the apathy of British psychiatrists.

By 1915 bolder advances were being recommended, and familar clichés, laments and battle cries were proclaimed. Hubert Bond, the senior Medical Commissioner of the Board of Control, told the students at the Middlesex Hospital that psychiatry was the Cinderella of medicine—too little money was being spent on it. There should be more diplomas. Although compulsory attendance at twelve lectures and twelve clinical demonstrations was a good thing for medical students, there should be a compulsory examination in the subject and more clinical teaching should be substituted for systematic lec-tures. Students should see 'borderland and incipient cases in the outpatient department' as well as 'asylum psychiatry'. Novices in psychiatry should begin their training in an asylum affiliated to a medical school and, finally, general hospitals must be persuaded to admit psychiatric cases to their wards, as (he pointed out) Guy's had done from 1724 until 1859—though the arrangement failed in that instance because the twenty patients admitted were usually incurable and the students learned nothing from them. Bond concluded by saying that though brains were more important than bricks, there must be outpatient clinics, laboratories and other facilities, of the kind proposed by Maudsley for his new hospital.

After the war the same champion (Hubert Bond) drew attention to the small number of people (less than a score) who had taken the Diploma at the five universities which had instituted it, and pointed out once more—what was too often forgotten—that an examination was all very well in its way, but the essential thing was a university-provided curriculum of postgraduate train-ing. He wanted Part II of the examination in clinical psychiatry to include psychopathology and the neuroses, as well as the relation of psychiatry to general and preventive medicine.

Bond's paper stirred up a discussion in which several speakers deplored

118

the unwillingness of teaching hospitals to admit the mentally ill. This resulted in 1923 in another missive to universities, a sort of R.M.P.A. encyclical which ran to the following effect:

'Notwithstanding the grave dislocation of educational work which occurred by reason of the war, definite progress has been made in the better systematic and scientific training and teaching of medical officers serving in mental institutions and others engaged elsewhere in psychological medicine. Much, however, remains to be done before the position of psychiatry as a branch of medicine can be considered satisfactory.... Thus psychiatry, though its renaissance during the past half century has been in many respects remarkable, still occupies a position of isolation: not until every centre of medical teaching has a modern and vigorous school of psychological medicine can the treatment of disorders and diseases of the mind hope to be on a level with that of the treatment of physical disorders and diseases; nor until then can it be constantly subjected to the stimulating and enlightening influences of the associated teaching of medicine in its several branches which occurs in the schools of medicine and which is so vital to progress.

The linking up of the mental institutions of the country with teaching and clinical centres of medicine would necessarily follow an expansion of this policy. The scattered situation of the former renders it necessary to have many more schools of psychological medicine to give it effect, which would also, in a large measure, overcome the difficulties now being experienced by the medical officers of mental hospitals in availing themselves of the opportunities afforded by the Universities and medical schools of obtaining a diploma in psychological medicine.'

An event which I would regard as more powerful and I hope more lasting in its effects occurred in the same year, 1923. The Maudsley Hospital was opened for the purpose that Maudsley had had in mind when he endowed it. Courses of instruction, organized in the first instance by Frederick Mott, were at once instituted. They were designed to prepare people for the diploma and were in fact intensive courses of lectures and demonstrations lasting six months. Besides members of the hospital staff, the lecturers included prominent teachers of the various subjects, e.g. Bernard Hart, Tredgold, Le Gros Clark, Norwood East, Hubert Bond. People flocked to the courses because they were in fact the only comprehensive preparation available for anyone who wanted to take the diploma; some systematic instruction was also provided in Edinburgh, but on a much smaller scale. But in spite of the distinction of the lecturers it must be conceded that the annual postgraduate courses at the Maudsley were in fact cram courses and that in themselves they did little more than ensure that those who attended them would acquire a good deal of predigested information. Thorough and organized training as we now know it was available only for a few.

The diploma course, in short, suffered from some obvious defects, not least from the gulf that then existed between the teachers in the course and the examiners for the Diploma: it has to be borne in mind that in almost all cases the diploma was obtained by an external examination, as the Conjoint D.P.M. still is. The best commentary on the diploma as it existed in the 'twenties and 'thirties is contained in the opening paragraph of the Royal College of Physicians Report in 1944:

'The institution of a diploma in psychological medicine in 1910 did much to raise the level of psychiatry in this country. It obliged most of the doctors who work in mental hospitals to acquire a basic knowledge of their subject, and it wiped away the old reproach that there were psychiatrists who had little psychiatry and less psychology. But an advance, however valuable, may fall short of what the times require. Even with the D.P.M. established as the requisite for promotion in the mental hospitals service, there were still many psychiatrists outside the mental hospitals who had not had this basic training; and inside the mental hospitals there were psychiatrists insufficiently equipped by clinical experience and training for work in outpatient departments and child guidance clinics. The causes of this were not simple, but prominent among them must be reckoned the relatively low standard and range of the D.P.M. requirements. A young doctor could obtain the diploma within a year after qualifying if he chose, and could do this without any remarkable abilities or extraordinary application, nor indeed need he have had anything to do as a doctor with the large group of mental disorders called neuroses.'

As the passage I have just quoted indicates, there was a growing awareness of the importance of extending the range of psychiatry far beyong the 'asylum psychiatry' which had so preoccupied the education reformers of the Medico-Psychological Association in previous generations. Besides the Maudsley, the Institute of Psycho-Analysis, the Tavistock Clinic and many child guidance clinics attested this; and then the special experience of the war with its emphasis on neurotic reactions to stress altered the complexion of educational demand. The questions asked in the diploma reflected this, but the clinical posts people held while preparing themselves to obtain the diploma were educationally insufficient.

The most powerful influence in bringing about a direct change in psychiatric education, both for postgraduates and for medical students, was provided in 1944 by the Report of the Interdepartmental Committee on Medical Schools (the Goodenough Committee). It is a pity that the eight pages of the report devoted to psychiatry are not more often read even now. Their recommendations in regard to the proper incorporation of psychiatry into the undergraduate curriculum have taken a long while to assert themselves, and we still have a good way to go. However, in regard to the training of psychiatrists after qualifying, their recommendations were in a few places fairly quickly put into effect. Two paragraphs of particular importance are the following:

'Insistence upon every specialist psychiatrist, whatever his particular field of interest, having an all-round training in psychiatry is necessary for the development of the general body of psychiatric knowledge and practice, and for the sound progress of the various divisions of the subject. Such training should include clinical experience in a mental hospital, psychiatric work in adult and child outpatient departments, experience in mental deficiency, both within and outside special hospitals, of industrial psychiatry, and of forensic psychiatry. In view of the intimate relationship between psychiatry and neurology, it should also include experience of neurology and neuropathology.

This postgraduate training and experience will have to be obtained in hospitals specially selected for the purpose and capable, on account of the high standard of their staffing and other facilities, of providing the requisite supervision and teaching. It is reasonable to expect that in course of time, as various medical teaching centres throughout the country build up their departments of psychiatry, each of these centres will participate in the production of specialists in psychiatry. Pending these developments, it will be necessary to look to Edinburgh and London as the principal centres.'

When the recommendations of the Goodenough Committee regarding the British Postgraduate Medical Federation were acted upon and the Maudsley, instead of being an independent school of the university as it had been since 1923, became one of the Institutes of the Federation, we stopped the six months intensive courses and instituted the curriculum, with which most of you are familiar, that now obtains here—in effect a three year course of education in relevant aspects of the basic sciences and clinical theory and practice.

There remained, however, the unhealthy gap between teachers and examiners, which was inevitable as long as the examinations for the diploma were purely external. Accordingly, the University of London brought to an end its external diploma in 1950 and instituted instead an academic diploma, more exacting and comprehensive in its requirements and accessible only to those who had received their training in the university. So far as the University of London was concerned, henceforward those who took the examination were known to have had thorough preparation and it was designed to confirm rather than to be the sole test of the quality of their systematic education in psychiatry.

As I have already mentioned, the reports of the College of Physicians which came out in 1943 and 1944, with their proposals for reforming the Diploma, also helped to improve the general standard. Since, however, the majority of psychiatrists took the Conjoint diploma of the two Colleges, the standards of training available to them in the mental hospitals in which they worked had a great deal to do with determining their fitness to pass the examination, and everyone who has examined for one of the external diplomas must, I think, have been at times pained by the sight of candidates who failed repeatedly, not because of their own lack of application or intelligence but because they had had so little or such bad guidance. In the hope of improving matters in this regard, a recommendation was made to the Minister of Health in 1955 by the Standing Mental Health Advisory Committee, which ran as follows:

'Existing facilities are unsatisfactory in many cases, particularly where hospitals are far from teaching centres. If suitable trainees are to be attracted, it is fundamental that good training facilities should be available. Where they cannot be provided the hospitals should cease to be a training unit. A systematic assessment should be made on the basis of objective criteria, of the suitability of each hospital for training purposes.

Reciprocal training arrangements between teaching and regional hospitals should be consireably expanded. Links with the Universities should be strengthened, and access to their training facilities improved.'

The Advisory Committee buttressed this recommendation with the following comment:

'Training is conditioned by many other factors (besides the situation of the hospital) e.g. availability within the hospital and in associated hospitals and clinics of a full range of clinical experience in all branches of psychiatry; the existence of adequate medical equipment and a medical library; active participation of the consultants in training work; and regular case conference studies. We have no complete knowledge of the facilities available in hospitals, but generally our information is that many of them do not provide full training. This must be a potent source of failure to obtain and to keep good recruits'. . . . 'It is appreciated that some hospitals, while unable to provide a full range of teaching facilities, may be excellent hospitals otherwise, and it is important that such hospitals should be able to obtain and keep a stable staff in the junior grades. This could be done by empoyment of junior hospital medical officers to the required numbers with sufficient inducement to remain in these posts'.

Unfortunately the recommendation fell on stony ground, and it is still true that almost any mental hospital is regarded as capable of giving tyros an adequate training in clinical psychiatry.

The recommendation also urged closer connexions with the universities. There has been, of course, a gratifying expansion of University Chairs— probably the most important development in psychiatric education that we have seen during the period I have been reviewing. In those universities, however, in which Professorial departments remain small and have heavy responsibilities in all three of three main branches—clinical work, research and teaching—it is extremely difficult, if not impossible, for them to give the postgraduate instruction which psychiatrists want and the university would no doubt like to give them. Fortunately there have been developments in several centres which point the way to much closer links between university departments and teaching hospitals on the one hand, and mental hospitals on the other, in education as well as in other respects.

I do not want to anticipate the discussion that will take place today and tomorrow about the role of the universities in this regard, since I am concerned here only with a summary historical review.

Two of the most contentious subjects when psychiatric education is discussed are the place of psychotherapy and the place of neurology. The strength of feelings that can arise was clearly shown in the deliberations of one of the committees set up during the war (1942–3). The sponsoring body was the British Branch of the International General Medical Society for psychotherapy, of which E. B. Strauss was then the President and Crichton Miller, Vice-President. Langdon-Brown was the Chairman of the Committee. In order to accommodate the point of view which insisted on formally acknowledged sub-specialties within the specialty, they proposed that on top of the unexacting ordinary diploma, there should be a more advanced, honours diploma, to be taken in one of the 'sub-specialties', psychoses, neuroses, mental defect, child psychiatry, forensic psychiatry and industrial psychiatry. The comments of the *Lancet*, were, I think, justified:

'The wisdom of having two diplomas, one for all-round competence and the other attesting more advanced and more specialised capacity within this specialty, is open to question, since it might split the subject up, parcelling out topics that are interwoven. Thus the child psychiatrist must consider constantly the adult problems presented by the child's parents, if he is to remedy some of the troubles arising out of parental mismanagement; he must be fully acquainted with the pathology and treatment of psychoneuroses; he will often be involved in forensic questions since juvenile delinquency is his affair, and in industrial psychology and psychiatry since in early adolescence questions of vocational placement and industrial conditions will often come under his notice; and he must possess advanced knowledge of mental defect. There is, one might say, more of a case for a general qualification in the specialty than for a special one; and this applies as much to an "honours" as to an "ordinary" diploma. In practice the committee's proposal might lead the abler men, after they had taken the ordinary D.P.M., to concentrate on one branch; consequently, employing authorities—such as health or education committees—would either have to create a variety of psychiatric appointments in the one locality, or (if they wanted their mental hospital staff to conduct also out-patient clinics for children and adults) would have to employ doctors who had no advanced diploma, or who had been concentrating on one of these branches only. The clause permitting a subsidiary subject would not materially lessen this difficulty. . . .

It seems possible that men who work full time in mental hospitals will in future have at least as great an interest and share in conducting clinics for neuroses and child-guidance as any other group of psychiatrists, and that we cannot take for granted the same rigid compartments as have hitherto kept several psychiatric groups out of sympathy with each other. What psychiatry needs is perhaps not more specialising within the specialty, but less. The Langdon-Brown committee's report mentions that two members considered that "special concentration of energy on organic disorders and on the techniques of organic medicine was a positive disadvantage to the student of medical psychology." Such views are more readily fostered when the ways of the exponents of the "organic" and the "functional" approach diverge early after they have once acquired a common diploma.'

Disputes not only within the Langdon-Brown committee but in others regarding the place of neurology in psychiatric training are a characteristic feature of the first half of this century. That particular debate has died down since our knowledge of the working of the nervous system, and its relation to behaviour, has been so much enlarged. In time the place of psychology in preclinical teaching and in the training of psychiatrists will similarly become steadily more secure and extensive, as its relevance becomes more manifest and its application more essential.

I have said nothing about the background of training in psychoanalysis, analytical psychology and other forms of systematized psychotherapy, chiefly because of their comparative recency and familiarity. In 1935 T. A. Ross devoted the Morison Lectures, which he delivered in Edinburgh, to the theme of how the neuroses should be taught to medical students. It was in many ways a forward-looking address. But, hitting out against psycho-analysts and psychiatrists with impartial vigour, he took it for granted that physicians in mental hospitals were not likely to be well fitted to conduct outpatient clinics, or to receive into their hospitals people with neurotic disorders. Consequently he disputed the growing acceptance of the opinion that general training in psychiatry should be a preliminary to such specialization as psychotherapy entailed. How much times have changed since then can be inferred not only from the way outpatient psychiatric clinics are now staffed, but also from Ross's remark:

The treatment necessary for the neuroses must always be active. There is an enemy to be routed. The treatment for the psychoses will seldom be active, but will as a rule be mainly on the lines of taking care of and leading the patient gently on.

I have also not thought it appropriate to consider those respects in which we have retrogressed, as we have, for example, in forensic psychiatry: twenty years ago a higher proportion of the Prison Medical Officers had had a psychiatric training than is the case at present. But these are better dealt with not as matters of history and background but rather as subjects that need contemporary scrutiny, and I have no doubt they will receive this during the subsequent proceedings of this Symposium.

REFERENCES

BOND, C. H. *J. ment. Sci.*, 1915, **61**, 3, and 1920, **66**, 10.

CONOLLY, J. *The treatment of the insane without mechanical restraints*, London, Smith Elder, 1856.

HART, B. *J. ment. Sci.*, 1912, **58**, 172.

Interdepartmental Committee on Medical Schools, London, H.M.S.O., 1944.

J. ment. Sci., 1923, **69**, 534.

Lancet, 1943, **2**, 294.

LAYCOCK, T. *J. ment. Sci.*, 1863, **9**, 444.

MERCIER, C. *J. ment. Sci.*, 1908, **54**, 557, and 1910, **56**, 373.

MOORE, E. E. *J. ment. Sci.*, 1885, **31**, 38.

NEWMAN, C. *The evolution of medical education in the 19th century*, London, O.U.P., 1957, p. 31.

PIERCE, B. *J. ment. Sci.*, 9114, **60**, 670.

ROSS, T. A. *Edin. med. J.*, 1953, n.s. IV, **42**, 445.

ROWS, G. R. *J. ment. Sci.*, 1914, **60**, 674.

ROYAL COLLEGE OF PHYSICIANS. *Committee on Psychological Medicine: Second Interim Report*, 1944.

THOMSON, D. G. *J. ment. Sci.*, 1908, **54**, 550.

9

THE EDUCATION OF PSYCHIATRISTS

ALAN GREGG recently said that the Rockefeller Foundation had spent most of its funds for psychiatric development in subsidies for the teaching of medical students and the training of young recruits to psychiatry because the recruitment, selection, and training of psychiatrists is of cardinal importance to any and every activity in this field. This, I think, is what most of us believe, but we have not acted on this belief: and if we mean now to make good training our chief immediate aim, we shall be forced to traverse some awkward country, throwing away goods that we have prized, and learning to distrust and redraw some of our time-worn maps.

The university is the institution in which higher education lives and develops. In emphasizing the place of the university in the training of psychiatrists I may seem to run perversely against the tradition of clinical instruction and hospital experience, in which the university played little or no overt part; but the influence of the university, the sun of the educational system, warms and refreshes clinical teaching in psychiatry, as in other branches of medicine.

STUDENT OPINION

Who are to be taught, and to what end are they to be taught? To the first question there can be no steady answer because every year the training of medical undergraduates is changing, especially in what they learn about psychiatry; and it varies much from place to place; yet this is what decides the knowledge and outlook to be expected of new entrants into the specialty. Upon it, also, and upon the credit of psychiatry as medical students learn to judge it through their training, depends the type of man and woman who will want to enter the psychiatric field. Unless psychiatry is well taught, and the conditions for teaching it well are provided in medical schools, there can be no hope that the abler students and those best suited to study and practise psychiatry will be attracted to it sufficiently. Eloquent appeals; arguments, however useful and true; enticements, whether in the form of material pros-

This paper was read as the Presidential Address to the Section of Psychiatry, Royal Society of Medicine in September 1946, and is reprinted from the *Lancet* (1947), **2**, 79–83.

pects in pay and promotion or as alluring chances for doing good and advancing knowledge—all these will, I believe, have little (or only adverse) effect in enlisting good recruits unless medical students see for themselves during their course that psychiatry is an absorbing field of medicine, one which gains the devotion of people whom students respect and would emulate.

Though the outlook of medical students is already becoming more favourable, no doubt in response to effective teaching, it is still commonly asserted in this country that medical students form a poor opinion of psychiatry and psychiatrists. They say the same in the United States, and at Yale Professor Kahn and his associates tried to discover how things really stood, by getting their students—who had just sat their final professional examination—to answer a detailed opinion-questionary, of the multiple-choice type. I have been able, through the generous co-operation of Dr E. B. Strauss and Dr Henry Wilson, to obtain and analyse voluntary and anonymous replies to almost the same questionary from 75 final-year students of two large London medical schools. Like the Yale students they show a more friendly and appreciative attitude towards psychiatry than some would have expected.

That it was not only the favourably disposed who answered is shown by the replies to several questions—e.g., that which ran: 'Do you intend to become a psychiatrist?' Of the 75, 26 said they had never thought of doing so and 23 more said emphatically that they strongly rejected the possibility. To the question whether they would refer a relative or friend with signs of a psychiatric disorder to a psychiatrist, 16 said they were rather uncertain whether they would or not. But in their answers to questions of a less directly personal flavour their attitude was more favourable. Rather more than half of them gave psychiatry as one of the fields (out of fifteen branches of medicine listed) in which a man going into general practice most needed to be trained; 47 would call a psychiatrist for a case of asthma that was difficult to treat; 55 liked their work with psychiatric patients; 46 considered the average psychiatrist's knowledge of general medicine adequate; 30 thought psychiatrists could be often, or very often, of assistance to physicians and surgeons in their clinical problems, and the rest (45) thought that psychiatrists could sometimes be of such assistance; 44 thought that psychiatrists on the whole had a better understanding of the life problems of the patient than had other physicians, and only 2 that psychiatrists had less understanding of such problems; 38 believed that what psychiatrists do frequently helps their patients, and 31 more believed that it is sometimes beneficial (only 4 thought it sometimes or often harmful); 11 were certain, and 41 disposed to believe, that psychiatrists have valuable techniques to teach other physicians and medical students; 31 felt fairly certain that they understood themselves better after their course in psychiatry, and 51 were disposed to say that after it they could understand the general problems of patients better.

Moreover, they were dissatisfied with the amount of clinical experience they had had in psychiatry: 61 said they had not examined enough psychiatric patients, and 35 wanted more guidance and advice in their work with such patients.

To one question, however, the answers were chastening: 22 of these keen young observers were fairly certain, and 21 others inclined to think that there are more odd and peculiar people in psychiatry than in other medical specialties: only 2 considered there are fewer oddities in our ranks than in the other specialties. But (apart from this curious lapse in discernment) it seems safe to infer from the replies of the 75 students that psychiatry is not now a laughing-stock or a closed book to the bulk of medical students but a serious and on the whole respected branch of medicine.

THE ALL-PURPOSE PSYCHIATRIST

How are psychiatrists chosen? Selection is impossible unless there are more applicants than vacancies that must be filled. This has hardly been the case with us. Nor could we truly say that we know the qualities desirable and detectable in the fledgling psychiatrist, apart from those that we would seek for in the fledgling paediatrician or the fledgling neurologist, or indeed in any good doctor: we could, of course, exclude some unsuitable people—stupid, immature, cruel, or leaden—but the positive goal, the ability to recognize peculiarly suitable people, is still outside our grasp. Guiding the right medical student, therefore, into psychiatry will seldom be a deliberate act by his educators, who have sized up his qualities, but often the unintentional, happy outcome of livening his interest and helping his aspirations until he catches fire and knows thenceforward that he would like most to work in one of the rooms in this rambling, rising house of psychiatry.

Since there are so many rooms, specialization within the specialty has been urged upon us, to follow a brief common training. This is at best a premature suggestion: unfortunately it has also in some cases been our over-hasty practice; the ill effects are now constantly bothering us. Every psychiatrist, surely, must have a good all-round training; and such a programme as that proposed by the Royal College of Physicians would make this possible, so far as a programme can.

The aim of the training is an all-purposes psychiatrist. When he is asked to treat a child, to report on a criminal, to explain the origins of a strange symptom, to supervise a course of insulin, to diagnose a high-grade defective, or to avail himself of the results of psychological tests, he should not have to choose whether he will excuse or hide his deficiencies; he ought not to be nonplussed and as much off his own ground as if had been called to deliver a baby. His all-round training is not designed to make him a sciolist who thinks he can answer every question, but to put him in the way of getting the experience that will give him scientific grounding, standards, and a sure frame of reference, and will fit him for the general practice of psychological medicine as our times require it.

The psychiatrist, like other specialists, must acquire knowledge, a technical skill, and an attitude fit for what he has to do: he cannot, for example, dislike human beings with a Swiftian rancour, he cannot view his patients' conduct censoriously or be indifferent to their motives and feelings, any more than he can afford to be clumsy in carrying out therapeutic measures or in getting patients to talk to him freely. He may, it is true, become an administrator, or a psycho-analyst, or a forensic expert, or even a professor—very diverse activities, but all requiring the broad training.

I do not believe that it is wise at the beginning of the psychiatrist's training to decide in what field his strength and interests will lie, and thenceforward to put most weight on that: time enough when he has boxed the psychiatric compass. Perhaps in a few exceptional cases now, and generally in that happy day when psychiatry will be taught to medical students with all the thoroughness and amplitude we could wish, it will be possible to curtail or amend the graduate's broad training, using elective courses and individual plans of study: but the time is not ripe for such economy.

You may be disposed to quarrel with my frequent use of the word 'training', as though a psychiatrist were an athlete or a circus elephant: and to remind me that I had chosen to speak of education. By the time a man enters on the postgraduate study of psychiatry, his general education should be able to look after itself and should gain from all his experience: if it cannot, the horse is out, and it will be idle to close the stable door by formal teaching. John Locke said, on a similar occasion, 'I have seldom or never observed anyone to get the skill of reasoning well, or speaking handsomely, by studying those rules which pretend to teach it.' The whole of the psychiatrist's postgraduate studies should train him in reasoning and understanding—what Thomas Lewis called the vital flame in education. And surely example and steady guidance, rather than precepts and 'a course', are the best corrective for defects in that general education which should fit a man to combine the scientific and the humane temper in his studies, as the psychiatrist needs to.

Coming from this high ground to the uneven plain where doctors are taught to be competent specialists, I see only two methods as essential there well-supervised practice (in hospital, laboratory, school, or clinic), and contact with more informed minds wherever these may be found—in books, seminars, educational films, lectures, and case-discussions, and on less formal and didactic occasions.

If the mind of the lecturer, of the author of the textbook, or the conductor of the seminar is dull and petrified, the student carries away no spoils, but only examination-fodder: or, if the teacher's mind, versatile and specious, throws out false speculations like sparks, luckless is the student who comes under its spell. Equally unrewarding is clinical work that is not supervised: hence comes the waste of zeal and the naiveté to which attention has been drawn by our critics. Walter Bagehot said that the self-taught and original man is dogmatic, decisive, and detestable. I think it might be said that the clinically self-taught and unoriginal psychiatrist is in danger of being feeble and frothy, and diligently futile.

Clinical teaching must be the core of the psychiatrist's education: 'taking cases', studying and treating individual patients, arranging and digesting the findings, formulating the problem, relating it to what may be learnt elsewhere than in the company of the patient—this is the body of psychiatric opportunity.

A recent writer, Karl Menninger, lists the devices that serve the ends of psychiatric education: assigned and recommended readings; the study and care of selected cases; systematic group conferences; individual weekly conferences or control sessions for at least nine months on individual cases under treatment; seminars and didactic lectures; subjective experiences—e.g., by being psycho-analysed, doing psychological tests, formulating one's autobiography. His list could be extended: educational films, demonstrations, the preparation of essays, carrying out a small original investigation, training in laboratory methods, 'field studies' of normal children and adults, participation in the work of courts, remand homes, prisons, homes for the aged, personnel departments in industry, social agencies; domiciliary visiting; and so forth. But the essential 'device' is clinical practice carried out under suitable direction.

There is much proper emphasis nowadays upon preventive psychiatry, extramural psychiatry, social psychiatry, psychiatry apart from the patient who wants to be treated for an illness: it is clearly necessary that these aspects shall be studied and pursued vigorously. But if they are not to become chimeras fed on catchwords and flighty pretentions, buzzing in a vacuum, then psychiatrists who follow them need clinical training with patients of every sort, just as much as do those of us who pursue more familiar therapeutic aims.

THE USE OF HOSPITALS IN TEACHING

The mental hospitals, which were long the sole, and always the main, training-ground for psychiatrists in this country, have produced so many learned and able men, famous for their contributions to medicine, that it seems impertinent to question their teaching methods. But when the diploma in psychological medicine was introduced, many voices declared the glaring faults of so-called training which consisted in letting psychiatrists learn by doing undisturbed by any regular instruction. Outstanding improvements have softened the charges then made, but it is still true that in many, if not most, mental hospitals the junior doctors serve an apprenticeship which flouts some of the principles of professional education. I think most of those who have examined candidates for the diploma in psychological medicine would wish the methods of training in mental hospitals improved.

The solution of this problem surely lies not in trying to turn every mental hospital into a postgraduate teaching hospital, but in selecting certain mental hospitals in each region, designating them as having teaching responsibilities for the men and women who begin their psychiatric career in that region, and ensuring that they have the staff and organization requisite for this. I assume that the new regional organization will permit the regional authorities to insist that entrants into the mental-health service of the region shall serve during their training years in the designated hospitals. The entrants are not likely to quarrel with this; objections are more likely to come from mental hospitals which do not enjoy the staffing and other advantages of the training hospitals: but these non-teaching mental hospitals will benefit in the quality and experience of the men who come to them after two and a half or more years novitiate in the training hospitals.

The designated hospitals would, of course, have outpatient and children's clinics connected with them, and the trainees would have opportunities for learning about mental deficiency and domiciliary psychiatry. The hospitals would, in brief, command all the clinical material needed for training: but this by itself would be of little avail. Sir Francis Fraser has lately repeated the familiar truth that—

... 'more is required than clinical material and the usual hospital equipment. The duties assigned to the candidates should be sufficiently light to enable them to study their cases thoroughly . . . they should be encouraged by group discussions to share their problems and experiences, they must have ready access to libraries . . . above all they must be guided and supervised throughout their period of training.'

These desiderata of specialist training cannot be forthcoming at any and every mental hospital—least of all at those with a small admission-rate or a propensity to entrust the junior members of the staff with the care of the least responsive patients.

THE SPECIALIZING CLINICS

Hospitals are more easily seen as elements in the postgraduate educational system than are the diverse voluntary clinics and institutes. Many of these have stimulated some kind of psychiatric activity neglected before their advent, while others have afforded certain educational services at a high self-imposed level; and however we view some of their claims and their divagations from the middle road, everyone must recognize that psychiatry owes them benefits. They are as anomalous educationally as they are in relation to organized health services. But calling something an anomaly is different from calling for its removal or repudiation. On the contrary, the valuable features of these clinics and centres in which a still disputed theory and practice are taught make it desirable that appropriate links should exist (for mutual advantage I hope) between certain of them and the postgraduate teaching institute of the university.

THE FOUNDATIONS OF TEACHING

Besides clinical teaching (which will include neurology in particular) there must be some laboratory experience in psychology, in biochemistry and electrophysiology, and in neuropathology. The first of these is a large topic in itself, intrinsically complex and made more difficult by uncertainty as to how much psychology the medical student will learn, what departments of psychology there will be in our universities, and what provision for psychological research and teaching in our psychiatric hospitals. Psychiatry cannot thrive if it is not soundly based on psychology, which is as important to it as physiology; yet no one would think psychiatrists believed this if he overheard some of them deriding experimental psychology or saw them abasing themselves before a psychological test result as though the Sibyl had spoken.

Finally, psychiatric education must include organized experience of healthy people of all ages and in many environments. How to get this and to keep a sensible proportion between the attention given to it and that given to the more traditional clinical material will be a crux. Joint field-research with psychologists and anthropologists may provide one medium of training. The question is connected with the need for psychiatrists to play a part in the health service for university students, where it exists. This means of demonstrating mental hygiene in action lies so obviously at the door of the university psychiatric clinic and has such patent educational value, if sensibly applied, that it should be striven for, in spite of the obstacles and the many reasons for sober restraint in developing it. It is demoralizing for a psychiatric institute to preach mental hygiene, or any other principles of professional conduct, if it does not practise them when it might.

DUTIES OF THE UNIVERSITY

What is the relation of the university psychiatric institute and hospital to all this? Is it to be a school through which pass all the psychiatrists in training in the region clustered around it, or is it to concentrate on the training of a much smaller number to fit them for posts as teachers and research-workers. There can be little doubt about the answer. The Goodenough Committee pointed out that the primary problem in psychiatric education is to build up an adequate supply of teachers. The training of such people, if it is to be as thorough as the furtherance of psychiatry and its relief from its present straits would demand, will absorb the major energies of any university postgraduate schools of psychiatry that may be set up. If schools of this kind are in due course created outside London and Edinburgh, parallel to the undergraduate psychiatric departments, they would still be insufficient to provide the larger part of the training of all recruits to psychiatry.

I say this with a full awareness naturally of the part which the Maudsley courses have played in the training of psychiatrists about to take the diploma in psychological medicine. If the training of psychiatrists could consist chiefly of lectures, demonstrations, and the kind of superficial tuition in case-taking and treatment which can be given to numerous 'clinical assistants', then the postgraduate schools could provide the bulk of the training for most or all psychiatrists-to-be. But the training of psychiatrists—even the least ambitious of them—clearly cannot continue to rest on so flimsy and outworn a basis, which, clinically, did little more than supply the deficiencies of under-graduate education in psychiatry, and on the theoretical side practised the vices of spoon-feeding and fact-cramming, which are inescapable in such compressed mass teaching.

There is no need to doubt that the last state of those who were thus prepared for the ordeal by examination was nevertheless often better than the first, and that much positive good has been done by 'D.P.M. courses'; but they do not answer the needs of psychiatry at its present stage of development. Although lectures and demonstrations will, of course, be a valuable part of psychiatric teaching in the future, they are, educationally of less account than supervised work in clinic and laboratory, seminars or discussions, guided reading, and tutorial sessions—all of which take up so much more teachers' time. Indeed there is a direct conflict of purposes: courses of the D.P.M. type become the bane of genuine psychiatric education if they occupy pupils and teachers alike to the exclusion of studies and work more appropriate to the complex task of psychiatric training.

Postgraduate institutes have therefore the choice of spending most of their energy on contributing all they can to this quasi-universal training, or husbanding their resources for the training of the honours men.

A third choice might lead them to concentrate on some division of psychiatry—for example, the forensic or mental deficiency—and to aim at teaching this on an intensive, or extensive, scale. But the more intensive, the more restricted to a select group; the more extensive, the more it will be of the universal spread-the-butter-thin type; so that what seemed a third choice is really a variant of the two main choices.

Between these two no true compromise seems to me possible: and I am convinced that it is intensive training that the university department should choose as its direct business.

This choice does not shut out the university school from the wider field of psychiatric education: its aim is to increase the influence of the university upon all such education, but that influence can be exercised indirectly and through systematic exposition of aspects of psychiatry and of its basic sciences which can be well taught to classes, rather than by the lowering of standards which necessarily accompanies the clinical teaching of large heterogeneous groups. It is wasteful to put the honours and the pass men in the same class.

I am assuming that, in future, teaching and mental-health services will be so related that the part-time teachers will be much more numerous than in the past, will be drawn from all branches of the mental-health service, will be available for postgraduate as well as undergraduate pupils, and will share in the work of the university clinic. It will be the primary concern of the university postgraduate clinic to find and train the men and women of outstanding promise—future administrators, psychotherapists, consultants, whole-time teachers—psychiatrists of every name and bent—who will have through their knowledge and achievement something valuable to pass on to others.

What I am proposing is perhaps open to the objection of privilege: you are pretending to separate sheep from goats (it may be resentfully said) with your 'honours men' and 'pass men', trying to skim off the cream, favouring smooth Jacob before homely Esau, reserving the honey for the queen bees (who may turn out to be drones). But in fact many psychiatrists seem to take a view of the training needed and attainable by most of those who practise our specialty that is far below anything implied or intended in what I have said. They hold that the clinical requirements laid down by the R.C.P. committee are far too exacting: many, for example, agreed with Sir Laurence Brock when he said in the twentieth Maudsley lecture that it would be disastrous to regard as psychiatrists only those who have taken a five years' course of preparation and training; and there was at one time support for the proposal to have a not very exacting common diploma for the bulk of psychiatrists, and a higher, more specialized, one for the illuminati. I hold, against such views, that psychiatry requires a high level of all-round training in everyone who practises it, and I would strongly oppose a two-level diploma: though I hold, equally strongly, that during professional training, as in every educational system, there is need to take account of those differences in endowment, interests and probable achievement of students which psychologists and psychiatrists realize better than any.

A three-year or five-year period of training would not, of course, be spent wholly within the university clinic and laboratories: just as the postgraduates who receive their nuclear clinical training in mental hospitals and attached outpatient departments would come to the university for certain lectures and studies, so the postgraduates of the university hospital would go to certain mental hospitals and other places for parts of their training.

What has the university clinic or institute to offer, that it can claim the chief place in the education of psychiatrists? First, I answer, the qualities that mark it off from the technical school. Vocational training is, of course, essential for the doctor, but by itself can produce a medical craftsman, not a physician, and least of all a psychiatrist. Students should find in the university clinic the ferment and the opportunity which Flexner had in mind, I think, when he said that medicine can be learnt but cannot be taught. The post-graduate student, bringing his own passion and energy, learns there to respond to the vigorous and often creative impact of other minds. Anyone who has worked in an active university clinic knows how much he owed to the congregation of fellow-students, to their ardent, critical, lively, disputations, reflective, eager minds.

More material advantages the university clinic also offers—its libraries and laboratories, its easy contact with other university departments, its facilities for research, its right to select and restrict its patients for the purposes of teaching or research: these are indeed solid advantages, but I see no reason why they should not be at the disposal also of those who pursue postgraduate studies in mental hospitals and other non-university institutions and clinics. And it is not in these material advantages that we find the true virtue and promise of the university clinic.

The relationship of the postgraduate to the undergraduate school will have to be considered. Where, as in London, there is an entirely separate post-graduate institute of psychiatry, and more than one undergraduate school with psychiatric beds, and appointments for house-physicians and registrars, the problem is very different from that which confronts the professorial psychiatric unit with undergraduate teaching as its chief duty, and no post-graduate institute alongside it: is such a unit to take the main responsibility for the postgraduate teaching of psychiatry in its region? The Goodenough Committee appeared to think this course desirable: they would encourage the assumption of such responsibilities by the teaching school and its associated hospitals 'to the fullest possible extent consistent with their primary educational responsibility for the training of undergraduate students'. While the benefits of this are patent, it seems a much less suitable plan for psychiatry than for most other specialties, because of the shortage of teaching staff in

133

the existing or contemplated undergraduate departments of psychiatry, and the relatively large number of entrants who will be required each year by the mental-health services: their instruction would be a drain on the teaching energy and time of the medical-school staff, which would conflict too much with their primary obligation to the undergraduates: even if desirable as an objective, it would be hard to put into practice generally during the critical decade before us. In that time it would surely be better to rely mainly upon the parallel non-university complex of selected mental hospitals and clinics to which I have referred as the inevitable and proper adjunct of the post-graduate institute of psychiatry, where that exists. Where the postgraduate institute does not exist, its advisory and adjuvant functions towards the selected non-university specialist hospitals could be carried out by the under-graduate department. There will always, of course, be a small number of men receiving postgraduate training in that department through resident and staff appointments.

SOME RECIPROCITIES

Then there is the relationship of the psychiatric institute to the university department of psychology. A psychological laboratory seems an essential part of any active psychiatric institute—a psychological laboratory, that is, not merely to meet the clinical needs of diagnosis and treatment, but with teaching and research in the front of its activity, staffed accordingly, and in the closest touch with the main university department of psychology. I can see no ground for conflict here, but only for mutual aid. No doubt the medical school would take a hand in the postgraduate education of psychologists, especially for purposes close to medicine; while the department of psychology might under-take some of the necessary psychological education of the psychiatrist, wherever the necessary administrative adjustments could be made.

The kinship between psychiatry and the social sciences raises similar issues, to be similarly handled by fraternal interchange and reciprocal increase. The truth is that for its various purposes the psychiatric institute must be able to take its problems, and its requests for aid in teaching, to any of its sister departments: statistics, genetics, pharmacology, industrial medicine, anthro-pology, paediatrics, psychology, and many more, as the occasion demands.

As to the relationship of the teaching psychiatric hospital to the treatment of the sick, it is now well understood that it is the duty of the teaching unit to select cases for its particular needs, rather than to accept all and sundry; equally it is its duty to treat the patients it accepts, in the most thorough, skilled, and effective way. The interdependence of teaching and research is generally recognized. Research projects moreover provide indispensable edu-cation for those at a stage to profit by taking part in them. One of the chief problems of the postgraduate institute is not to reconcile research with teach-ing, but to preserve for both the conditions favourable to them against clinical and administrative encroachments—what Sir Thomas Lewis has called 'the crippling routine which the care of numbers of patients renders inevitable', 'attendance at committees, and numerous additional chores'. The responsibilities of each university medical school in assisting the development of the National Health Service in its region will for the next few years throw a further burden on the psychiatric in common with other departments—a necessary burden, but one not easily to be carried if the full obligation to teach and study disease is being shouldered as it ought. A professor, like the bishop of whom Hugh Latimer preached, cannot be two men: he 'hath his office, a flock to teach, to look unto; and therefore he cannot meddle with another office, which alone requireth a whole man: he should therefore give it over to whom it is meet, and labour in his own business.'

For kindred reasons, it might be desirable that it should fall to the associated non-university training hospitals and clinics, rather than to the postgraduate institute, to conduct courses for refreshing the knowledge of qualified psychiatrists or of general practitioners, and for educating special sections of the public. There will, I daresay, be far more teaching to be done than teachers to do it: we psychiatrists shall need to agree on our teaching provinces, therefore, in a condominium, and will feel no temptation to scramble for sovereign rights and the power of veto.

Child psychiatry and psycho-analysis—igneous topics these. As for child psychiatry, I see no valid division in the training of psychiatrists which could depend on the age of the patient, and I have no doubt that presently the psychiatry of the old will likewise become a prominent part of our branch of medicine. The chief problem in respect of children is how to ensure that the psychiatrist shall have a good knowledge of general paediatrics (equivalent to his knowledge of general medicine) without adding to the length of his training: and the second problem is to place the main period of experience with children at the most suitable stage of the psychiatrist's three years of all-round training, before he devotes himself more exclusively to that or any other division of psychiatric study and practice.

Psycho-analysis is an older and thornier educational problem. It would be absurd to state the arguments or offer a tentative solution here. It can be assumed that for a good while to come, at any rate, psychiatrists will be free to choose whether they will be psycho-analysed or not, and that those who teach psycho-analysis will be free to choose whom they will analyse, and when. But it is unseemly that a postgraduate institute, if it holds that psycho-analysis may be valuable in the training of some psychiatrists, should shut itself off from that work, or profit by it without taking responsibility for it, as we have profited—and how much we have profited—by the bold and enlightened educational effort of American and European centres of psychiatric training, at which so many of us, in the last thirty years, have been nourished or polished. Means must be found, therefore, whereby those pupils of the postgraduate institute for whom psycho-analysis is judged a useful and necessary part of their training should be able to get it under university auspices, just as we aim to provide at home as wide and good a training as the best foreign schools afford. Not of course that we want to forego the advantages of study abroad (a year of such study should be almost obligatory upon 'honours men') nor want the university institute to take over—if it could—all the functions and convictions of the Institute of Psycho-analysis.

The last, and the most practically urgent, question to consider is the determination of the criteria, and the means, through which approval may be given to non-university hospitals and clinics at which doctors can learn psychiatry. At the present time this is attended to, in a blithe and blanket fashion, by the examining bodies which grant a diploma in psychological medicine. The Goodenough Committee propose that—

... 'any hospital outside a medical teaching centre that is used for pre-registration house-appointments should be specially approved for the purpose by a university.... A university, after approving any hospital, should notify the General Medical Council and that body from time to time should publish a complete list of approved hospitals'; specialist trainees should obtain practical experience 'particularly in the hospitals approved by the various universities for the purpose of pre-registration house-appointments.'

This is well enough as far as it goes, though naturally it does not allow fully for the peculiar distribution of psychiatric cases. It does, however, put the onus of approval on the universities, and since it is proposed elsewhere in their report that the award of a diploma in psychological medicine should be solely vested in the Royal Colleges, the committee evidently decided that the bodies which should grant or withhold approval ought to be not the diploma-giving but the education-giving institutions. This is rational, and puts the primary duty of approval in the hands of those qualified to judge the fitness of the hospitals and clinics in their region. It could only be exercised fairly if minimal criteria of approval were laid down, and some open method of inspection and appraisal used.

*   *   *

It is hard to tell how soon it will be possible to come at the full means for realizing aims now generally agreed upon by all of us. To realize these aims I think we must get away from the D.P.M. outlook, as I may call it, in psychiatric education. At its worst this attack has created psychiatrists who are bare empirics, and teachers of psychiatry who are like the sophists that Aristotle denounced—'they used to suppose that they trained people by imparting to them not the art but its products.'

What are its outstanding faults? Too many examining bodies have made a uniform standard almost impossible, and a high standard quite impossible. The psychiatrist has been encouraged to nibble at many branches of knowledge instead of studying them, and has often come to regard the experts in these—for example the psychologist—as rivals or subordinates, as technicians, as academic playboys, as masters of strange and efficacious arts, as anything but scientists and collaborators on whom he intelligently depends. His training has not saved him, in psychopathology, from a weak syncretism. Therapeutic effort has prospered at the expense of therapeutic discrimination.

Perhaps I lay too much of this at the door of the 'D.P.M. outlook'; these things may bespeak wider faults than inhere in the D.P.M. course and examination: and we have now in any case the promise of a better system of psychiatric education, and a better D.P.M., likely to advance psychiatry greatly. But, mindful of much public misunderstanding of what psychiatrists can do and what psychiatry stands for, we can heed the assurance of a Victorian, 'Depend upon it, there is only one way of really ennobling any calling, and that is to make those who pursue it real masters of their craft, men who can truly do that which they profess to be able to do.' If the education of the psychiatrist does that, and produces men capable of adding to the knowledge that will advance psychiatry, then, whatever its shortcomings, it will have deserved well of our generation.

IO

PSYCHIATRIC EDUCATION
AND TRAINING

A. INTRODUCTION

OF ALL the branches of medicine which are taught to medical students and specialists none is so difficult to consider in isolation as psychiatry. Both the content and the manner of instruction will vary according to the conceptions of psychiatry's role as a medical service, and of its scientific status, which prevail in medical circles and in the community at large. The manner in which medical education as a whole is viewed must greatly influence the teaching of so controversial, wide-ranging, important and unsettled a subject as psychiatry. The personal qualities of those who study medicine or who choose to train as specialists will govern the quality and outlook of the teachers of psychiatry, and affect the educational goals they set out to attain. It is easy to demonstrate that countries which, on a superficial view, subscribe to the same psychiatric tenets, accept the same body of psychiatric knowledge and use the same almost international textbooks, nevertheless devote very different amounts of time to the teaching of this subject to medical students and concentrate on quite different aspects, while for graduates who aspire to become psychiatrists they likewise make very discrepant provision. Often it can be readily discerned that the discrepancies are more directly connected with the economic, cultural and institutional conditions prevailing in the respective countries than with the state of medical knowledge in them or the structure of their medical curriculum. It is noteworthy that in reply to a questionnaire circulated in 1950 to twenty-five national medical associations, fifteen expressed the view that insufficient emphasis was laid on mental aspects of disease in the teaching of medical students, yet among these many gave much more time to the teaching of psychiatry than did those who were satisfied on this score (World Medical Association, 1950).

It will be assumed in this article that the purpose of psychiatric instruction for the medical student is not to fit him to practise psychiatry, nor even to be technically competent in applying psychiatric procedures of treatment in

Reprinted from *Psychiatrie der Gegenwart*, (1961), 3, 111–29.

general practice. A university is not a technical school, and the medical student can no more be equipped for psychiatry than he can for surgery (Black, 1957). 'The primary purpose of the undergraduate medical course within the university is to train the student's mind so that he can collect and verify facts concerning health and disease in man, and so that he can form a balanced judgment on issues that affect both individuals and groups. If this has been achieved in the undergraduate curriculum, then the special requirements of scientific and vocational medicine can be erected, in the postgraduate period, on a firm foundation. Moreover the student is equipped to learn so that in his, future professional life he will have little difficulty in keeping abreast of advances in thought or knowledge. It is not the function of the undergraduate curricula to turn out fully fledged general practitioners or specialists, nor to turn out men who have detailed knowledge of the basic sciences.' (Pickering, 1956).

What this university education must equip the medical student with, quoad psychiatry, is a trained and informed mental attitude towards the psychological phenomena of health and disease, distinguishing between exact knowledge and empirical trial-and-error, relating both to the patient's needs, and evaluating with sober judgment what purport to be new findings and therapeutic progress. This is true not only of psychiatry but of medicine as a whole. 'The present state of knowledge does not allow of the recognition of a corpus of essential knowledge. The picture of disease is constantly changing, not only from individual to individual, but from year to year. This change depends on the complexity of aetiology, the constantly changing nature of man and his environment, and the impact of new knowledge. Furthermore the proportion of what is known in medicine to what is yet to know is very small indeed. It is therefore necessary for medical men to have a flexibility of outlook which will enable them to revise and amend their knowledge in conformity with progress. Above all it is necessary to educate them to recognize false prophets who, like weeds, tend to choke true knowledge.' (Arnott, 1954.)

Psychiatry, which may in many respects fairly be regarded as in much the same state as medicine was at the end of the eighteenth century (Shryock 1956), cannot be presented to the medical student as an adequate theoretical system or as a body of established and classified facts about causes, pathology, course and treatment of mental diseases. If it were to be so presented the intelligent, sophisticated student, well educated in other branches of medicine, would be puzzled or repelled, and might scorn it; the mediocre student might accept what he is told uncritically, and be thereafter at the mercy of every subsequent swing of the pendulum of psychopathological or therapeutic fashion. Equally, however, psychiatry cannot be presented as just a holistic point of view, a commonsense appraisal of salient personal and environmental facts about the patient, since this ignores the wealth of observational data, in longitudinal or dynamic terms as well as in cross-section, which has been amassed by the labours of psychiatrists, psychologists and social investigators. Whether the happy mean can be found, avoiding the extremes of the system-maker, the empiric and the self-sufficient manipulator, must depend on the policy of the medical school and its climate of educational effort, as much as on the psychiatric teachers.

In the medical schools of some countries psychiatry and neurology have, by long tradition, been as firmly conjoined as Siamese twins. Though the interdependence of these two branches is beyond dispute, their combination in one department under a single Professor has not conduced to the progress of psychiatry, or given students that broad conception of its scope and relations which is the purpose of medical education. Occasionally a brilliant teacher could triumph over the limitations imposed by the joint obligation, but with the growth of both subjects and their scientific foundations in physiology and psychology, this is hardly now to be hoped for.

In some other countries, in which psychiatry has independent status, it is taught with more emphasis on the neuroses and 'psychosomatic' conditions which bring it into close relation with internal medicine than on the psychoses, so that the main teaching locus is not the mental hospital or the clinic but the outpatient department and the wards of the general hospital. In such medical schools the policy adopted may reflect the clinical interests of the teachers, their practical facilities (which may be very restricted, so far as control of psychiatric beds is concerned) and their belief that stress on the potency of dynamic psychological forces is the chief element in sound psychiatric teaching.

The few countries in which the social sciences have won for themselves a respect comparable with that given to the biological sciences have some medical schools which are including psychology and sociology as serious academic subjects, and not merely as ancillaries of medical progress, in the preclinical courses of instruction; they are as ready to train the student in the application of these social sciences as in the application of physiology and anatomy, with due allowance for the very different stage of development the social sciences have reached. The roots of this policy lie in extra-medical soil. Countries with a long and distinguished philosophical tradition approach the incorporation of psychology into medical teaching in a different spirit from those which distrust all speculation that cannot be tested or refuted by experiment. What appears on the surface to be an outcome of the convictions or prejudices of medical educators, as exhibited in the teaching of psychiatry, can often be traced to the ethos and changing institutions of the society in which it occurs. What is true of the society as a whole, is a fortiori true of the smaller society constituted by the medical school. 'Learning to be a physician, like complex learning of other kinds, is not only a function of intelligence and aptitude, of motivation and self-images; it is also a function of the social environments in which learning and performance take place ... Learning and performance vary not only as the individual qualities of students vary, but also as their social environments vary, with their distinctive climates of value, and their distinctive organization of relations among students, between students and faculty, and between students and patients.' (Merton *et al.*, 1957.) In schools

140

where prominent and admired teachers of other branches of medicine adopt a frankly derisive attitude towards psychiatry, or where they patently judge its attainments by lower standards than in their own field, the effect upon students learning the subject can be more withering than if they were getting much less instruction in it, but doing so in an environment where they could recognize that it was a subject respected by those whom the students respected.

B. THE MEDICAL STUDENT

The primary considerations are: What is the aim of psychiatric instruction? Should all the students receive the same psychiatric instruction? Should the instruction be chiefly through clinical apprenticeship or by didactic lectures and demonstrations?

I. THE AIM

Some writers have frankly expressed the view that the chief purpose is to 'humanize' the future doctor, to induce him to see each patient as a person, rather than as the assembly of organs and functions which his scientific studies may have made him contemplate and which the cruder of his surgical and medical teachers may have seemed to think they were treating. The more mechanistic the thinking and the more indifferent the attitude of some teachers in the medical school towards the feelings and human dignity of their patients, the more strongly is the development of proper regard for the patient as a person likely to be stressed as a major aim in psychiatric teaching. With this may go a lessened concern for detailed knowledge of the phenomena and course of illness (dismissed rather contemptuously as 'descriptive psychiatry') and there may be also an aversion for physical methods of treatment, distrust of physiological explanations of the pathology of mental illness, and denial of the part played by heredity in determining the recurrence, form and course of such illness.

There can be little doubt that his contacts with psychiatry increase greatly the student's awareness and understanding of the important part played by emotions, needs and drives in every patient, and correct any tendencies to regard sick people as a veterinary surgeon regards sick animals (Proc. 4th. Conf. Psychiat. Educ. 1938; Rümke, 1954). But it would be unrealistic to suppose that a boorish, unsympathetic, tactless student will be converted by some psychiatric lectures and demonstrations into a man well-fitted to practice medicine, or that the mollifying and civilizing effect of psychiatric teaching will be greater than that produced by the example of kindly and humane teachers of the other branches of medicine. A decent regard for the feelings and needs of sick people is one of the products of all medical education. Psychiatry contributes to this end, but cannot arrogate to itself primary responsibility for it (Sinclair, 1955).

The aim of psychiatric teaching, according to a representative American

141

group (Whitehorn *et al.*, 1951) is to develop in the medical student ability to interview; ability to diagnose the condition of patients who are emotionally disturbed and who may be expressing their distress in physical, psychological or social symptoms; and, finally, understanding of what the physician who is not a psychiatrist can or should do, and what he cannot and should not do, in the care and treatment of the mentally ill. This is a series of practical objectives. What they omit is as significant as what they include: they do not mention ability to evaluate critically theoretical and practical issues affecting mental health, though they include 'knowledge and realistic appraisal of the scope and limitations of modern methods of treatment of the mentally sick', and they sum up the basic aim of the teaching as 'to equip the student with a reasonably adequate knowledge of the facts of human nature'. Unfortunately we are still ignorant of much we should like to know about human nature, and we are at intervals exposed to waves of enthusiasm for new methods of treatment. It should therefore be a further aim of psychiatric education to cultivate and train in the student a capacity for weighing evidence and examining speculations about the intangible material of psychiatry, which can be so much more elusive and deceptive than somatic phenomena.

II. UNIFORMITY OF INSTRUCTION

The question whether all students in a given medical school should receive the same psychiatric instruction is more pertinent in a British or an American university than in a German one where tradition works so strongly in favour of the student's freedom to move from university to university, and where the influence of the professor's personal teaching is so dominant in each school (Pfeiffenberger and Smith, 1956; Holldack, 1957). In any English university students of most faculties choose whether they will 'read for honours' or for an ordinary pass degree: the former entails a more exacting course of studies and a more searching and discriminating examination. The faculty of medicine is an exception: medical students do not differ from one another in their curriculum at the same university except during the preclinical period (when they may elect to spend an extra year reading for an honours degree in physiology or other basic science). Some medical teachers, including psychiatrists, regret that medicine does not permit the abler students to move faster and delve further than the average. They would like to admit, by corresponding differences in the organization of studies, that some students are the men who may be expected to further medicine by their research and other outstanding abilities while some of their contemporaries in the student body are likely to become competent, dependable doctors without academic interests or capacity: both sorts are needed, but it is unwise to force both, while students, into the same Procrustean training (Anderson and Johnson, 1958). This point of view is not generally shared, and hardly does justice to the actual differences brought about by the student's choice of the teachers they will work under and the natural interest of teachers in the most promising students; but it raises the question of elective courses (e.g. in certain branches of psychiatry) and the undeniable difficulty that some students have in grasping psychiatric principles (MacCalman, 1949). This difficulty is sometimes an intellectual one, but more often springs from emotional sources and inexperience. To teach the immature student how sexual conflicts affect mental health may require an approach or a form of exposition which is ill-suited to an older, more balanced, more sensitive and experienced fellow-student. So long as all medical students who have reached a certain stage in their course receive the same psychiatric tuition, it is almost certain that some will be puzzled and unedified, while others will be stimulated and enlightened, and yet others perhaps bored. The smaller the group taught and the more the seminar method of teaching is employed, the less is this problem a troublesome one. The same holds good, though to a much lesser degree, of controversial features in psychiatry, of which psychoanalysis is the best example: some students are much attracted, others repelled by it, and the uncertainty thus engendered can be better coped with by a teacher dealing with a small group of students than by a professor demonstrating to a large audience.

III. MEDIA OF INSTRUCTION

The third primary issue turns on whether lecture-demonstrations by a senior teacher are to be preferred, as the main medium of psychiatric instruction, to an apprenticeship whereby the student, attached to a clinician at the teaching hospital, watches him at work by the bedside and in the outpatient department, takes him as his 'role-model', insensibly copies his methods and attitudes, acquires from him a stock of knowledge, and blends all this with the more formal and orderly teaching he receives in systematic lectures; the lectures then rank with textbooks of psychiatry as elements in his education which are necessary but less durable and formative than psychiatric 'clerking'. It is not here a sharp antithesis that must be faced, but a distribution of emphasis. Whereas in the medical schools of Continental Europe (Schaefer, 1957; M. Schneider, 1957) the series of lectures given by the Professor bulks as much more important in the student's teaching programme than the practical clinical work which he may carry out, in the best medical schools of Great Britain and the United States and others drawing their tradition and practice from these countries, clinical responsibility is laid on the student from the outset; lectures are subordinated to 'case-taking' and other ward-work (which will include search into the literature relevant to a particular patient's illness), and he will be left in no doubt that he can learn much more from his patients and from his own efforts to apply clinically his knowledge of pathology, physiology, biochemistry—and psychology—than from didactic lectures. So far as psychiatry is concerned, there is usually a close correspondence between the size of the teaching staff in the psychiatric department and the extent to which clinical work is preponderant in the student's training programme. Where the staff is relatively small, more of the student's time may be spent in listening

143

to lectures than in examining patients: where the staff is larger, the bulk of his time is allocated to work in the outpatient department and the wards. The reasons are obvious. There is undoubtedly (K. Schneider, 1958) much to be said for the system which has produced a rich harvest of great psychiatrists, but insofar as paucity of staff precludes experiment with alternative methods (Kolle, 1958) it is to be regretted.

IV. INTEGRATION INTO MEDICAL CURRICULUM

The fusion of psychiatric education with the rest of medical teaching has not been fully attained anywhere, as far as can be judged. There is always a gap, which is probably haunted by the ghost of Descartes.

Professing to view the human organism as a single biological unity, mind-body inseparable, we all—or nearly all—use the conceptual language of dualism: and students are quick to see the unbridged gulf between our psychopathology and our pathology, our way of observing and inferring the dynamics of emotion, on the one hand, and the dynamics of secretion or metabolism, on the other. Complete integration of psychiatry into medical education must wait for the integration, or rather the fusion, of physiology and psychology. In the meantime, much can be accomplished to bring before the student the relevance of psychiatry, in its various aspects, to the other branches of medical knowledge and practice. The General Medical Council, which has the duty to see that medical education in the United Kingdom attains a proper standard, stated firmly in its new Recommendations (General Medical Council, 1957) that 'during his study of all clinical subjects the attention of the student should be continuously directed by his teachers to the importance of the inter-relation of the physical, psychological, and social aspects of disease'. This sound injunction, echoing the theme of countless symposia and articles, has a major weakness—it is easier said than done. In the days when psychiatry could be presented as a branch of neurology—in the days, say, of Meynert and Wernicke—the problem was less awkward, for the psychological aspects of a disease were construed as the epiphenomena of its physical reality, and the social aspects were simple because we had no inkling then of the harvest which could be yielded by sociological inquiry into the causes and consequences of disease.

There has been vigorous experimentation in the United States, following on much discussion of how to bring psychiatry out of the special department and into the general arena in which students organize all they are learning into a serviceable whole. Integration has become the watchword of some bold, almost revolutionary medical schools of great influence. These schools, aware that the enormous growth of medical knowledge has made it absurd to attempt to teach the student everything that it would be useful for a practising doctor to know, have recast their whole programme of medical education (Dietrick and Berson, 1953). Thus Western Reserve University (Ham, 1958) decided after much preliminary study to treat the medical student as a

144

graduate, capable of assuming steadily increasing responsibility for the care of patients and for furthering his education in his own way: he was therefore given much free time (one and a half days each week), with opportunities for research and for elective studies. The student was put in direct and prolonged personal contact with individual patients and their families from the beginning of his medical studies: all the medical, psychological and social problems that cropped up in these families were his concern, to ponder over, inquire about, and, where he could, to give help. Teaching was consequently not based on individual departments and branches of knowledge but on 'subject-areas'; an inter-departmental group planned the teaching in each of these subject areas (Caughey, 1956). Commenting on the development of such experiments, a close observer reported that these efforts to break down barriers between departments have resulted from the development of psychiatry and preventive medicine; 'because these infiltrate into all areas of medical knowledge and care, the two disciplines of preventive medicine and psychiatry have, indirectly, played an interesting and influential role in focussing attention on the need for ... constructive integration and correlation of many facets of medical education.' (Turner, 1958.) It is therefore natural that psychiatry enters into the nexus of teaching opportunities at many points in these experimental programmes. Several of them link it closely to social medicine, its congener and ally, others to the biology of growth and development. The student, either early in his education or in his fourth year, is introduced into a home where a confinement is due: the obstetrician, the pediatrician, the psychiatrist and the teacher of social medicine take him under their joint guidance (Bakst and Malamud, 1957) at weekly or daily conferences. At another school it is the teachers of psychiatry, psychology, social sciences, social casework, preventive medicine, and anthropology who meet, at regular conferences where they use the illustrative material afforded by patients, to acquaint the student with 'human ecology' (Hargrove, Ham and Fleming, 1957). This multi-disciplinary method of teaching, admirable in its intention and thoroughly in keeping with the present spirit of American research which stresses the need for team-work, has disadvantages and risks. It makes great demands on the teachers' time, and often on their patience and adaptiveness; it exalts freshness and breadth, sometimes at the expense of learning and thorough mastery of some limited field; and it interferes with the kindling influence which a single teacher, acting independently, can exert with signal advantage upon the mind of a receptive student.

The experimental American schemes referred to will be judged by their results, which are not yet available. They are bold and honest efforts to recast medical education, now that traditional methods are proving unequal to the demands made by accumulating knowledge, changing medical functions, and a distribution of emphasis, which gives psychiatry much greater prominence than in the past (Ewing, 1956). The same boldness characterizes the latest American approach to the problem of preclinical training, where normal psychology should logically take its place alongside anatomy, physiology, biochemistry, and pharmacology. This problem is hardly recognized as such in some countries, and in many others it is cursorily handled (World Medical Association, 1950).

In Great Britain there is no rigid view as to what teaching in psychology should be provided or who should provide it at the preclinical stage. The range is therefore wide. At University College, London, a series of lectures has been designed and delivered by the Professor of Psychology, to acquaint medical students with the scope and scientific outlook of modern psychology. At other schools the instruction is given by a psychiatrist and is then as a rule 'medical psychology', i.e. psychoanalysis in varying degrees of dilution and flavouring, or a slightly old-fashioned combination of commonsense psychobiology with the psychology of the abnormal, very broadly outlined. Nowhere are the dry-as-dust aspects of psychology shown to the student, and nowhere—as yet—is an attempt made to teach him the subject seriously in its own right, as he is taught physiology. The Royal College of Physicians considered that 'it is desirable that (the course) should deal with aspects of the subject which will be of value to the student when he meets with clinical problems' (Royal College of Physicians, 1943). There is, however, a rapidly growing realization that modern psychology, as it is studied in departments of psychology and used in research, is a powerful instrument for enlarging our knowledge of mental disorder and perhaps in learning to control it: it can no more be treated Cinderella-fashion in medical education than can any other science basic to medicine.

One of the greatest of American medical schools, Johns Hopkins, refuses to allow the future physician, whether psychiatrist or not, to cast aside his interests in the social sciences (in which psychology is included) when he enters the medical school. Since it is desirable for the optimal development of medicine that psychology, sociology and anthropology should be established as basic to medical education, the new curriculum planned for Johns Hopkins students includes in the first year two humanistic or behavioural subjects of their own choice, in the second year cultural anthropology, social psychology, history and philosophy of science, medical psychology, and one elective course in one of the liberal arts or social sciences; and in the third year (when clinical work has begun) one such continued elective; psychiatry comes then in the fourth and fifth years. The sceptic may wonder if the ambitious scheme will work; but recollecting how the ambitious schemes of Johns Hopkins Medical School have worked, to the permanent advancement of medical education, since its beginnings seventy years ago, he will probably suspend his doubts. It is at all events easy for the psychiatrist to agree with the assertion of the Hopkins teachers that there is 'an acknowledged need in medical education for a better understanding of social and environmental factors in illness; of the social resources and processes concerned in convalescence and rehabilitation; of the humanistic values which are significant in our culture, but which sometimes appear trivial and obstructive to the technologically-absorbed physician. It seems unlikely that these deficiencies can be remedied by such devices as lectures in human ecology or exercises in social service. Rather the encouragement of deep and earnest study of these matters by interested medical students under inspiring scholars seems better calculated to produce enduring results.' (*Johns Hopkins Magazine*, 1957.)

In European medical schools (Ey, 1955; Kauders, 1946) the time allotted to the teaching of psychiatry is grudging and inadequate. In a recent comparison it appeared that in West German Universities and in Paris less than five per cent of the time allotted to teaching clinical medicine was devoted to psychiatry; in Strasburg the proportion was somewhat higher (Gärtner, 1957; Kolle, 1958). This is in contrast with the time—amounting to as much as 560 hours in one case—given to the subject in some American medical schools (American Medical Association, 1957). In Great Britain there are fairly wide variations, from 26 hours to 130 hours; the average time given to psychiatry is 60 hours.

It is often urged by psychiatrists that the amount of time devoted to the subject in the medical curriculum should be commensurate with the wide distribution of mental illness and its patent importance in social, economic and human terms: teachers of other branches of medicine, in direct contrast, sometimes say that psychiatry has not yet reached the stage of development which could justify using it largely as a vehicle for the education of the medical student. The dispute is an unprofitable one, and the situation calls for experiment rather than dialectic. There is, particularly in American medical schools, vigorous experimentation at present, but it is either too early to judge whether any particular experiment has succeeded in doing what it meant to, or too difficult to evaluate its effect, since that entails judging the value as doctors of the men educated by it: certainly it would be the height of folly to judge the merits of any innovation in the teaching of psychiatry by looking at examination results or technical attainments. There are therefore no sure grounds as yet for holding that a particular way of teaching psychiatry is preferable to other ways; there are indeed excellent grounds for holding that in the hands of one teacher or in the conditions of one medical school a method may be extremely good whereas with another teacher or environment it works very badly. It follows that there is no recommended pattern or programme, of general application and validity. The nearest approach to it is a combination of lectures, seminars, demonstrations, joint conferences, responsible clinical work interviewing and examining patients in ward and outpatients department, and guided reading. This amounts to accepting internal medicine as a model, copying its teaching framework, and filling this in with content that is co-ordinated and illustrates the principles of psychiatry as the individual psychiatric teachers see them. The duty of the head of the Department is not to dominate the teaching but to ensure that the teachers have been well chosen and that they educate the students in, rather than stuff them with, psychiatry. What proportion of time is spent in teaching about the neuroses, or the organic psychoses, or dynamic psychopathology, or 'psychosomatics', or the behaviour disorders of children, or the forensic aspects and delinquency, or mental defect, is clearly a matter for the head of the Department to consider, in conjunction with his colleagues, but it is subordinate in importance to the spirit of intellectual integrity, scholarship and zest for inquiry which informs the best medical teaching, no matter what the subject.

The technical aids to psychiatric teaching have multiplied of late years. The one-way screen, the tape-recorder, the cine-strip and documentary film, are now in use in many medical schools to teach interviewing methods, illustrate technical procedures and stimulate the student's interest (Millar, 1954), but on the whole it cannot be said that they have proved of much value to the experienced or gifted teacher. He does better to rely on the direct contacts between him, the student and the patient, rather than on the material at one remove which audio-visual aids can offer. Teachers who believe themselves dull and jejune sometimes have recourse to the recorded interviews, with commentary, which may now be obtained on gramophone discs, to illustrate how a psychiatrist should conduct therapeutic and other interviews (Gill *et al.*, 1954).

Since psychiatry covers a wide territory, with all of which the student cannot be acquainted, a decision has usually to be taken regarding what shall be given prominence and what omitted. Mental deficiency usually suffers when this decision is made: it is considered to be more dispensable than neurotic disorder, in the opinion of some, and than the major psychoses, according to others. This is questionable policy. Insofar as education in psychiatric principles, rather than imparting information, is the main purpose, mental deficiency is an admirable subject, which clearly illustrates the application of psychological, pathological, chemical, genetic and sociological knowledge to the clinical problems of prevention and treatment (Royal College of Physicians, 1943; O'Connor and Tizard, 1956).

In the United States there has been a tendency in some schools to teach psychiatry mainly on patients who are not in the psychiatric department—'psychosomatic' cases. In such schools the students see very few psychotic patients. The objections to this distorted presentation of psychiatry are manifest: the medical student is hardly likely to grasp abstruse psychopathology such as will be offered him in psychiatric comments on ulcerative colitis or obesity, whereas the broad issues in, say, manic depressive psychosis are well within his scope (Bowman, 1952).

It is not unknown for students to be alienated from a subject because of the way it is taught them (Ross, 1935). It by no means follows that putting a great deal more time and effort than hitherto into teaching psychiatry will have the desired effect of giving the students a psychiatric outlook and understanding. The same caveat applies to an examination in the subject: useful as examinations are to test factual knowledge, they are of little value as a criterion of capacity to discriminate, to observe, and to weigh all relevant evidence. The clinical examination in which the student sees a patient, himself collects the findings, and discusses their significance, is much to be preferred to the written question-and-answer type of examination (Bull, 1956).

148

Just as medical students develop hypochondriacal fears during their surgical and medical training, the experiences they will pass through in their psychiatric course may disturb them emotionally. Here again the tutorial system of education is advantageous, since it permits closer acquaintance with the student and early recognition of his difficulties. The judicious teacher, in dealing with such students, steers a midway course between neglect of a potentially serious mental disturbance and, on the other hand, over-intensive concern about a transient upset (Fry, 1942).

C. THE PSYCHIATRIST

Some of the greatest psychiatrists of the last century were self-taught (e.g. Griesinger, Maudsley) but it would be difficult to maintain that a psychiatrist can nowadays become proficient if from the beginning of his psychiatric career he has had no guidance, no systematic teaching, no school except his own mistakes and successes (Blacker, 1946; Interdept. Committee, 1944). Wherever university psychiatric clinics were set up, their educational value was quickly recognized, but these could provide teaching only for a minority of the doctors who entered the specialty: the rest 'picked it up' as they went along, unless they were fortunate enough—as many were—to serve their apprenticeship in a mental hospital at which they would have the guidance and encouragement of an experienced psychiatrist who could teach and who enjoyed teaching.

In some countries (notably Great Britain and the United States) psychiatric training, like that for some other specialties, is the prelude to an examination; success in the examination indicates that the doctor has attained at least a minimum standard of skill and knowledge. The history of this development is instructive (Lewis, 1949; Whitehorn et al., 1952). By insisting that candidates must have completed stated periods of instruction in order to become eligible to sit the examinations, those controlling them are in a position to determine the pattern of training. They have undoubtedly influenced, and in many respects raised, the quality (as well as the quantity) of training, but less so than their ostensible powers permit. Where the examining body is a university, awarding a diploma to its own students, the examination is geared to the teaching, rather than the converse; if the examining body is a National Board, it must be careful not to lay down requirements too hard for average psychiatrists to satisfy. For a University diploma, the examination is a minor feature of the whole postgraduate educational process; for a Board certificate or diploma, however, the examination is crucial, and the preliminary requirement usually amounts to no more than a stated period of residency in approved hospitals or clinics.

Psychiatry has certainly not reached the stage at which a uniform pattern of postgraduate education is to be desired. Nor is it feasible. Apart from differences in educational policy within each country, there are divergencies reflecting the cultural, social and medical institutions of different countries, especially the organization of their welfare and medical services, the financial provision for graduate students and the financial and social rewards for different sorts of psychiatric activity; there is also the importance attached to special forms of training, in particular psychoanalysis (Boshes, 1956).

Extreme views have been the bane of psychiatry. They can certainly become the bane of psychiatric training. One group of extremists holds that psycho-dynamics is the alpha and the omega of the subject. Another group insists, with bigoted sincerity, that physiological interpretations, chemical and tissue pathology, and physical methods of treatments are the only proper meat and drink for the fledgling psychiatrist. A third maintains that in the training of psychiatrists of a particular complexion, psychiatry as Esquirol and Kraepelin, Bleuler and Maudsley and Adolf Meyer understood it need play no part at all: it is boldly urged that the psychiatrist of childhood, for example, need be only a pediatrician who has qualified as a psychoanalyst (Winnicott, 1958).

These are ill-advised and harmful views. A broad training is essential, giving the postgraduate student full opportunities to learn about the varied conditions comprehended within psychiatry and teaching him the ways of differentiating them, assessing their prognostic indications and carrying out their treatment (Meyer, 1933; Lewis, 1947; Royal College of Physicians, 1944; Whitehorn, 1957). When he has been given these opportunities to acquaint himself with the whole broad front he will be in a position to cultivate a particular aspect or division of psychiatry intensively, if he chooses.

I. SELECTION OF PSYCHIATRISTS

The practice of psychiatry makes demands on a doctor which are in some respects different from those of surgery or obstetrics or other branches of medicine. It has not been possible, however, to determine what sort of doctor can best meet these demands. Some doctors who are attracted to psychiatry are themselves in need of psychiatric treatment. It is generally assumed that these should be steered away from the specialty, since their mental condition may disturb their clinical judgment and expose their patients to risk. The kind of risk will depend on what sort of mental disturbances the doctors in question are prone to and the kind of psychiatric work they are going to undertake: an anxiety state is a very different matter from an insidious paranoid condition, and these will have very divergent effects according to whether the psychiatrist so affected practises psychoanalysis exclusively, or is in a busy outpatient department, or has charge of patients in a hospital where convulsive therapy, continuous narcosis and leucotomy are generously used.

When the would-be psychiatrist has pronouced character traits, an opinion of his fitness for psychiatry will be judged by much the same criteria as his fitness for any profession that entails dealing with people in a highly responsible way. Some who have reviewed the problem urge that emotional warmth in personal relationships is essential, others that sensitiveness and intuitive understanding are more valuable, and that this is particularly important if the psychiatrist undertakes the treatment of schizophrenic patients (White-horn and Betz, 1957). On the whole, however, it is sufficient if the would-be psychiatrist has the intelligence, integrity and balance that one would like in every doctor.

In most countries the supply of psychiatrists is less than the demand. It is therefore only in the university clinics and hospitals which offer coveted opportunities for postgraduate education that there is room for choice between applicants for training. Psychoanalytic institutes are also able to select those whom they will train in analysis. The bulk of psychiatrists, how-ever, enter the specialty without any 'screening', and in the present state of knowledge about the desirable combination of personality characteristics in a good psychiatrist this self-selection is not a matter for regret. It is, however, very much a matter for regret when doctors who have failed in other branches of the profession, because of mental disturbance, alcoholism or character defects, find a haven on the staff of a mental hospital.

Where the candidate for psychiatric training can be selected—usually be-cause he applies for a post as registrar or resident in a teaching hospital—his previous medical experience since qualifying must be taken into account. But here also rigid standards are objectionable. Some candidates have spent a few years in internal medicine, neurology or pediatrics—or, it may be in general practice—before taking up psychiatry; others have acquired special knowledge of psychology, or physiology, or philosophy; others, again, have been engaged in laboratory studies such as pathology or bacteriology and wish now to cultivate a less detached, more human branch of medicine. No one can say that such experience will be of no value to the psychiatrist, or that one kind of experience is in all cases more to be prized than another. This also holds true of psychoanalytic experience (though some psycho-analysts think otherwise).

II. PROVISION OF TRAINING POSTS

A thorough training, lasting several years, can in most countries be obtained without hardship through paid appointments, though in countries which have not a coherent National Health Service like that of Great Britain, which is deliberately planned to facilitate graduate training, the would-be specialist may have to make economic and other sacrifices in order to train at a good centre. In all countries, however, the psychiatrist who wants to train as a psychoanalyst must be prepared to give much time, and a good deal of money, to attain his end. Although economic considerations do not normally call for any consideration in a *Handbuch* article, it is necessary to emphasize that in most countries psychoanalytic training is closely connected not only with the choice of subsequent career, but with the necessity to recover the heavy costs of such training. Psychoanalysts are no more mercenary than other physicians, but young graduates can as a rule only meet the heavy expense of a training analysis, lasting perhaps four years, if they see a good prospect of recouping themselves in the ensuing years in private practice. The fairly sharp division in the United States between the psychiatrists in mental hospitals and the psychiatrists in private practice is not unrelated to this necessity and its by-products (Hollingshead and Redlich, 1958).

Whether a psychiatrist learns most while working in a mental hospital with its associated outpatient departments, or in a university hospital and medical school, depends not only on the custom of the country, the clinical facilities in particular mental hospitals or university clinics, and on the particular interests of the learner, but far more than these, on the personal qualities of the staff, junior as well as senior, with whom they will associate. The atmosphere of lively curiosity, serious and sustained inquiry, intellectual integrity, and eager, well-informed, penetrating discussion must be of crucial importance. (Ebaugh and Rymer, 1942; Lewis, 1947; Stengel, 1958; Levine, 1953; Whitehorn, 1957). Similarly the psychiatrist may learn through joint or reciprocal seminars with internists (Engel, *et al.*, 1957).

III. PROGRAMME OF STUDIES

The central feature of postgraduate training in psychiatry must be contact with patients in a medical capacity. Psychologists, nurses, social workers and occupational therapists have close contact with patients in their several professional capacities: but the relationship manifestly differs in some important respects from the medical relationship: as does indeed also the relationship of the research worker, whether medically qualified or not, if his approach to the patient is exclusively that of an investigator to his experimental subject. The psychiatrist's training can be along no royal road which by-passes prolonged medical contact with the mentally ill, and medical responsibility for them. How long this clinical training, which determines the length of the whole training, should go on is unclear. In principle, it need hardly be said, it never ends: but the neophyte may be regarded as ceasing to need tutelage after three, four or five years. In most countries, the period of required psychiatric clinical training is formally about five, but in practice three. There are, however, so many variations, so many differences in the application of such requirements in accordance with local conditions, and so little uniformity in the control of psychiatrists who claim the status of specialists without having satisfied the requirements of examining or administrative boards, that it is justifiable to infer that nobody knows what is the desirable duration of clinical training, that it cannot really be laid down in hard and fast rules which ignore the quality of the trainee and the social needs of his community, and that it is sensible to equate it with the duration of clinical training expected—or insisted on—for all the other specialist branches.

Each postgraduate school has its own teaching programme, based partly on the educational conviction of its teachers, partly on the demands and critical suggestions of its graduate pupils and partly on the special strengths and balance of its facilities. In the most active schools, there is a constant gradual readjustment reflecting the lessons drawn from their current experience and the changes in their teaching staff.

A typical programme at a university postgraduate centre launches the trainee on the clinical waters by entrusting to him the examination and care of a limited number of patients (not more than twelve or fifteen at a time) with a variety of psychotic conditions, since it is usually easier for him to find his way with such patients than if he is confronted with neurotic, psychopathic or 'psychosomatic' patients who demand from him psychotherapeutic assistance which he is too inexperienced to give them. Concurrently he is given (through tutorial classes, ward conferences and seminars) guidance in clinical procedure, and especially in diagnostic appraisal, etiological and psychopathological formulation, and the broad issues of treatment. Systematic lectures, tutorials and demonstrations during this first year of his training acquaint him with the history and fundamentals of psychiatry and as much physiology, biochemistry, neuroanatomy, genetics and psychology as it seems appropriate to offer a psychiatrist to assure his scientific foundations. At the Institute of Psychiatry in London 112 hours are devoted during the first year to this systematic instruction in the normal: of these 46 hours are given to physiology and biochemistry, and 51 to psychology.

When the student has completed this first stage—the counterpart in his graduate training of the mainly preclinical phase of his medical student curriculum eight or nine years before—he enters upon further clinical training, alongside which go tutorials, lectures and seminars. In few of the latter is imparting facts the main purpose of the teacher: his concern is far more how he can help the student to learn from his patients, to reason well about his findings, apply to current clinical problems the knowledge he has gained in his basic studies and in his reading, and to recognize the limits and the possibilities in each clinical situation he encounters (Royal College of Physicians, 1944).

The clinical range of the trainee should be wide. It is desirable that he should have adequate experience of forensic problems, of child psychiatry, of the rehabilitation of patients with chronic illness, of the accepted forms of physical, social and psychological treatment, and of outpatient, day-hospital and domiciliary practice. Through teaching others (his juniors among the graduate students, or nurses, or social workers) he has himself learnt; through 'journal discussions' he has become familiar with the critical evaluation of technical literature and with the lines of current progress; and through follow-up inquiries and a review of his successes and failures he has attained a just appreciation of prognosis, protecting him against becoming the dupe of his own or other people's hopes.

Experience suggests that rapid alternations of clinical duty are detrimental to training: six months is, as a rule, the minimum period which a trainee should serve on a specific clinical attachment in which he deals with the same members of staff and the same type of clinical problem: in certain instances, e.g. secondment to prisons and remand homes to gain experience of forensic and criminological problems, three months may suffice, but continuity and time to 'settle down' are so essential to learning psychiatry and digesting current experience that half a year must generally be regarded as the least period for a given tour of duty.

There is, during clinical training, ample opportunity to try the advantages of audio-visual and other technical aids. In Montreal, for example, the post-graduate students are supplied with tape-recorders 'in much the same way as a student in pathology is provided with a microscope', because of the belief of the teachers there that the recorder is an invaluable means of detecting problems and showing how the student's psychotherapy is proceeding (Cameron, 1958).

The development of systematic training has been less rapid and the demand for it less insistent in most European countries than in Great Britain and the United States. There are now, however, in several countries comprehensive programmes, related to the official requirements for recognition as a specialist. Governmental interference of this kind in postgraduate training is foreign to the British, Canadian, and American tradition, but it has the logical basis that it extends to specialist education that concern which the State everywhere shows in the content and standards of undergraduate medical education (Neumann, 1957; Ehrhardt, 1955).

In France, by a decree passed in 1949, the certificate of special studies in neuropsychiatry which is necessary for specialist status could be obtained after three years of clinical, theoretical, and practical or laboratory studies: a year and a half devoted to neurology, and a year and a half to adult and child psychiatry. During the first year the student would study the anatomy and physiology of the nervous system in health and disease, neuropathology, electroencephalography and other clinical and laboratory aspects of neuro-logical disease. In the second year he studies psychopathology, experimental psychology, mental tests, and the theoretical and clinical aspects of mental disorder and defect, including its medico-legal problems. The third year would be occupied with the neuropsychiatry of childhood, further clinical experience of general psychiatry, and a small investigation in the line of the postgraduate student's interests and capacity. This programme was modified by a decree issued in July 1957, which laid it down that whereas the first years must be spent in appropriate teaching hospitals associated with the university, the third clinical year could be in a wide variety of hospitals, but that the requirement of a third year of clinical work could be dispensed with in the case of doctors who had held a post as resident (chef de clinique) in the university hospital or obtained special experience in certain other hospitals. At the end of the student's period of training he has clinical, practical and written examinations, and his examiners take into account the record of his performance during the various stages of his training, and any scientific work he has published (Pichot, 1958).

If this programme is compared with that of the Academic Diploma in Psychological Medicine in the University of London (University of London,

1957) and with the requirements of the American Board of Psychiatry and Neurology (Amer. Board of Psychiatry and Neurology, 1954), the general similarity in content and purpose is clear, though there are considerable differences of detail, method and examination criteria. A catalogue of requirements and a syllabus can, however, give no true picture of the vitality of a course of training nor of the laxity or rigour with which it is actually conducted and its results assessed. In the long run any national or local scheme of postgraduate psychiatric training must be judged by the way psychiatric services develop in that area and by the contributions to the advancement of psychiatric knowledge which come from the men so trained.

IV. SPECIAL DIVISIONS OF PSYCHIATRY

Some teachers do not subscribe to the tenet that the student should obtain experience of all aspects of psychiatry, if possible. They prefer to emphasize the psychodynamic aspect, the contacts and overlap with other branches of medicine, and the acquisition of psychotherapeutic skill and insight: or they would reserve, say, child psychiatry for study after the completion of a 'standard', or general, psychiatric training (Capes, 1955).

It is clear that every aspect or branch of psychiatry demands a close and long application from those who would concentrate on it. That is, however, a different matter from training, which can be concentrated within a comparatively short period of the specialist's professional life. The period of training can, however, be appreciably lengthened if the psychiatrist wishes to become highly proficient in psychotherapy and believes that he must therefore qualify as a psychoanalyst—or, it may be, as a Jungian analytical psychologist.

Training as a psychoanalyst has no predetermined duration, but seldom takes less than four years. If, as many think desirable, it is begun only after the physician has spent two or three years in psychiatry, it prolongs his total training to six or seven years—or longer if those who analyse him and supervise his analysis of patients remain for a considerable period doubtful of his fitness to practice analysis. The organization of strict psychoanalytical training tends to be on a formalized pattern, in the later stages of which compulsory lectures and seminars play a considerable part (Institute of Psychoanalysis, 1957; Schlumberger and Marty, 1956). It varies in stringency and average length from country to country, but the International Psychoanalytical Association has an effective influence in maintaining approximately similar standards of training and acceptance. The training is not without its critics, even among psychoanalysts (Glover, 1955), and is considerably modified in several of the more or less dissident groups which have sprung from the parent stem. The training in analytical psychology, given by the Institutes which follow in the footsteps of C. G. Jung, now extends over about five years.

Psychotherapy existed before psychoanalysis, and methods of teaching it according to a particular method—for example suggestion or persuasion—likewise came into being in France, Switzerland and elsewhere. More recently particular countries have shown a penchant for a special method—such as autogenous training in Germany and Daseinsanalyse in Switzerland, while in the United States Carl Rogers, Percival Symonds, Lakin Phillips and other psychologists have developed and taught varying methods of treatment: these may be investigated, and perhaps in part incorporated, by psychiatrists who wish to amplify the scope and simplify the procedure of psychotherapy so long as it can be done without detriment to the quality of the treatment. For the most part, however, American psychotherapists regard a conventional psychoanalytical training as desirable for the psychotherapist, even if he is not going to restrict himself exclusively to psychoanalytic practice.

In those countries where psychoanalysis has been accorded the leading place in the training of psychotherapists, there is manifest flux and readiness to experiment in this matter. Doubts and discontents are expressed because of the dangers of premature crystallization of theory and practice. The development of group psychotherapy has powerfully modified earlier attitudes (Foulkes and Parkin, 1957; Sutherland, 1952), as has also the effort to extend the range of psychotherapy for schizophrenia and other psychoses (Bally, 1956). In some countries of Western Europe there is moreover a semi-philosophical strain in current conceptions of psychiatry which would transcend the scientific limits—or limitations—of our branch of medicine; the adherents of this view of the psychiatrist's function emphasize those human features in a psychotherapeutic relationship which cannot be analysed or taught (Kuhn 1956; Kretschmer, 1951).

V. TRAINING FOR RESEARCH

Prominent among the obligations of those who provide postgraduate education is the duty to recognize and further whatever talents for research their students possess. The fields within which psychiatric research is carried on are so wide that there is scope for many kinds of interest and ability; the complexity of the problems is so daunting, however, that it is profitless, and can be unkind, to encourage competent clinicians to attempt scientific investigations beyond their powers. But besides outstanding men who give a great impetus to the study of a subject, there is always need for steady, less brilliant workers who nevertheless accumulate indispensable findings (Schilling, 1958). Since psychiatry clearly requires both kinds of investigator, it can seek them out and cultivate them in the ranks of non-psychiatrists—biochemists, psychologists, statisticians, physiologists—as well as find them among psychiatrists themselves. There is no dilemma or sharp choice here, since the joint labours of non-psychiatrists and psychiatrists are called for to advance our knowledge. It would, however, be an ominous situation if the special training of psychiatrists did little to promote their activity in suitable research.

How this can be achieved is a matter of opinion. Some hold that exposure to an atmosphere of lively inquiry and direct contact with good research workers is the only way, others that formal instruction in scientific method and supervision in allotted investigation are effective (N. D. C. Lewis, 1953). It is ideal when all these formative influences can be combined. Though there can be no substitute for personal enthusiasm and ability in the student and the corresponding qualities in teacher or exemplar, much can be accomplished by a steady insistence, in all clinical work, on recognizing problems that planned inquiry might illuminate, or even solve, and by guiding the student in the design and execution of a manageable investigation which he himself has chosen. This can lead up to a dissertation, which may be required of every candidate for a psychiatric diploma or for approval as specialist; or it may provide the material for his doctoral thesis. A good library is indispensable; the postgraduate institute which has a poor library or which does not teach its students how to use a library properly, grossly handicaps them.

Those psychiatrists who have genuine gifts for research will commonly need further training in scientific method and techniques, beyond what they have received as medical students. Special grants and fellowships to enable them at an appropriate stage of their clinical training to be seconded for this purpose to appropriate departments and laboratories (in the postgraduate institute or elsewhere) have proved of the utmost value. In a large institute, with several scientific departments engaged in active research, whole-time secondment may not be necessary; the selected psychiatrists may spend about half their time in the relevant laboratories, and the other half in teaching and clinical duties. It is imperative, if such arrangements are to work on a fairly large scale, that it should be easy for those psychiatrists who have devoted themselves almost wholly to research for a period of two, three or more years, to return to a clinical career, if they wish, without suffering from any disadvantage because they have been climbing a different ladder (Medical Research Council, 1953).

The foregoing article has been restricted to the teaching of psychiatry to medical students and to would-be psychiatrists. Other physicians (Kolb, 1956; Engel et al., 1957), psychologists, social workers, clergymen and many other professional groups are nowadays given psychiatric instruction in one form or another, but to discuss such teaching would go beyond the limits of this presentation.

REFERENCES

AMERICAN BOARD OF PSYCHIATRY AND NEUROLOGY: 'Requirements', J. Amer. med. Ass., 156, 539–41 (1954).

AMERICAN MEDICAL ASSOCIATION. '57th Annual Report on Medical Education in the United States and Canada', J. Amer. med. Ass., 165, 1413–14 (1957).

ANDERSON, D. G., and JOHNSON V. 'Influence of changing dimensions of medical knowledge upon medical education', J. Amer. med. Ass., 167, 54–7 (1958).

ARNOTT, W. M. 'The aims of the medical curriculum' in Proceedings of the First World Conference on Medical Education (ed. H. Clegg), London, Oxford University Press, 1954.

BAKST, H. J., and MALAMUD, W. 'Combined teaching in human ecology', J. med. Educ., 22, 603–9 (1957).

EDUCATION

BALLY, G. 'Die psychotherapeutische Ausbildung an einer psychiatrischen Universitätsklinik', *Schweiz. Arch. Neurol. Psychiat.*, **77**, 427–80 (1956).

BLACK, D. 'A modern liberal education in medicine?' *J. med. Educ.*, **32**, 751–66 (1957).

BLACKER, C. P. *Neurosis and the Mental Health Services*, London, Oxford University Press, 1946.

BOSHES, B. 'The responsibility of the graduate educator in neurology and psychiatry', *J. Amer. med. Ass.*, **161**, 1213–19 (1956).

BOWMAN, K. M. in *Psychiatry and Medical Education: Report of 1951 Conference on Psychiatric Education*, (eds. J. C. Whitehorn *et al.*), p. 53, Washington, American Psychiatric Ass., 1952.

BULL, G. M. 'An examination of the final examination in medicine', *Lancet*, 1956, **II**, 368–72.

CAMERON, D. E. 'The teaching of psychiatry', *J. ment. Sci.*, **104**, 492–503 (1958).

CAPES, M. 'The training of the child psychiatrist', in *The Child in Hospital: Bull. Wld. Hlth. Org.*, **12**, 449–52 (1955).

CAUGHEY, J. L. 'Medical education based on interdepartmental co-operation', *J. Amer. med. Ass.*, **161**, 697–99 (1956).

DEITRICK, J. E., and BERSON, R. C. *Medical Schools in the United States at Mid-Century*, New York, McGraw-Hill, 1953.

EBAUGH, F. G., and RYMER, C. A. *Psychiatry in Medical Education*, New York Commonwealth Fund, 1942.

ENGEL, G. L., GREEN, W. L., REICHMAN, F., SCHMALE, A., and ASHENBURG, N. 'A graduate and undergratuate teaching program on the psychological aspects of medicine', *J. med. Educ.*, **32**, 859–71 (1957).

EHRHARDT. H. 'Mitteilungen der deutschen Gesellschaft für Psychiatrie und Neurologie', *Nervenartzt*, **26**, 452–3 (1955).

EWING, J. A. 'The role of psychiatry in medical education', *Brit. med. J.*, 1956, **11**, 503–6.

EY, H. (ed.). 'La psychiatrie dans le monde', *Annexe au Traité de Psychiatrie Clinique. Encyclopedie Médico-Chirurgicale*, Paris, 1955.

FOULKES, S. H., and PARKIN, A. 'Outpatient psychotherapy: a contribution towards a new approach', *Internat. J. soc. Psychiat.*, **8**, 44–8 (1957).

FRY, C. C. *Mental Health in College*, New York, Commonwealth Fund, 1942.

GÄRTNER, H. 'Welche Anregungen ergeben sich aus einer Analyse der ärztlichen Ausbildung in Frankreich für die Reform des deutschen klinischen Medizinstudiums?' *Dtsch. med. Wschr.*, **82**, 1659–62 (1957).

GENERAL MEDICAL COUNCIL. *Recommendations as to the medical curriculum*, London, General Medical Council, 1957.

GILL, M., NEWMAN, R., and REDLICH, F. C. *The Initial Interview in Psychiatric Practice*, New York, International Universities Press, 1954.

GLOVER, E. *The Technique of Psychoanalysis*, London: Baillière, 1955.

HAM, T. H. 'Current trends in medical education: a research approach', *J. med. Educ.*, **33**, 297–309 (1958).

HARGROVE, E. A., HAM, G. C. and FLEMING, W. L. 'Multi-disciplinary teaching of human ecology in the first year of medicine', *J. med. Educ.*, **32**, 697–702 (1957).

HOLLDACK, K. 'Medical education in Germany', *J. med. Educ.*, **32**, 631–4 (1957).

HOLLINGSHEAD, A. B., and REDLICH, F. C. *Social class and mental illness: a community study*, New York, Wiley, 1958.

INSTITUTE OF PSYCHOANALYSIS. *Training Prospectus 1957–1958*, London, British Psychoanalytical Soc. and Institute of Psychoanalysis, 1957.

INTERDEPARTMENTAL COMMITTEE ON MEDICAL SCHOOLS. *Report*, London, H.M.S.O., 1944.

JOHNS HOPKINS. 'A revised program of medical education at Johns Hopkins', *Johns Hopkins Mag.*, **8**, (1957): reprinted in *J. med. Educ.*, **33**, 225–33 (1958).

KAUDERS, O. 'Der psychiatrische Unterricht innerhalb des medizinischen Bildungsganges', *Wien. klin. Wschr.*, **58**, 709–14 (1946).

KOLB, L. C. 'The psychiatric viewpoint in training residents', *J. Amer. med. Ass.*, **161**, 21–4 (1956).

KOLLE, K. 'Neuordnung der ärztlichen Ausbildung', *Münch. med. Wschr.*, **100**, 586–92 (1958).

KRETSCHMER, E. 'Zur Frage der Lehranalyse und der Analyse Gesunder', *Nervenarzt*, **22**, 122 (1951).

KUHN, R. 'Über die Ausbildung zum Spezialarzt für Psychiatrie', *Schweiz. Arch. Neurol. Psychiat*, **77**, 457–72 (1956).

LEVINE, M. 'A note on the methods of teaching psychiatry', in *The Psychiatrist, His Training and Development: Report of the 1952 Conference on Psychiatric Education* (eds. J. C. Whitehorn *et al.*), p. 175, Washington, Amer. Psychiat. Ass., 1952.

LEWIS, A. 'The education of psychiatrists', *Lancet*, 1947, **II**, 79–83. (See also this vol. pp. 125–37)

LEWIS, A. 'Postgraduate study in mental health in Britain', *Brit. med. Bull.*, **6**, 185–7 (1949).

LEWIS, N. D. C. 'The place of research in psychiatric residency programmes, in *The Psychiatrist, his Training and Development: Report of the 1952 Conference on Psychiatric Education* (eds. J. C. Whitehorn *et al.*), Washington, Amer. Psychiat. Ass., 1953.

MACCALMAN, D. R. 'The place of mental health in the medical curriculum', *Brit. med. Bull.*, **6**, 188–91 (1949).

MEDICAL RESEARCH COUNCIL, MINISTRY OF HEALTH and DEPARTMENT OF HEALTH FOR SCOTLAND. *Clinical Research in Relation to the National Health Service*, London, H.M.S.O., 1953.

MERTON, R. K., READER, G. and KENDAL, P. L. *The Student Physician*, Cambridge (Mass.), Harvard Univ. Press for Commonwealth Fund, 1957.

MEYER, A. 'Preparation for psychiatry', *Arch. Neurol. Psychiat.* (Chicago), **30**, 1111–1125 (1933).

MILLAR, W. M. 'Teaching methods in psychiatry', *Brit. J. med. Psychol.*, **27**, 30–6 (1954).

NEUMANN, H. 'Die Entwicklung der deutschen Facharztordnung, *Nervenarzt*, **28**,' 278–9 (1957).

O'CONNOR, N. and TIZARD, J. *The Social Problem of Mental Deficiency*, London, Pergamon Press, 1956.

PFEIFFENBERGER, J. M. and SMITH, D. H. 'Current status of West German medical schools', *J. Amer. med. Ass.*, **161**, 1072–7 (1956).

PICHOT, P. Personal communication (1958).

PICKERING, G. W. 'The purpose of medical education', *Brit. med. J.*, 1956, **II**, 113–16.

PROCEEDINGS OF THE FOURTH CONFERENCE ON PSYCHIATRIC EDUCATION: *Undergraduate Instruction*, New York, National Committee for Mental Hygiene, 1938.

ROSS, T. A. 'The teaching of the neuroses to medical students', *Edinburgh med. J.*, **42**, 445–75, 505–36 (1935).

ROYAL COLLEGE OF PHYSICIANS. *Interim Report on Undergraduate Education in Psychiatry*, London, Royal College of Physicians, 1943.

ROYAL COLLEGE OF PHYSICIANS. *Second Interim Report on Postgraduate Education in Psychiatry*, London, Royal College of Physicians, 1944.

RÜMKE, H. C. 'The teaching of social psychiatry', in *Proceedings of the First World Conference on Medical Education* (ed. H. Clegg), London, Oxford University Press, 1954.

SCHAEFER, H. 'Medizinische Studienreform', *Münch. med. Wschr.*, **99**, 613–14 (1957).

SCHILLING, H. K. 'A human enterprise', *Science*, **127**, 132–4 (1958).

SCHLUMBERGER, M., and MARTY, P. In *La Psychoanalyse d'Aujourd'hui* (ed. S. Nacht), Paris, P.U.F., 1956.

SCHNEIDER, K. 'Der psychiatrische Unterricht in Deutschland', in *Festschrift für H. Delgado*, Lima, 1958.

SCHNEIDER, M. 'Zur Organisation von Lehre und Forschung an unseren medizinischen Fakultäten', *Dtsch. med. Wschr.*, **82**, 1117–23 (1956).

SHRYOCK, R. H. 'The history and sociology of science', *Items*, **10**, 13–16 (1956).

SINCLAIR, D. C. *Medival Students and Medical Sciences*, London, Oxford University Press, 1955.

STENGEL, E. 'Reflections on the undergraduate and postgraduate teaching of psychiatry', *J. ment. Sci*, **104**, 772–82 (1959).

SUTHERLAND, J. D. 'Notes on psychoanalytic group therapy: therapy and training', *Psychiatry*, **15**, 111–17 (1952).

TURNER, E. L. 'The education of a physician in the United States: the current scene', *J. med. Educ.*, **33**, 259–71 (1958).

UNIVERSITY OF LONDON. *Regulations for internal students*, 1957–1958, 2062–65, London, University of London, 1957.

WHITEHORN, J. C. *Psychiatric Education and Progress* (Salmon Lecture), Springfield (Ill.), Thomas, 1957.

WHITEHORN, J. C., and BETZ, B. J. 'A comparison of psychotherapeutic relationships between physicians and schizophrenic patients when insulin is combined with psychotherapy and when psychotherapy is used alone', *Amer. J. Psychiat.*, **113**, 901–10 (1957).

WHITEHORN, J. C., BRACELAND, F. J., LIPPARD, V. W. and MALAMUD, W. (eds.). *The Psychiatrist, His Training and Development: Report of 1952 Conference on Psychiatric Education*, Washington, Amer. Psychiat. Ass., 1953.

WHITEHORN, J. C., JACOBSEN, C., LEVINE, M. and LIPPARD, V. W. (eds.). *Psychiatry and Medical Education: Report of 1951 Conference on Psychiatric Education*, Washington, Amer. Psychiat. Ass., 1952.

WINNICOTT, D. 'Child Psychiatry', in *Modern Trends in Pediatrics. Second Series.* (ed. A. Holzel and J. P. M. Tizard), London, Butterworth, 1958.

WORLD MEDICAL ASSOCIATION. *Standards of Medical Education: Report 1*, New York, World med. Ass., 1950.

ADDRESSES

II

PHILOSOPHY AND PSYCHIATRY

I AM grateful for the honour of being invited to give the second Manson Lecture. Dr Manson believed that the study of sick people leads into the widest fields of thought, but that increasing specialization within medicine diverts the doctor from seeing man and his nature whole: the chief question seems to be (he wrote in 1930), 'whether medicine is in the bondship of practice, whether it is a skilled art, or whether it can emerge to give its own contribution to abstract thought and philosophy' [1]. Indeed, pleading with doctors to join this Institute of Philosophy, he declared that medicine should be the most philosophic of the professions. In this he was reviving an ancient claim: the arguments for it have lately been restated with much Aristotelian piety by Scott Buchanan. Now here I find myself in a difficulty at the outset: I am to speak of the relationship between philosophy and medicine, at a lecture founded by a passionate believer in their conjunction, yet I am engaged in a particular branch of medicine which was for longer than any other preoccupied with philosophy and dependent on it, but had so little profit from its fidelity that it reckons progress from the time when it struggled away from this allegiance. Psychiatry has not been able to refrain since then from many a backward glance at the older philosophy she once swore by, and she has been much influenced by the philosophies of later times: she has—doubtless in punishment for her defection—become entangled now and then in bad, unrecognized philosophy of her own making. She has, at all events, never achieved more than a temporary indifference to philosophic thought. She has, moreover, this signal virtue, that she tries constantly to avoid the tyranny of a limited specialization: she seeks to occupy herself with man in his whole nature, body and mind together. Her faults are, on the whole, much the same as the faults of philosophy—schematization without sufficient evidence, uncritical trust in the adequacy of language, and contention because the contenders do not agree about their axioms or fail to make them explicit.

I shall therefore consider first how it has come about that psychiatrists, who

This paper was first delivered as the second Manson lecture to the British (now Royal) Institute of Philosophy in March 1948. It is reprinted from *Philosophy* (April 1949), **24**, 99–117.

of all doctors might be expected most to value philosophic training and thought, do not as a rule think much of philosophy. I shall then speak of some psychiatric observations on certainty, and their relevance to the intuitive knowledge or self-evident propositions on which philosophers have built so much. Insight and knowledge of self have an intimate bearing on certainty, and I shall refer to depersonalization as a striking disorder of self-knowledge, which also raises the inevitable question of the inter-relation of body and mind. Finally I shall speak of the closely connected question of the nature of consciousness, viewed from a psychiatrist's standpoint.

The connection between psychiatry and philosophy was, as I have said, intimate for many centuries. There are strong reasons in the nature of psychiatry why this should be so. The psychiatrist has to ponder on the relation of mind to body, in resolving the clinical problems of every patient he sees; he must address himself to questions of value whenever he has to decide whether a patient has become healthy after he has been ill, or whether a particular disturbance of mental activity is a sign of illness; if he is at all reflective, he must examine the validity and limitations of human knowledge, gained through means upon which he relies for his understanding of himself and his patients, while at the same time recognizing how deceived those patients can be when they too rely upon such means of knowledge; and, finally, the problem of causation is thrust on his notice so insistently that even the most unsophisticated psychiatrist is aware that common sense will hardly serve his turn here. The psychiatrist then is confronted, whether he likes it or not, with many of the central issues of philosophy. It might be expected that he would therefore value a philosophical training. But this is far from being the case: he philosophizes as best he can with little or no help from the schools; or he denies that he has any concern with philosophy: for him it is not charming, nor for that matter harsh and crabbed, but just useless. Such an attitude is not limited to those innocent of philosophic discipline. Of living philosophers, the only one, I think, who has been a psychiatrist of note is Karl Jaspers: and Jaspers, in his well-known book on Psychopathology [2], writes that thorough philosophical study has no positive value for the psychopathologist, except in fitting him to meet methodological objections. It has, he goes on, a further negative value in that by it he is protected against many formulations, superfluous discussions and clogging prejudices 'die bei unphilosophischen Köpfen in der Psychopathologie—dem Gegenstand dieser Wissenschaft entsprechend—nicht selten eine Rolle spielen'. Yet even this grudging credit is withdrawn in an ensuing passage in small print which says that those who make valuable discoveries often state them badly so that by formal logic the new statements can be shown to be contradictory and incorrect; therefore, says Jaspers, a philosophical training can be damaging rather than helpful for those who must be alive to fresh points of view in such a field as psychopathology. Evidently Jaspers the psychopathologist has had little help from Jaspers the philosopher.

The psychiatrist's desire to reject or ignore philosophy is closely paralleled in the history of psychology. During the many centuries when psychology was a branch of philosophic thought, it remained sterile, and later suffered in comparison with the emancipated natural sciences. Psychiatry, whose progress depends so much on psychology, was in similar straits, and the intuitive or deductive approach to its problems yielded little of value except systems of classification. The best that a kindly historian can say is that 'the influence of philosophy on psychiatry is indisputable and yet imperceptible, almost elusive. Abstract philosophy and introspective psychology remained united. Consequently . . . (the) contribution to psychology was more methodological than substantial. . . . Summarizing the keen speculations of the philosophical psychologies of the seventeenth century we may say that they did give the spontaneous, empirical orientation of the physician a certain dignity of philosophical depth. Introspection . . . and empirical descriptions of various details of human behaviour became the substance of psychiatry.'[3] This view is somewhat superficial, for psychiatry was materially furthered through its impregnation by philosophic ideas but the advance made during the eighteen hundred years in which it was yoked to philosophy and theology were small in comparison with those of the last hundred and fifty.

There is, moreover, a widespread belief among psychiatrists, as among other empiricists, that the 'creativeness of a thought does not depend on its being truthful or even reasonable'. Hence their readiness to accept irrational or naïve hypotheses which lead to useful action, especially in treatment: for example, the theoretical assumptions upon which Egas Moniz based his operation of prefrontal leucotomy for mental disorder. The complaisant attitude of the 'eclectic' psychiatrists towards diverse systems of psychopathology is another instance of pragmatism and, often, of lack of consistency: whereas in everything somatic and quantitative many such psychiatrists have strict requirements, in the field of 'dynamic psychology' they give way to despair and ask of a method only 'does it work?' and of a theory only 'is it consistent within itself?'

Some psychiatrists have interested themselves more in philosophers than in philosophy. Speculative systems, it has often been said, have more to do with the personality and even the mental illnesses of the philosopher who propounds them than with the world as it really is: they are, in short, his illusory projections of himself upon the larger screen. The pathographers, as they have been called, of Schopenhauer, Fechner and other philosophers labour to demonstrate this. Since the constant aim of the natural sciences, in which doctors are trained, is to minimize or eliminate subjective bias in observing and interpreting the world, the more the personality and individual experiences of the philosopher are seen to colour his system, the poorer the opinion the doctor has of it as knowledge. Such summary judgment is clearly faulty, and would be improper in the psychiatrist, of all people. The philosopher, like everyone else, is, at any age, the product of his heredity and all the passing accidents of his life, and it is futile to hope that his thoughts can ever be separated from what he is. Much of his thought may have been recognizably coloured and shaped by illness and misfortune, or by some happy concurrence of events, and it is surely profitable to discern this. Perhaps I can illustrate this influence by a very simple instance taken from the writings of Kant. Kant, as you know, was interested in the nature and forms of mental disease, and in one of his lesser-known writings [4] says of depressive hypochondria 'I have paid attention only to its mental manifestations, without wanting to look into its roots, which really lie in the body, and have their chief seat in the organs of digestion rather than in the brain. . . . These sad discomforts, as long as they are not hereditary, have a fair prospect of recovery; and the man whose help is chiefly to be sought in them is the physician. Still, for the honour of my faculty, I should not like to exclude the philosopher, who could prescribe the right mental diet—on condition, that is, that he take no payment for his services.' Much later, in his *Anthropologie*, 1798, he returned to this question and put forward his well-known classification of mental diseases, based on the conceptions of mental structure and function which played so important a part in his philosophy. In this classification he gives much importance to Hypochondria (Grillenkrankheiten), which he described with much particularity and insists, as he had twenty years before, that it is caused by bodily changes especially in the stomach. The clue to his concern with this question and the explanation for his error may be found in another of his writings [5] where he gives a scrap of autobiography: 'Because of my flat and narrow chest which affords too little room for the movement of my heart and lungs, I have a natural disposition to hypochondria, which in earlier years made me weary of life. But the reflection that the cause of this oppression of my heart was perhaps only a mechanical matter and was irremovable, brought me to the point of disregarding it: so that whilst I felt the oppression in my chest, in my head there was peace and cheerfulness which I could communicate to others, when in company. . . . I still have the opression, for the cause lies in my bodily structure: but I have mastered its influence on my thoughts and actions, by turning my attention away from it as though it were no concern of mine.' And a little later, in the same paper, he illuminates his metaphor of 1764 about the philosopher prescribing die Diät des Gemüts, for he now remarks 'Thinking is a nutriment without which a scholar cannot live, when he is awake and alone.'

I have dwelt upon this simple instance of dangerous dependence upon personal experience because its very crudity drives home the likelihood that in more subtle and remote ways also the thoughts of a Kant, and of any philosopher, are significantly influenced perhaps distorted, by his personal circumstances and constitution. It is, at any rate, an assumption of psychiatry, with its present genetic bias, that you may have to study the inheritance, and the upbringing and daily life of a man if you would understand his mental products. This is not to say that it is thus you assess their value.

So much for the attitude which the majority of psychiatrists, I think, have adopted towards philosophers and philosophy. I doubt whether philosophers, on their side, have paid much attention to psychiatry. Yet it is scarcely to be denied that the phenomena which the psychiatrist studies throw light on many questions of great interest to philosophy, especially those touching on theory of knowledge. The psychiatrist has to attend to disorders of belief, errors of perception and reasoning. His clinical experience sometimes enlightens, sometimes clouds his understanding of writings on philosophy. When he reads, 'je jugeai que je pouvais prendre pour régle générale que les choses que nous concevons fort clairement et fort distinctement sont toutes vraies', [6] he is reminded of all the people he has seen who if they applied this to themselves, would have assuredly fallen into error: and his painful doubt is not relieved when he reads on: 'il y a seulement quelque difficulté á bien remarquer quelles sont celles que nous concevons distinctement' [6].

No doubt it will be replied that Descartes was here speaking for himself and for other men of intact philosophic mind; it would be absurd to suppose that he maintained that simpletons and madmen as well as ordinary human beings could recognize truth in those things which they conceive very clearly and very distinctly. This would perhaps be the end of the psychiatrist's difficulty, if all men could indeed be divided into philosophers, ordinary human beings, simpletons and madmen. But the psychiatrist early learns an important lesson about men's minds; that there are no sharp qualitative divisions which separate wise men from fools, or rational men from lunatics. Descartes was seeking to determine what it is that gives him the conviction of certainty about the proposition 'I think, therefore I am': a personal quest and a personal certainty. The certainty about truth arising, as Descartes says, from a very clear and very distinct conception, may be found in many people manifestly insane and in many people who are mentally healthy yet whose certainty is in part subject to the same determinants as that of the insane, and is correspondingly attached to a false proposition.

Certainty, or conviction, has been studied, though not very fully, in relation to belief, especially religious belief. William James, agreeing with Bagehot that conviction carries intense emotion with it, pointed out that it might be pathologically exalted 'as in the nitrous oxide intoxication in which a man's very soul will sweat with conviction' [7], but that 'as Descartes made the indubitable reality of the cogito go bail for the reality of all that the cogito involved, so we all of us, feeling our own present reality with absolutely coercive force, ascribe an all but equal degree of reality, first to whatever things we lay hold on with a sense of personal need and second to whatever farther things continuously belong with these' [7]. I shall return to this presently when I come to speak of depersonalization.

The reasons for the cartesian rejection of sensory data—because they may deceive us (men being subject to notorious error through illusions)—are equally reasons for rejecting the cartesian assertion that our thinking is an empirical certainty: about our thinking we may as unwittingly be certain yet mistaken as about our sensations. What Locke called 'bare intuition, without the intervention of any other idea' [8] is common in mental disorder: and what he said of this kind of knowledge 'the clearest and most certain that human frailty is capable of' applies perfectly to what patients experience in respect of their 'primary delusions': this knowledge is 'irresistible and like bright sunshine forces itself to be perceived, as soon as ever the mind turns itself that way, and leaves no room for hesitation, doubt or examination, but the mind is presently filled with the clear light of it' [8]. These words of Locke's are very close to those which patients use when they tell us of what they know with absolute certainty, requiring no proof: truth suddenly and decisively made clear to them in an immediate intuition. But Locke, whom I have been quoting, takes up this difficulty when he comes to write about enthusiasm: he uses almost the same words to describe the false certainties of the enthusiasts as he had for the intuitive certainty upon which truth partly rests: 'When once they are got into this way of immediate revelation, of illumination without search, and of certainty without proof, and without examination, it is a hard matter to get them out of it. Reason is lost upon them; they are above it; they see the light infused into their understandings, and cannot be mistaken; it is clear and visible there, like the light of bright sunshine; shows itself and needs no other proof but its own evidence' [8]. In rebutting the claims of the enthusiasts that the truth is revealed to them, he undermines, I think, the original assertion about intuitively known truth: 'light, true light, in the mind is or can be nothing else but the evidence of the truth of any proposition; and if it be not a self-evident proposition, all the light it has, or can have, is from the clearness and validity of those proofs upon which it is received.' All then turns on the distinction between self-evident propositions, intuitively known, and those arrived at by reason or sense. But no one can determine what is self-evident except him to whom it is so: and much that is false appears self-evident to the healthy man, and still more to the mentally sick man. Professor Stace, in his recent provocative article about unreasoned beliefs in *Mind*, classed together under this head 'instinctive beliefs' about the material world, declarations of 'common sense' about sundry matters, moral 'intuitions', metaphysical 'insights', the procedures of mathematical infant prodigies, and the 'flairs' and 'hunches' of common men in all matters [9] and he deplored the lack of empirical material which would afford a proper psychological description and analysis of the process whereby such unreasoned beliefs are reached. He is emphatic that unreasoned beliefs, held to be immediate intuitions, play a large and harmful part in the thought of philosophers, and of ordinary people. If psychology is to illuminate the process, as he wishes, it cannot ignore the extreme instances which the psychiatric clinic offers. Targowla and Dublineau, in their monograph give a telling account of the phenomenon: 'il se revéle d'un seul coup, complet et total, dans un éclair qui brusque la réflexion, lui jette les données d'une réalisation, mais en bloc. . . Cette intuition, du fait qu'elle est, ne comporte pas, ne suppose même pas la discussion. Elle ne comprend aucune perception et élimine par là la necessité du raisonnement. . . Il n'y a pas de preuve á fournir appuyant la réalité ou la signification de constatations, pas de rapport à établir. . . . Les preuves qu'il ne cherche pas, le malade les refuse

168

aux autres; il n'essaie pas de convaincre: Ne me demandez pas d'explication; je le sais . . . mais puisque je vous dis que c'est une intuition. Surgissant spontanément à la conscience sans intermédiaire sensoriel ou intellectuel, 'synthétique et directe', l'intuition fournit une connaissance pure, parfaite d'emblée, precise. . .' [10] It is undeniable that to the patient experiencing them, whatever his intellectual level, these intuitions are self-evident truths; truths beyond doubt. The distinction Locke draws between the convictions of the enthusiast and the intuitive truths of the philosopher can hardly be sustained here. Self-evident 'truths', however definite and clear, may be as false as demonstrative beliefs arrived at through erroneous reasoning. And this falsity can be found, not only in the intuitive knowledge of the insane but also, though less dramatically, in that of the neurotic subject—the hypochondriac, for example, or the depersonalized patient. It is moreover common as a sign of deficit, as in the patient recently reported by Babcock [11] who had had a prefrontal leucotomy and was absolutely certain he was correct in his answers to psychological tests—largely, it would seem, from lack of any critical judgment. What determines this self-deception through certainty in the various sorts of mental illness has not, I think, been sufficiently ascertained, though in the individual patient the influence of emotions and needs can be discerned: there are, however, as I said, sufficient points of identity between these phenomena in the mentally ill and those observed in healthy people, to justify the conclusion that some of the same causes of distortion operate in the healthy and the sick.

It may be said that the healthy man has insight into the falsity of his intuitions, whereas the sick man has not. But although this is true in the extreme cases, it is by no means true of the greater number of those false thoughts which we experience with such immediacy and certainty that we cannot doubt them when they first occur. Perfect insight, in the clinical use of the term, is indeed a fiction: it can never be wholly realized since there is no means of determining for a particular man what is the 'correct' or 'healthy' attitude towards his own perceptions and thoughts; yet every judgment of insight presupposes first, that we can know or infer what a man's attitude is towards his own mental events and secondly that we have a standard against which we can range this attitude. What we commonly do, in clinical practice, is: we accept communicated introspections at face value, and we compare the patient's attitude to the content of these with our own; we compare it with what, from previous instances and observation, we believe would be our attitude if we were like the patient in everything except his mental ill-health. Clearly this is to attempt the impossible and the attempt is not made any more respectable because a feat resembling it can be crudely and confidently performed whenever a patient reports patent absurdities to us with evident conviction. All that we can say is that certainty may accompany mental events which lead to a false proposition about the external world, or to a false proposition about the subject himself. The falsity of the proposition may, however, lie in its verbal statement: for example, it is not uncommon for people in an attack of acute anxiety to feel certain that they are about to die: this is a direct experience, reported in what is ostensibly a false statement about the immediate future of their physical body, but is actually a true statement about their present feeling—which can only thus in part be conveyed to us or verbally expressed to themselves. It is therefore proper to say that certainty may accompany a mental event of which the account seems to the listener to contain a false statement, because the resources of the subject's language are insufficient to express it adequately or because his experience is unique or novel and communicable only in approximations such as metaphor and analogy provide. To say, then, that the subject lacks insight because the statement is false is in such cases to give insight a superficial meaning. But there are convictions which arise suddenly and clearly and are indisputably false: for instance, a conviction that the physician is putting obscene words into the patient's mind. Here it may justly be concluded that the patient's insight is faulty (if we judge his insight by his awareness of existing relationships between objects and himself): is it possible for the insight of a healthy man likewise to be at fault in respect of a thought which comes to him with certainty and great clearness? I believe so, though in him the correction through reasoning may follow almost at one. Leaving aside religious experience, with the absolute certainty of its ecstasies—an appeal to which might be thought to beg the question—there is ample evidence of the sudden rise of mistaken beliefs of love and hate, accompanied by certainty, in healthy people—convictions that reflect their wishes and fears, their unsatisfied needs and unrecognized conflicts. I think it is plain that in these matters there is no sharp division between the mentally healthy and the mentally unhealthy; and that in the mentally unhealthy we can see very gross examples of undue doubt and undue certainty, such as we see also, though much less often and less manifestly, in healthy people: the *folie du doute* of the obsessional patient is in this respect as continuous with the 'normal', as is the *intuition délirante* of the schizophrenic. It is however, the case that psychiatrists have been far more ready to admit that excessively misplaced doubt occurs in healthy people regarding true propositions than to recognize that misplaced certainty occurs in the healthy regarding false intuitions.

What I have been saying about the deceptiveness of immediate certainty could be amply illustrated by the morbid perceptual phenomena which the psychiatrist meets. The patient with acute alcoholic hallucinosis, for example, may have no doubt whatsoever about the insulting voice he heard, and his certainty may persist after he has recovered from his illness. But the problems of perception are too difficult, and, in many ways, too well-explored in psychology and philosophy as well as in psychiatry, to deal with briefly. Perception has, in psychology and psychiatry, passed of late through phases far removed from the traditional philosophical standpoint. Perception was accounted for until fairly recently in terms of sensation and association, but now perceptions are viewed as organized mental structures, selectively taken from the unstructured stimulus field. Perception is not isolated from affect

170

and memory: as F. C. Bartlett put it, 'inextricably mingled with it are imaging, valuing, and those beginnings of judging which are involved in the response to plan, order of arrangement and construction of presented material. It is directed by interest and by feeling, and may be dominated by certain crucial features of the objects and scenes dealt with.' The psychiatrist by no means regards hallucinations as essentially distinguishable from delusions, from states of feeling, memories or fantasies: he has given up the exclusively atomistic and reductive approach to mental functions. He recognizes the inseparability of events which it may be convenient to classify as cognitive, affective, and conative. He sees also that the patterns imposed by social institutions and human relationships provide a frame of reference or anchorage for subsequent mental activities (including acts of perception): consequently he cannot examine with any fullness the delusions, hallucinations or other symptoms of a patient unless he also looks closely into the patient's personality—that unitary synthesis and outcome of all the past impacts of the environment upon inherited potentialities. This idiographic approach to personality which the psychiatrist adopts, brings up the problem of how to understand the individual, to which Dilthey and Spranger paid so much attention. Consequently some influential psychiatrists have laid great stress on the distinction between causal explanation and psychological understanding of personality. Jaspers, who gave this currency, insisted that in psychology phenomenological study permits true causal sequences to be discerned; these cannot all be understood. The genetic understanding of psychological phenomena requires no theoretical foundation, as explanation does: it is concerned only with immediate data, and, indispensable though it is, it may lead the investigator into error because an understood relation need not be a real or a constant one. The teaching of Jaspers has had much influence on psychiatrists everywhere: but in this country the violently opposed psychoanalytic theory, in which genetic understanding is all-important, has prevailed over it, so that even those who are not psychoanalysts mostly accept in their psychopathology the view that understood relations are the true ones, or at any rate are the ones they will 'work with': the non-analysts, in conceding this, concede a deficiency in themselves, since they lack the fuller 'understanding through trained experience' which is conferred by a personal psychoanalysis—though whether this specially acquired understanding would be regarded as understanding by Jaspers is questionable. In any case, the psychiatrist's clinical material is often such as to put understanding beyond his reach: even if a personal psychoanalysis has made familiar or certain to him sequences which to others are strange and dubious, there will still be much in his patient's symptoms and their succession which cannot be paralleled and understood from his own immediate experience.

Knowledge of one's own personality is necessarily partial: yet it is the starting point for all our understanding of the personality of others. 'Of the whole of our own natures we are never directly aware, nor of any large portion of the whole. At any single moment the range of consciousness is remarkably slight. It seems only a restless pencil point of light entirely insufficient to illuminate the edifice of personality. Yet, for all its feebleness, it provides each of us with the one and only sure criterion of our personal experience and identity. The past is drawn out in successive and overlapping conscious moments, backwards, twenty, thirty, or forty years to early childhood, and the future extends, vaguely, but still intimately, before us in each overlapping moment of planning and imagination. It is through this dovetailing of the successive moments of consciousness with imbrication of temporal reference and content that we arrive at the conviction that we do somehow possess consistent personalities surrounding the momentary conscious 'core' [12]. This self-consciousness, upon which so much depends, is curiously perverted in 'depersonalization', a morbid state which merits our further attention. Here normal assurance of the continuity of personality is lost: 'I am a stranger to myself . . . I have stopped being . . . I am not the same person that I was before.' Such feelings as these are fairly common; they are often accompanied by privation of bodily awareness and of affection, and—more significantly for my theme—by a morbid detachment. Thus a patient will say 'I suddenly realized I was me. I suddenly got outside myself and saw myself. I am since then absolutely conscious of being conscious.' Or she may say 'everything I do reminds me of "her", that is, of myself (as I was). All the time the galling pictures of all "she" did and what "she" was going to do and all "she" has in the world to live for, are driving me to floods of hopeless misery and anger.' 'I am analysing myself on the surface all the time, but there is nothing underneath.' In these phenomena the subjective core, the continuous thread running though all our conscious states has been destroyed, and with it much else goes—the just appreciation of time, the capacity to picture absent people or places, and—most striking of all in many such patients—the perception of the outside world as real is also impaired, the meaning of things is lost. This suggests a tempting speculation: if a few philosophers had had this syndrome—as Amiel did—and produced their philosophical works while suffering from it, no doubt their systems, or at all events their epistemological arguments, would be different from those we know; psychiatrists with a metaphysical bent might wonder whether depersonalization is not a *reductio ad absurdum* of extreme subjectivism. But I do not know of any detailed philosphical consideration of this remarkable syndrome, which is compatible with intellectual lucidity and objectively accurate perception of physical attributes. It may be thought that what occurs only in disease is hardly the concern of the philosopher. I doubt if there is any force in such an argument. The gradations between health and disease are not abrupt; depersonalization may occur, for a brief space, in healthy people, and the feeling of change in one's own personality can occur, for example, at puberty, without any other suggestion of mental illness. The symptoms of disease, moreover, are as much part of the phenomenal world as anything else, and might deserve as much regard from the philosopher as he gives to other philosopher's introspections. It is surely a defect in the thought of philosophers if they draw their ontological conclusions only from data provided by the operations of presumably healthy minds.

Depersonalization brings forward, as almost all psychiatric problems do, the inescapable question about the relation of body and mind. Here is a condition that often comes on abruptly, bringing with it profound changes in the consciousness of self and especially in the perception of one's body. It has been known to occur in patients with physical disease, epilepsy, tumour of the brain, encephalitis, cerebral arterio-sclerosis. It is almost identical with the state that can be produced deliberately in healthy people by giving them a drug, mescalin, which has its action largely on the brain. The assumption, therefore, is often made that this syndrome must have its physical substrate in the brain. But the methods of morbid anatomy show no disease in the brains of these patients; therefore the change is assumed to be 'physiological' or 'metabolic': no constant physiological accompaniment being demonstrated, it is assumed that although the abnormality as yet eludes our crude methods of investigation, there must nevertheless be some eventually detectable chemical or physical abnormality of the brain. Tenacious indeed is the faith of the psychiatrists who think like this. They are offset by other psychiatrists who regard such speculations and hopes as profitless, and who search in mental structure and function for the pathology of this disorder: these have the advantage—if it can be called so—that their method and theory make it almost impossible for them to fail to discover underlying abnormalities which can be related to the symptoms.

It is obvious that a preference for somatic or for psychological explanation of depersonalization depends on something other than direct evidence about the pathology of the condition. Depersonalization therefore affords a better example of the implicit attitude of psychiatrists to the body-mind problem than a disorder like agnosia or aphasia which is due to demonstrable damage to parts of the brain. A large number of psychiatrists, perhaps the majority of us, profess a monistic view, while talking the language of dualism. It is easy to see how this comes about. We have had a medical training in which it is constantly stressed that study of the functions of the body and its structure in varying circumstances has been the indispensable condition of advance in knowledge. In psychiatry we find this standpoint seemingly tenable when we are dealing with the numerous mental disorders that accompany disease of the brain (such as the syphilitic condition, dementia paralytica). But there are other considerations forced on us, which are by no means new in medicine and in the sciences on which medicine stands, but which until lately the medical student was often allowed to ignore. The integration of bodily activities, reminding us that physiological statements about the functions of parts may be incomplete; the occurrence of severe mental disturbances without any discoverable physical or chemical change in the body, which yet disappear after physical interference with the body, for example, by electrically induced convulsions; the association of emotion with bodily changes, and of temperament with physique—all these make it hard for the dogmatic materialist in psychiatry—and hard, too, for the dogmatic idealist. The new-comer to psychiatry finds, moreover, that the prevalent psychopathology makes use of an abstruse language in which mature somatic phenomena and functions are neglected; though those of the infant are heavily drawn upon. It is true that the teacher of physiology will have drawn the medical student's attention to the work of Cannon and Sherrington, and that the psychoanalyst will press for psychological study of all disease; but the two languages are far apart though often used in the same discourse. Urged to examine and denote his philosophical position, the psychiatrist may range himself as idealist or materialist without too nice a regard for consistency; or he may declare his monistic belief that man is a 'psychosomatic unity'. The psychosomatic unit is made up of integrated parts, describable in differing language according to the hierarchical level of the integration: 'the concepts of mental and physical must undergo a readjustment . . . science deals with a world of things, facts and relations appearing in several distinct levels or types of integration. Physics deals with one set of aspects . . . chemistry with another . . . physi-ology with a biological level, that is, those objects and their parts which grow by reproduction and metabolism; and as psychobiology we treat the func-tions of total organisms which blend, with more or less consciousness, in a manner constituting a special level of integration which has been especially and most characteristically enriched by the interindividual and social develop-ment of language. . . . All that constitutes psychobiology to the physician is therefore physical as well as mental. We can further recognize an ultra-biological level of facts when we consider the products of such functioning, as logic and mathematics or theory of relations. . . . In this way we obtain an orderly perspective of the various sciences, but eliminate the contrast between physical and mental.'[13] I have been quoting from a manifesto by the most influential American psychiatric teacher of his day, Adolf Meyer, in which he said 'each individual has his own mental activity, but to say that we can-not see it and make it accessible and understand it in others is a philosopher's scare like the statement that we can never know whether the world exists because we know only mental states or processes. . . . By making of mind something like the religious or philosophic concept of the soul, something opposed to the body instead of a function of the individual as a whole, traditional philosophy and psychology have rendered us a poor service.' In the first of these quotations the influence of Lloyd Morgan may be suspected: but I think that the two quotations together illustrate the way psychologists and psychiatrists came to believe, in the first quarter of this century, that philosophers in their concern with ontology have troubled themselves about unreal problems which could be by-passed—though the by-pass often seems strangely like a well-trodden philosophic road: empirical realism, for example. Those who think in this way constantly invoke integration—'all the facts of experience prompt us to see in mentation a biological function, and we are no longer surprised to find this product of integration so different from the nature and functions of all the component parts. All the apparent

discontinuities ... are shown to be a general feature of nature and of facts.'
Sherrington, who has done more than anyone to develop the concept of
integration found the energy-mind difficulty insoluble: whether his refusal to
consider mind as energy be sustained or rejected, it is evident that integration
was not for him at any rate a sufficient explanation for the emergence of mental
activity. I think the biologically more sophisticated and elaborate argument
which Leo Loeb recently put forward, indicates the weakness of any attempt
to make 'integration' the conceptual key to the problem of a psychosomatic
unity. Thus Loeb, after stressing the stable, highly differentiated individuality
which—through homoeostasis as it were—achieves relative independence of
the unstable environment says: 'there has thus taken place an evolution of
two types of individuality. The first is connected with the differentiation of
the organ differentials and with the evolution of the individuality differential
and its manifestations, from a very primitive character to the state of great
refinement reached in mammals. The second is connected with the evolution
of the psychical-social factors, leading to the gradual creation and refinement
of the individual in the psychical-social sense. The second evolutionary
process is related only indirectly to the development of the individuality
differentials; it depends directly upon the increasing complexity and refinement of certain organ differentials, especially of the nervous system. There
is therefore no perfect parallelism between these two evolutionary processes.
While in the first process a gradual, step-by-step development of the individuality differential occurs, in the second process the most important far-
reaching change has taken place suddenly in the transition from anthropoid
apes to man.'[14]

The growth of our knowledge regarding the nervous system during the last
two decades has permitted closer correlation of mental events with bodily
function; such a book as the A.R.N.M.D. symposium on the interrelation-
ship witnesses to the advances now being made: it is, however, still true, as
John Stuart Mill said a hundred years ago, that to construct the theory of the
mind solely on such data as physiology at present affords, seems a great error
in principle and an even more serious one in practice, for psychology is in a
'more advanced state than that portion of physiology which corresponds to it,
and to discard the former for the latter appears to me an infringement of the
true canons of inductive philosophy'.

How, then, you will again ask, does the modern psychiatrist look at this
ancient problem of mind and body? I think there may be many answers. But
most psychiatrists will still say that the question is a spurious one: and their
reasons amount to a declaration either that the question is put in a form
which fails to satisfy the requirements of logical syntax, or that it is put in a
form which includes sentences asserting what is not testable; consequently,
they say, traditional statements about the relation of mind and body, which
infringe the rules of logical syntax or are without meaning when subjected to
the operational procedure, need not be further considered. The standpoint
of many psychiatrists is close to that of the American realists, with their

monistic conception of neutral-stuff. In practice as I have said the psychiatrist uses a double vocabulary and justifies it on grounds of necessity: he compares his hybrid language to the stereoscope which enables pictures of the same object taken from different angles to be superposed and fused. He knows it is a dangerous practice and he gives alarmed assent to such declarations as this: 'The greatest difficulty confronting the abstractor will be descriptions made under the spell of pseudo-problems: syntactically combinations in the same sentence of terms from the language of the psyche with terms of the language of physics. When this is done, at one end of the gradation of consequences, where the terms of the psyche are operationally redefinable, the statement may be translated into usable form. In this instance the least that may be said is that the terms of the psyche are unnecessary. At the other end of the scale is utter confusion, and the statements are lost. Sentences which seem to tell as much about the observer as about the observed and actually nothing definite about either, are of no use.'

It is impossible to leave this subject without speaking of consciousness. Psychiatrists commonly regard consciousness not as the essential feature that characterizes mental activity but as a function of the human organism in action. It varies in relation to the state of the organism; it can be conceived in quantitative terms; it is not restricted to the cognitive sort of mental happening—as Spearman put it 'a person tends to know his own sensations, feelings and strivings' (any lived experience tends to evoke immediately a knowing of its own characters and experiences). Consciousness individuates relatively late in the evolutionary development of the higher organisms, and is indispensable for the epitomizing, organizing and symbolizing activities which enable human beings to carry out very complex adjustments to their environments and needs. It does not in itself differentiate man from all other living beings as man's capacity to handle propositional symbols, to think about things, probably does, and it is dependent on physico-chemical happenings, occurrences of the whole organism describable in electrical, metabolic and other concepts and known to occur in large measure in other living beings too: the extent of the differences between consciousness in man and in animals or plants can be inferred from behaviour. These, I think, are the views of the psychiatrist today. If 'consciousness' be defined wholly in subjective terms, we cannot, it is true, be certain of it in non-human living beings, but neither can we be certain of it in other men, since we can only infer it: we will infer it from their behaviour, or we will rely on their similarity to ourselves in so many other respects and especially their use of the same words about contents of consciousness as we use. The psychiatrist, of course, is continually meeting disorders of consciousness; these demonstrate to him how dependent it is on the intact functions of the organism and chiefly of the brain, but they also demonsrtate how the flame of consciousness can be made to flicker, to flare up or die away without any crude or recognizable physical interference with the organisms, e.g. consciousness may be affected through hypnosis. The psychiatrist therefore is far from desiring to seat consciousness in any group of cells: he will go no further than to hold that in general the integrity of some of the cerebral cortex and its thalamic connections is an indispensable condition for consciousness and, probably, for the exercise of discriminative and educative powers characteristic of conscious intelligence. Much work is at present being done on the anatomical and physiological connexions between cell-aggregations in the central nervous system. But it is not on structures, or collocations of cells but rather on their physico-chemical state that the psychiatrist now turns his hopeful eye when he thinks of defining the conditions of consciousness.

You will perhaps wonder how a psychiatrist can talk of consciousness thus far without referring to 'the unconscious', which plays so large and active a part in the theory of psychopathology. The unconscious, however, is unhappily named: so positive a concept should not have so negative a verbal symbol, and it is, I think, legitimate to say that privation of consciousness is not the essential characteristic of the events to which the psychoanalyst applies the adjective 'unconscious'. It seems to me a paradox of psychoanalysis that in its psychology of the unconscious it has tended to perpetuate a form of dualism which would never have arisen were it not for the vast importance men attach to their conscious thoughts—an importance which psychoanalysis set itself vigorously to undermine. Psychoanalysis has not fared well at the hands of philosophers: even so favourable and well informed a critic as Dalbiez says that Freud's empiricism is not consistent; 'le plus souvent, les formules freudiennes rendent un son empiriste trés banal. Il y a pourtant ça et là dans les écrits de Freud des passages qui impliqueraient logiquement une philosophie rationaliste' ... 'l'incohérence de l'attitude de Freud par rapport à la métaphysique et à la théorie de connaissance se prolonge dans tout ce qu'il a écrit sur les diverses valeurs spirituelles.' [15] The recurring difficulty in psychoanalysis, for the psychologist as well as the philosopher, is the proliferation in it of concepts by postulation which cannot with any confidence be checked experimentally or empirically by appeal to directly observable fact. There is thus an unbridged gap between concepts with denotative meaning drawn from immediate clinical and laboratory observation and on the other hand the intricate network of concepts with connotative meaning which are designated by the postulates of psychoanalytical theory: the designation, moreover, is unsure because the concepts— for example, 'introjected object': 'instinct': 'unconscious fantasies': 'id': do not have their properties specified unambiguously in the postulates of the theory so that rigorously logical deductions can be made from them. You will remember that Freud's standpoint was bluntly empirical, and that he attacked philosophy for clinging 'to the illusion that it can produce a complete and coherent picture of the universe, though in fact that picture must needs fall to pieces with every new advance in our knowledge. Its methodological error lies in the fact that it overestimates the epistemological value of our logical operations, and to a certain extent admits the validity of other sources of knowledge, such as intuition.' There is clearly much to be said about psychoanalysis, and, for that matter, about systems like C. G. Jung's which have likewise been developed to meet medical needs and have in due course expanded far beyond the confines of medicine: but I shall not enter upon it, hoping that someone better qualified in philosophy and psychoanalysis will do so in some later Manson lecture. It is a theme Dr Manson would have approved, for he was a member of that Committee of the British Medical Association whose report gave psychoanalysis its certificate of medical respectability in this country.

I have wandered too discursively and, I fear, ignorantly over some of the ground which is necessarily traversed by the psychiatrist and the philosopher. There is so much else in psychiatry which can be recognized as grist for the philosopher's mill—questions of language and symbolism, of perception, of value, of moral judgment, of causality and purpose—that it is likely future Manson lecturers will often have occasion to revert to aspects of the same subject. Some of them, believing with Scott Buchanan, that 'modern empirical science is frustrated science, and its present dogmatic aversion to metaphysics a sign of an internal blindness that threatens the value of basic routine research and practice', may go on to assert, as he does, that medicine is the medium and perhaps the focus in which the problems of wisdom and science meet. Certainly psychiatry is a field of medicine in which science needs metaphysics, if by metaphysics we mean as William James did, 'an unusually stubborn effort to think clearly'.

REFERENCES

1 MANSON, *British Medical Journal*, 1930, **2**, 266.
2 JASPERS, *Allgemeine Psychopathologie*, Berlin, 1923, p. 12.
3 ZILBOORG, *A History of Medical Psychology*, London, 1941, p. 274.
4 KANT, *Versuch über die Krankheiten des Kopfes*, 1764.
5 KANT, *Der Streit der Facultäten in drei Abschnitten*, 1798. Dritter Abschnitt.
6 DESCARTES, *Discours de la Méthode*, Quatrième Partie.
7 JAMES, *Principles of Psychology*, vol. 2.
8 LOCKE, *Essay on Human Understanding*, bk. iv.
9 STACE, *Mind*, 1945, **54**, 138.
10 TARGOWLA, and DUBLINEAU, *L'Intuition Délirante*, Paris, 1931.
11 BABCOCK, *Journal of Abnormal and Social Psychology*, 1947, **42**, 470.
12 ALLPORT, *Personality*, London, 1937.
13 MEYER, *Journal of the American Medical Association*, 1915.
14 LOEB, *The Biological Basis of Individuality*, Springfield, 1945.
15 DALBIEZ, *La Méthode Psychoanalytique et la Doctrine Freudienne*, Paris, 1936, tome 2.

12

HEALTH AS A SOCIAL CONCEPT

THE SOCIAL implications of health and disease are very great, but they are obscured by uncertainty as to what these two terms refer to, or, more correctly, how to know when health is or is not present in individuals. It is particularly in respect of mental health that this doubt comes up; but the same essential uncertainty prevails also about physical health. So soon as we pass from obvious good health, or obvious disease, into the penumbra where the dubious cases lie (such as the congenital deformities, the symptomless lesions and so on), we see that the concept of health needs to be clarified: and we realize that it is hardly to be defined without reference to the material and the social environment within which each individual lives.

If my theme were the social causes and the social consequences of disease, or if it were the social conditions propitious to the maintenance of health, my task, though not easy, might be easier than the one I have chosen. A great deal of factual knowledge exists on these matters—they lend themselves to lively speculation, they can be illustrated by telling clinical instances, and there is less danger of an expositor losing himself in a tangle of intersecting paths.

Such studies commonly presuppose that we already know what health is, and can always distinguish it from disease. But we cannot safely operate with ambiguous words and concepts, such as health and disease now are. If we are determining the needs that must be met in the National Health Service, we must first estimate the prevalence of disease; yet for mental disease, in all its forms, this is at present impossible, largely because we are unsure what is to be included. Similarly we cannot agree on the duration of illnesses and on the efficacy of treatment because we have no accepted criteria of recovered health: this may sound extravagant, but there is abundant evidence that it is so.

I shall therefore be dealing tonight largely with a problem of definition. I shall not be considering how the forms of illness are classified and defined, that is, I shall say nothing of the principles and criteria of diagnosis, but shall

---

This paper was first delivered as a lecture to the British Sociological Association. It is reprinted from the *British Journal of Sociology* (1953), **4**, 109–24.

examine only the criteria of health in general. And although the matter demands theoretical discussion, the purpose is a practical one—to apply the criteria, whatever they may turn out to be, to the enumeration of sick people and healthy ones; to the selection of healthy people for various social opportunities and obligations; and to the further study of the social conditions of health and disease. Since this is the practical aim, there is no harm in accepting certain working assumptions, such as that dualist language is unavoidable here, and that the fictions, health and disease, serve a useful intellectual purpose, though we know they refer merely to uplands and lowlands in a continuously graded and terraced country.

When people say, in joke or seriously that surely we are all a little mad, or that it is the neurotic people who contribute most to the arts and keep the world moving, or that crime should be treated as a disease and prisons turned into hospitals, they are implying, I think, that there is a social concept of health, no less important than the traditional concept which had until lately been taken for granted. The modern dilemma has been stated in an extreme form by Erich Fromm:

'The term normal or healthy can be defined in two ways. Firstly, from the standpoint of functioning society, one can call a person normal or healthy if he is able to fulfil the social role he is to take in that given society—if he is able to participate in the reproduction of society. Secondly (or alternatively) from the standpoint of the individual, we look upon health or normality as the optimum of growth and happiness of the individual.'

There is high sanction for the prima facie assumption that health is partly a social concept, for it is explicit in the definition adopted by the World Health Organization five years ago. The opening passage of that body's international charter says that 'health is a state of complete physical, mental and social well-being'.

A proposition could hardly be more comprehensive than that, or more meaningless. But to condemn it because it is meaningless is to ignore the history and complexity of the idea behind it. In describing health as a state of perfection, such as was enjoyed perhaps by archangels and by Adam before the Fall, the charter-writers of W.H.O. were reverting to an ancient formula of unattainable wholeness of body, mind and soul, realized in the Golden Age but long since forfeited.

The workaday conception of health can best be examined in connexion with the physical activities of the body. I shall therefore begin by considering the concept of physical illness, and its possible social component. Then I shall pass to the much more difficult field of mental illness, and see whether adaptation to the social environment is a criterion of mental health, or whether other criteria—notably disturbance of psychological functions—are the only essential and useful ones. After that I shall consider sexual perversions, psychopathic personality and suicide, to see whether social deviation spells mental illness, and I shall point out that illness cannot be defined as that which doctors treat. After a brief review of some awkward consequences of an ill-defined

180

concept of health, I shall conclude by suggesting that we should keep social well-being conceptually distinct from health so that their interrelations can be better observed and analysed.

Now, if the various organs work well enough not to draw attention to themselves, and their owner is free from pain or discomfort, he usually supposes that he is in good health. The criterion is then a subjective one. But if he avails himself of the mass X-ray service and in consequence learns that his lung shows strong evidence of tuberculous disease, he ceases to consider that he is in good health: the criterion he now adopts is an extraneous one, viz. the assertion of a physician who relies on objective or pathological data. It is evident that the physician's criteria of physical health are not the same as the patient's, and that, in practice, it is the presence of disease that can be recognized, not the presence of health. There are no positive indications of health which can be relied upon, and we consider everyone healthy who is free from any evidence of disease or infirmity.

The constitution of the World Health Organization, however, which I have already quoted, roundly asserts the opposite: the whole passage runs: 'Health is a state of complete physical mental and social well-being and not merely the absence of disease or infirmity.' That idealistic statement seems to forget that the abstractions health and disease do not represent distinct states but rather areas in a continuum. Where health ends and disease begins is arbitrary, but health cannot be restricted to a narrow area at one extreme.

How difficult, if not impossible, it would be to recognize disease, or health, as an absolute is illustrated in Health Surveys. Most western countries have realized that mortality statistics do not afford sufficient basis for planning health services and detecting trends in the form and incidence of disease. Morbidity statistics are therefore required, to provide the data about all illnesses that had hitherto been available only for the notifiable diseases. Material for such statistics can be drawn from various sources: from the general practitioners; from the hospitals; and from health insurance records. As soon as the matter was looked at, it was seen that quite divergent figures would be derived, according to which of these sources was drawn upon. What the patient counted as illness would not always come within the ken of the practitioner, nor be always conceded by him to be illness; and similar difficulties would arise in using statistics derived from hospital in-patient records and from insurance certificates, which are concerned with special sections of the population or special groups of illnesses. Any conclusions about the prevalence of health and disease in the population must therefore be qualified by a statement of how the primary data were obtained.

The criteria of physical illness and health depend upon: first, the patient's account of how and what he feels, i.e. upon subjective statements; secondly, manifest signs of satisfactory or impaired function and structure; and thirdly, occult signs of such adequacy or impairment, detected by special instruments and procedures.

Each of these presupposes a norm. But since they are not identical norms, they must be considered in turn. The patient will report some change in what he has come to regard as his normal state of well-being—a state which may allow for a fairly wide range of variation or on the other hand may be a narrow and fixed mode, according to his temperament, constitution and experience. The quality of the change he has noticed will also determine whether he disregards it (which is much the same as regarding it as healthy) or construes it as a symptom of illness: pain, for example, may be treated differently from fatigue. The norm of bodily perceptions, roughly related to the external or internal stimuli which might be supposed to evoke them, is supplied by every man for himself. There is not, and cannot be, any convention about this norm, which is built up from past, incommunicable experience. To evaluate a report of any departure from it, one must guess something about the man who makes the report; about his habits, the demands he makes of his body, the attention he pays it, and the language he uses to describe its sensations. What a patient tells about his symptoms, and what he concludes about his health are therefore data which will be used by the physician only after a further process of interpretation which may transmute them and yield a different conclusion from the patient's.

The physician is of course trained to relate signs of disturbed function and structure to the norm. His personal experience and the accumulated experience of others are at his disposal. For some organs he has much fuller and more exact information at his disposal than for others: he can, for example, with much more confidence judge the state of the heart than that of the liver. But for each organ and system he has a body of knowledge about the range of normal function and the evidences of normal structure, so that equally well-trained physicians would agree about whether a particular system is working normally (which, in this context, is the same as being healthy). I do not want to overstate this: there can be much difference of opinion in difficult cases or regarding organs difficult to assess as to their functional and structural integrity: but on the whole the criteria are well known and become sharper with every advance in physiology, biochemistry, pathology and anthropometry.

I have spoken of organs and systems: but these are, of course, strictly, artificial abstractions from the total living organism. Perhaps the most important functions of the organism are those that affect a balance and unitary working of the separate systems, ensuring that a change in one is compensated for or reinforced by an appropriate change in another. When this regulatory or integrating function is disturbed, illness is certain. As Professor Ryle put it: 'The term "health" as affecting the individual, should embrace (in addition to those of sensory well-being and structural integrity) ideas of balance and adaptability; these in turn reflect the co-ordinated activity of component parts each functioning within its normal range.' The physician therefore must concern himself not only with the evidence of normal structure and function in parts of the body, but in its total working. If the internal milieu, as it has been called, of the body is not kept constant, the physician must detect this;

but for the purpose he cannot use structural changes (which will be late consequences of disturbed integration, or local causes of it); instead he must rely on estimation of the total performance of the patient, as well as on the performance of separate parts of him, isolated for convenience as organs or systems: all should be working in responsive harmony. A great many pathologists and physicians have sought to make this the touchstone of health, which they define, or rather sum up, as 'a state of physiological and psychological equilibrium', whereas they view disease as the organism's reaction to a disturbance of its inner equilibrium.

At this point we are again adrift, away from objective, well-studied norms. The adequate performance of the body working as a whole is highly individual; the range of variability in the human species is wide; performance is not the same in different races, in different climates, at different ages, in the two sexes, under innumerable conditions of past and present environment. And no instruments of precision, no application of recent discoveries in chemistry or physics can remove the difficulty. In short, for the most important of bodily functions, that which regulates the working of the whole, norms are so wide in range, or need to be so extensively hedged around with qualifying conditions that in clinical practice the physician must take the patient pretty much as supplying his own norm of total performance or behaviour, and proceed by rough and ready appraisal of whether there has been any departure from this, when due allowance has been made for the environment in which the patient has been living.

So, even in regard to physical illness, we cannot disregard total behaviour, which is a psychological concept, and the environment, which, so far as it consists of human beings and their institutions, includes a social concept. When we go on to mental illness, we may be inclined to think that the human environment is all-important, or even that the concept of 'mental illness' is essentially a social, rather than a clinical or pathological one.

In general discussion it is customary to assume a monistic standpoint and to infer a physical aspect to all mental health and illness, just as we infer a psychological aspect to all physical illness; but in practice the limits set to our observations and knowledge compel us to talk a dualist language. I am therefore accepting as much distinction between physical illness—or health—and mental illness (or health) as between the subject matter of physiology and of psychology.

Mental health, ideally, might be a state of perfect equipoise in an unstable system. It has been described by some as a state in which one's potential capacities are fully realized. But unless some capacities are characterized as morbid and excluded from the generalization, this is absurd. We all have deplorable potentialities as well as desirable ones. It is hardly necessary to dwell on the emptiness of an ideal notion of mental health, perfect and unattainable. The serviceable criterion commonly employed to define mental health is the absence of mental illness. This shifts the difficulty, and slightly lessens it.

What then is mental illness? Can it be recognized, as physical disease often is, by the qualitatively altered function of some part of the total, by disturbance of thinking, for example, or disturbance of perception? This is possible: we very frequently recognize a man to be mentally ill because he has delusions or hallucinations. But not always, for if the disturbance of part-functions is without influence on his conduct, or falls within certain categories which we regard as 'normal', we do not infer 'mental illness' from their presence. Thus in their *Phantasms of the Living* Myers, Podmore and Gurney devoted a chapter to the hallucinations of the sane. The procedure is then semantically confused: we have a class of perceptions judged abnormal on statistical grounds, which can be assessed as normal by certain value-judgments. The confusion is manifest in the discriminatory use made of certain signs of disturbed thinking: if a man expresses an irrational belief, e.g. that he has been bewitched, we do not call it a delusion, a sign of disease, unless we are satisfied that the manner in which he came by it is morbid. This would not necessarily be the case if he had been brought up among people who believed in witchcraft, whereas if he is an ordinary twentieth-century Londoner who has arrived at such a conviction through highly individual, devious, suspicion-laden mental processes, we call the belief abnormal and the man who holds it unhealthy.

Two criteria have apparently been applied, then, to changes in function: a psychopathological one paying regard to the process, and a statistical one paying regard to the frequency of its occurrence.

When the psychopathological criterion is looked at, it shows its kinship with the pathological criterion applied in evaluating physical diseases. Unless the phenomenon to which it is applied is gross, it can be used only by experts: just as the decision whether a tumour is malignant requires a highly trained judge, so does the decision whether a queer belief or a turn of mood is due to a pathological process. 'Pathological', however, often has elusively vague referents. Most commonly the highly trained judge equates it with 'unbalanced', i.e. lacking in stable internal and external adjustment.

The body and the mind have remarkable powers of internal adjustment: compensating, balancing and checking. In the body these adjustments may result in extraordinary departures from the conventional structure of parts —hypertrophy of one kidney, for example, to take over the work of the other when this has been destroyed or removed. In the mind, where ignorance of anatomical substrate and other factors make it harder to delimit functions with confidence, the adjustments are more subtle and elusive, but every system of psychopathology has to pay much attention to the internal devices whereby a working unit is maintained. The psychoanalytic system is, of course, in the main an elaborate metaphorical account of how these checks, compensations and balances may be supposed to work in order to keep mental activity integrated and healthy, and how they can, in certain circumstances, get out of hand and defeat their object. That integration is never wholly attained, is a sad truth. 'The basis of much frustration and many conflicts is in this universal circumstance, that no man ever fuses all his self-reactions into a single, unambiguous, coherent whole.' But this imperfection can be overstressed. In healthy individuals a regulatory function is at work which keeps the organism internally adjusted and ready to meet changing external conditions. We have arrived at the same point as we reached in considering physical disease: there must be adjustment of functions within the organism, keeping its internal milieu steady: there must be adaptation of this integrated organism to its surroundings so that it remains unharmed, in spite of changing conditions.

'Adjustment' and 'adaptation' are words often used as though their meaning were unequivocal. They deserve closer examination. Adequacy of adaptation is today the chief yardstick of mental health, for many people. The Education Authorities provide special schools for 'maladjusted children'. What is meant by adaptation, or adjustment, and how failure in it may be detected, is clearly important.

In the last few years the 'general adaptation syndrome' has had a vigorous run in purporting to explain how phenomena of physical disease are produced in response to stress. Here adaptation is considered as a biological phenomenon; men respond to stresses with 'adaptive' patterns of reaction that are conservative and protective. They may be designed to provide extra fuel and energy for vital parts of the organism, or to defend some threatened part:

'The organism may sacrifice at such times some functions or capacities for the sake of promoting others that are most important to meet the adverse situation. Although there is a degree of specialization in the sense that one or other protective arrangement is dominant, discrimination is not exact. In a threatened man it is common to find a variety of protective reactions, some of which are extremely pertinent, others less so and still others minimally effective.'

So far indeed may the reactions be from pertinence or effectiveness that they are noxious to the individual. In other words, there is no dividing line between the protective mechanisms of adaptation and the same mechanisms when they are harmful: the notion of 'adaptation' is then stretched to cover all the responses of the organism to external stress, irrespective of whether these are to be classified as healthy or morbid. Although the multitudinous writers on the subject are not as a rule explicit, it is, I think, plain that they take the same standpoint as McIver when he writes:

'Fresh air will stimulate our lungs and poisonous gas will destroy them; physically the one is no less an adaptation than the other. ... Nature everywhere makes demands whatever the conditions are ... whether in the eyes of men they are favourable or unfavourable, good or evil, this unconditional physical adaptation remains with all its compulsion. ... Purely physical adjustment is always ongoing, is never "maladjustment".'

Such a view of adaptation cannot be sustained when social adaptation is in question. Here value judgments must be made, and adaptation is distinguished from maladaptation according as a particular valued state is favoured, or jeopardized. Social adaptation, by itself, is therefore rather an empty term: it must be qualified by an indication of the state desired. Consequently mental

185

health cannot be equated with good social adaptation, as many have proposed, without risk of tautology: the valued and desired state which adaptation is to attain or maintain may itself turn out to be health.

According to the most widely used of current textbooks, psychiatry is concerned with 'the study of the individual as a psycho-biological organism perpetually called upon to adapt to a social environment', but unfortunately we have not an agreed touchstone for his success or failure in this inescapable exercise. Failure in it, moreover, need not betoken mental illness. One can be sociopathic without being psychopathic.

Although social disapproval has obviously played a large part in deciding what shall be called social maladaptation, and is its main feature in current psychiatric usage, it cannot be accepted as a satisfactory criterion, varying as it does according to the group of people who express the disapproval. It is necessary to describe behaviour in terms that specify the social situation in time and place, but perilous if we must describe the behaviour further in terms of who approves it, before it can be held to show good social adaptation. It is true that behaviour indicative of social maladaptation will very often be disapproved by almost the whole of society, but there will also be forms of social maladaptation which enjoy social approval, at any rate for a time or by a section of society. Where then can we find a less shifting barrier between success and failure in social adaptation of the individual? Until we have this we are hardly in a position to examine whether such maladaptation bespeaks disease, or delinquency, or (passing from medicine and law to theology) sin.

Social maladaptation of the individual is not total, any more than malfunction of the physical body can be total; different social relations will be variously affected. But like physical malfunction, social maladaptation in any one regard may have some effect upon all that individual's social relations. It is therefore permissible, but sometimes lax, usage to consider social maladaptation as taking restricted forms, such as are seen in alcoholics or in religious fanatics.

It might be urged that the most useful criterion of whether an individual is socially maladjusted is non-conformity—non-conformity to the institutions, the mores, the verbal and other customs prevailing in his society. Social maladaptation of this sort could, of course, be a good and admired thing. It is at present usual to express it in terms of social role. A person is maladapted when his own version of his social role is not in conformity with society's version: and in so far as each person has many social roles, it is the dominant role, or those which have precedence in the daily organization of his activities, that are important here. Conflict can easily arise. Cultural lag, clashes, transitions during phases of development (as at puberty) and involuntary changes of social status will clearly favour conflicts over a man's own conception of his social role and that which society fastens upon him, and will so lead to non-conforming behaviour. Such behaviour can, of course, betoken mental illness.

One thoughtful student of the problem, Edwin Lemert, believes that the

186

psychopathic variety of social deviation is characterized by symbolic distortion of the attitude to one's self and one's social role ('symbolic' here referring to the product of emotional and cognitive activites, which are most covert): 'The "me" of the self (the reflective part of the symbolic process) no longer approximates within normal limits the socially objective estimates and designations of the person's role and status.' The observable aspect of this in behaviour appears as 'abnormal variation in the amount and form of self-expression'. Although Lemert contends that this formula covers 'practically all of what is called "neurotic" and "psychotic" behaviour', it seems to me to be applicable mainly to some forms of insanity and near-insanity, and to be too vague to serve for differentiating psychopathic from other forms of social maladaptation. Similar objections may be made against other sociological attempts to state the denotative characteristics of mental illness. They do not stand on their social legs, but are propped by medical struts and stays.

Let us revert then to the traditional medical criteria already mentioned. They are threefold: (1) the patient feels ill—a general, subjective datum; (2) he has disordered function of some part of him—a restricted objective datum; (3) he has symptoms which conform to a recognizable clinical pattern —a typological datum. Social criteria play no part except in so far as disturbance in capacity to meet social demands, e.g. ability to work, may provoke the question: is this man ill? Difficult cases can be cited, it is true: for example, the typhoid carrier who feels well and has no reduction of capacity but who can infect others and may, because of this social consideration, be segregated and treated as though he were himself ill, perhaps even be constrained to have his gall-bladder removed. Yet I do not think anyone regards such a man as actually ill, since he does not satisfy any of the three criteria I have just listed—he has no subjective malaise, no demonstrable disorder of function, no familiar clinical symptoms and signs.

These traditional criteria were applied long before our current modes of thought about the origin and nature of disease had been developed. They accompanied the animistic notions of disease which prevailed for many centuries before systematic study of causes and of morbid anatomy was undertaken; pathological studies of disease were a comparatively late outcome of technical advances in microscopy, physiology and chemistry. For most people, over long stretches of time, ill-health has meant feeling ill, suffering pain or incapacity, and going in danger of death or mutilation. Whether this state could be traced to some structural change in the cells of the body did not enter into consideration in deciding whether a man was healthy or ill. Nevertheless, when, as in insanity, the unusual state affected the patient's whole conduct and not the activity or well-being of a limited part of his body, it was by no means invariably held that this was illness; the old animistic conceptions of disease were invoked—demoniacal possession, witchcraft, and so on. There were, however, always physicians who regarded these too as forms of ill-health. Why did they do so? What principle led them to bring insanity and physical disease under one heading, while leaving crime, for example, apart?

187

The common feature was, surely, the evident disturbance of part-functions as well as of general efficiency. In physical disease this needs no demonstration; in mental disorders it is shown by the occurrence of, say, disturbed thinking as in delusions, or disturbed perceptions, as in hallucinations, or disturbed emotional state, as in anxiety neurosis or melancholia. Deviant, maladapted non-conformist behaviour is pathological if it is accompanied by a manifest disturbance of some such functions. It is true, as I have already said, that functions are an artificial construct, and that disorder in any particular function will be commonly accompanied by less conspicuous disorder in many other functions—just as in the body. But, for illness to be inferred, disorder of function must be detectable at a discrete or differentiated level that is hardly conceivable when mental activity as a whole is taken as the irreducible datum. If non-conformity can be detected only in total behaviour, while all the particular psychological functions seem unimpaired, health will be presumed, not illness.

The disputes about the relative merits of structural psychology and functional psychology, coming after the excesses of faculty psychology, justify a wary approach to the listing of mental functions. There is, however, at present general agreement about the importance of the following:—perception, learning, thinking, remembering, feeling, emotion, motivation. The main objection might be that the list is not exhaustive. However, these fall into the traditional divisions—cognitive, affective, and conative; and each of them can be subdivided into many varieties, according to the fullness of the data provided by psychology or by clinical psychiatry. Motivation is the least satisfying and probably the most important: under it needs or drives, conflicts and social responses fall to be considered. As P. T. Young has pointed out, in regard to the great diversity of methods used in studying emotion and motivation, the difficulty lies in the extreme complexity of the processes and their basic significance for understanding conduct. A list of functions, such as that just given, is provisional: the history of psychology underlines that it must be so for the present. Physiological functions likewise are subject to revision. The fuller our exact knowledge of functions, the more definite our conclusion that there is a disorder of one or several, constituting illness. It is possible now, as may be seen in a textbook like that of Landis and Bolles, to classify the phenomena of mental illness in terms of disordered function.

There are some forms of socially deviant behaviour which raise nice problems—sexual perversions, for example, such as homosexuality or exhibitionism. To settle whether sexual perversions are necessarily pathological, in the light of the suggested criterion of illness, would require closer and more extensive consideration than is here possible of the place of sexual needs and activities among mental functions. In the psychoanalysts' strictures on Kinsey's findings the wide difference can be seen between a statistical criterion of what should be included within the norm of sexual function and a value-criterion of this.

The crucial difficulty arises with psychopathic personality. Every textbook of psychiatry discusses this abnormality, but almost always ambiguously because the authors do not make clear why it should be regarded as an illness. Though no definition of the term has received general assent as far as I know, the following description, taken from Norwood East, indicates what sort of person it is generally understood to cover: 'A person who although not insane, psychoneurotic or mentally defective, is persistently unable to adapt himself to social requirements on account of quantitative peculiarities of impulse, temperament and character which may require specialized medical and rehabilitative treatment. . . '

The category evidently embraces a particular group of people whose socially deviant behaviour arises from some non-cognitive psychological deviation. Furthermore, the condition may call for medical treatment; but as this is not an invariable requirement we may neglect it here.

Peculiarities of character and temperament are not acceptable indications of illness: they are, of course, very common in the general population, and it is hardly justifiable to classify all people who exhibit them as psychopathic. There remains the quantitative abnormality of impulse: this is prominent in medico-legal discussions of the matter, possibly because it is so often urged as a medical explanation for lessened responsibility in crimes of violence, especially murder. But impulse is, psychologically, an imprecise and somewhat old-fashioned term. With the dethronement of Will in modern psychology, it is not easy to specify abnormalities of conative function in terms of impulse, and it is certainly impossible to measure them.

It would seem, then, that until the category is further defined and shown to be characterized by specified abnormality of psychological functions, it will not be possible to consider those who fall within it to be unhealthy, however deviant their social behaviour.

Although social danger is a common feature of insanity, as of much physical illness also (e.g. the infectious diseases—smallpox, venereal diseases and the like), the social harm is a contingent, not a necessary feature: in its absence, the condition is still an illness because of the changes in the individual. The truth is that though the social effects of disease, like the social causes, are extremely important, it is impossible to decide from them whether a condition is healthy or morbid.

The concept of disease, then—and of health—has physiological and psychological components, but no essential social ones. In examining it we cannot ignore social considerations, because they may be needed for the assessment of physiological and psychological adequacy, but we are not bound to consider whether behaviour is socially deviant: though illness may lead to such behaviour, there are many forms of social deviation which are not illness, many forms of illness which are not social deviation.

It is necessary at this point to draw a distinction between illness and what doctors treat. If the view were taken that everyone who goes to the doctor and receives treatment is ill, we would have a simple operational criterion, but its defects are obvious: it will fluctuate enormously from place to place and from time to time, it will depend on an attitude by the patient towards his doctor, and it will certainly fail to indicate many people whom, by any common-sense standard, one must call ill.

Moreover it must be remembered that the doctor is not necessarily acting outside his proper scope if he attends to people who are not ill. Congenital defects of bodily structure and function (e.g. malformations and benign metabolic anomalies) are not strictly illnesses but they are the concern of doctors. Pregnancy and childbirth, after all, are not illnesses either. Extension of the doctor's province has gone very far in psychiatry. The psychiatrist learns a great deal about normal and abnormal psychology which is relevant to the treatment, or the prevention, of some non-pathological states that are socially deviant. He is nowadays often, and quite properly, asked to investigate and treat disturbances of behaviour in children which can hardly be included within any warranted conception of illness (though of course they may be the prelude to illness). He may likewise investigate or treat criminals, drug addicts, prostitutes and sexual perverts. It may be that there is no form of social deviation in an individual which psychiatrists will not claim to treat or prevent—the pretensions of some psychiatrists are extreme. That time has not come, fortunately. Nevertheless it is clear that psychiatrists, and other doctors, look after plenty of people who are not ill: and conversely that there are many sick people who think as Montaigne did and would hold it absurd to commit themselves to the mercy and government of the doctors—at any rate for a nervous illness. Psychiatrists in our day are much exposed to strictures and suspicions like those which Montaigne expressed against the doctors of the sixteenth century.

Suicide illustrates the problem in deciding between social deviation and illness. No one disputes that suicide is often an outcome or symptom of illness; no one, I think, disputes that it can be the act of a mentally healthy person. If it occurs in a society which sanctions suicide in given circumstances, as ours does, and if the circumstances of the act are the approved ones, it is assumed that the act does not bespeak mental illness nor, of course, social deviation. That is, socially approved behaviour is not usually reviewed to see if it evinces mental illness; and in such a case, suicide is regarded like marriage, or any other isolated but decisive act of choice which is socially approved. But even in a society which does not disapprove of suicide, the act may be a sign of mental illness; and it may be suspected to be such for two reasons: because of the circumstances in which it occurs, and because of the disorder of psychological functions which the person displays, apart from his suicidal behaviour. When the circumstances indicate that the act is not in conformity with the social roles which the person is required to enact, this is not sufficient to denote illness, though it excites inquiry into the matter. The decision about illness must be made in the light of a further inquisition, into psychological functions. If these are found disordered, then the suicidal act may be assumed to have been also an evidence of mental illness—but even this would not be true unless the suicidal act fitted into the total pattern of

190

disordered function which the person displayed. A person may be mentally ill, yet his suicide may be extrinsic to this, or represent, so to speak, a normal and even healthy response to the situation in which he finds himself. It may seem absurd to talk of suicide as in any circumstances a healthy response, but it is absurd only if one holds to the opinion that biological adaptation is the true and final criterion of health. By any biological standard the suicide of a person who has not reproduced is surely a supreme instance of maladaptation.

The psychoanalytical concepts of mental health and illness call for special consideration. Though there is no unanimity among psychoanalysts on the matter, they concentrate on inner psychological criteria, and some of the terms they use for definition would make it impossible to tell whether an individual is mentally healthy unless he has been psychoanalysed or his behaviour interpreted on psychoanalytic lines: the criteria, in short, are technical psychoanalytical ones. It is also common for psychoanalysts to describe mental health in loose general language: thus Karl Menninger says: 'Let us define mental health as the adjustment of human beings to the world and to each other with a maximum of effectiveness and happiness.' A more serious effort to grapple with the problem has been made by Ernest Jones. He lists three features of the normal or healthy mind: first, the 'internal freedom' of feelings of friendliness and affection towards others; secondly, mental efficiency, i.e. 'the fullest use of the given individual's powers and talents'; and finally, happiness which is 'probably the most important of the three'—a combination of the capacity for enjoyment with self-content. These criteria are approximately those which he applies to a practical matter—viz. determining whether, and when, treatment has been successful: 'The analytical success betokens the highest degree of the favourable results I described just now when speaking of the therapeutic criteria. One may then expect a confident serenity, a freedom from anxiety, a control over the full resources of the personality that can be obtained in no other way than by the most complete analysis possible.' Such language leaves room for honest but absurdly wide differences of opinion between a psychoanalyst and another person—say a psychiatrist, a general practitioner, or a relative of the patient—about whether a psychoanalysed patient, or indeed anybody at all, is mentally healthy. Yet this is no remote and theoretical matter. Partly because it has not been settled we are still without exact information about the comparative effects of psychoanalysis and other methods of psychotherapy, or of the indications that a successful outcome will ensue from psychoanalytical treatment of a particular patient. Yet a Health Service which promises adequate treatment to the whole population is in an awkward position when a demand that much more psychoanalytic therapy be provided is refused on the ground that such treatment is costly and its efficacy open to doubt. Every psychiatrist has seen patients who, he is told, have recovered after treatment of their mental disorder but who seem to him still ill. It is not a problem that affects only the assessment of psychoanalytic treatment: it comes up quite as often after

191

physical methods of psychiatric treatment, like leucotomy. The inherent difficulty of the concept of mental health is underlined when we find the psychoanalyst, so expert in the microscopy of mental happenings, unable to dispense with equivocal and cloudy terms in stating his criteria of recovery.

Another psychoanalyst, Lawrence Kubie, has looked more closely than most into the social implications of health. Beginning with the assertion that 'psychoanalysis is uncompromising in its concept of mental health', he goes on to say that the analyst is not 'content to use conformity to the cultural mores of any time or place as his criterion of normality' ...

... 'nor does the difference between normal and neurotic conduct depend upon the degree to which an act contributes either to the welfare of society or to its destruction, or on whether the behaviour is extravagant and fantastic or orderly and sedate. Certainly from the point of view of society all of these are important attributes of human behaviour; but they are neither constant nor explanatory as a basis for the distinction between the normal and the neurotic process. ... The critical difference lies not in the act, nor in its setting, but in the psychological mechanisms which determine the act. ... What passes for normality in our world to-day is not in any fundamental sense normal. It is rather the unstable equilibrium between conscious and unconscious phenomena. ... The activities which result may not be peculiar or strange in themselves. They may be socially acceptable and even valuable; and they may meet all the demands of conscience. ...'

but they are residues of the unresolved neurotic problems of childhood, they are the 'veiled and universal neurotic component of "normal" human nature'. He concludes that on pragmatic grounds we may call any act normal if conscious processes predominate in it; he holds that every act is the product of biological forces and superimposed conscious, preconscious and unconscious psychological forces, all of which bear the imprint of many social pressures and are in a state of continuous unstable equilibrium. This is another way of looking at the efficiency of certain functions. But the functions are those which psychoanalysts emphasize in their account of mental organization. They are difficult functions to consider outside the psychoanalytical frame of reference, and the concept embodying them accordingly difficult to apply to the recognition of health and disease.

To deny a social content in the idea of health in no sense implies denying it a social context. Anthropologists and social psychologists have arrayed overpowering evidence showing how highly dependent we must be on knowledge of the social and cultural background when we would appraise conduct and the efficiency of psychological functions. No practising psychiatrist can be unmindful of this, and it is needless to cite the standard examples— Kwakutl and Shasta, Crow Indians and Ekoi, Yakuts and Dobuans—in order to underline it.

But in our own society the prevailing confusion about the quality and nature of health has begotten some dangerous errors. Thus during the last war many people assumed that a man who had neurotic illness would be less capable in social relations and work than a healthy man. A rather similar assumption is often made about would-be university students, and about entrants into a wide variety of careers and jobs. But the evidence for this is not conclusive, and much of what purports to be evidence is vitiated by the use of a concept of neurotic illness which takes account of occupational or social inadequacy, and a concept of occupational inadequacy which is much influenced by considerations of health. Unless the criteria of ill-health are independent and clear, it is difficult or unsafe to use data based on them for purposes of selection.

In the investigations of the Research Unit with which I have been connected this problem has come up in many forms. When we were trying to find out what influence a neurotically sick worker might have on others, and how his own output was affected by his health, it was necessary to have means for detecting such illness in men who were not under a doctor's care and were not complaining: should one attach any weight to occasional bouts of drinking, or frequent absences from work, or the way a man got at loggerheads with other people at the factory and with his wife or family. Hitherto such social data have often been given a pathological value. This may account for some divergent figures. Thus Russell Fraser, and later Morris Markowe, found that about 10 per cent of light engineering workers had suffered from definite neurotic illness, and a further 20 per cent from minor forms of neurosis, during a period of six months; whereas Lemkau found a much lower prevalence rate in a much less selected population. The prevalence rate of psychopathic personality in an American city (Baltimore) was 13 per 10,000 in 1933, but in 1936 it had fallen to 5·2 per 10,000: it seems highly probable that social considerations may have entered to a large extent into this ostensibly medical census. Indeed, the main American investigator in the Baltimore inquiry says that

... 'in 1933, early in the depression years, there was a tendency for the sources on which the survey was dependent to interpret inability to earn a satisfactory living as an evidence of psychopathic personality. By 1936 the seriousness of the depression had become more clearly recognized, familiarity with unemployment had made it less a mark of defective character, and consequently the diagnosis of psychopathic personality was more rarely used.'

And he adds that in the last war the incidence of psychopathic personality among men examined for military service in the United States was eight per 1,000: rejections from military service for this reason accounted for more than a quarter of all rejections because of mental disease. Social considerations weighed very heavily in deciding whether these men were healthy, or ill, and the confusion of social deviation with illness may explain away the improbable fluctuation in prevalence of a supposedly constitutional disorder. In the more recent work of the M.R.C. Unit I referred to, an effort is being made to keep the estimation of mental health clear of direct occupational and other social considerations. This is especially necessary in the investigations made by the Unit into the employability of high-grade mental defectives. Mental defect has two characteristics—a deficiency in intelligence and a disorder of personality. The latter tends to be judged largely by social criteria, since the social consequences are so important, legally and administratively. The incidence of high-grade defect in the general community may therefore seem to fluctuate from place to place. The social findings have to be kept as distinct as possible from the psychological and pathological findings, in order to avoid getting spuriously high correlations between morbidity and social adjustment.

The curious implications of using a social criterion for health and illness are apparent when a whole society is characterized as unhealthy. So long as this is a literary usage, there can be no objection but it has been seriously formulated and close analogies have been drawn between a sick society and a sick individual. If failure to conform to one's social role is a requirement of illness, a given society can only satisfy it, I suppose, if there is some larger community or world-polity within which the individual society takes the wrong road, or if, at the other extreme, the social role of a given society is that assigned to it by its individual members acting collectively. It is fairly clear that only by a bold metaphor can a society be called healthy or sick. There are plenty of other and more suitable terms we can use to praise a society or to indicate that it is disorganized.

If I now try to pull together my argument, it is this. Health is a single concept: it is not possible to set up essentially different criteria for physical health and mental health. We commonly assume a break between health and ill-health, for which there is no counterpart in the phenomena but which we cannot yet replace by a continuum because we lack means of measuring some of the necessary dimensions. Besides subjective feelings and degree of total efficiency, the criterion of health is adequate performance of functions, physiological and psychological. So far as we cannot designate formal, major functions of the human organism and lack means for judging whether they work efficiently, we are handicapped in recognizing health and illness in a reliable and valid way. The physiological functions can be thus designated and judged far more satisfactorily than the psychological. We can therefore usually tell whether an individual is physically healthy, but we cannot tell with the same confidence and consensus of many observers, whether he is mentally healthy. Though our estimate of the efficiency with which functions work must take account of the social environment which supplies stimuli and satisfies needs, the criteria of health are not primarily social: it is misconceived to equate ill-health with social deviation or maladjustment. If we avoid this error, we shall find it easier to study the relation between health and social well-being and so, one may hope, learn how to further both.

13

BETWEEN GUESSWORK AND
CERTAINTY IN PSYCHIATRY

IT IS the common state of reflective and inquiring minds to be somewhere between untrammelled guesswork and certainty. It would be discreditable if psychiatrists were huddled at either extreme, wholly engaged in guessing or ignorantly certain. We are, however, sometimes suspected of luxuriant speculation and of invincible faith in our tenets: and I propose to consider how this reputation has arisen.

More than most branches of medicine, psychiatry can be regarded as an art. One of its distinctive procedures—psychotherapy—manifestly depends on subtle relationships and incommunicable qualities of personality. But in the proportion that it is an art, psychiatry is a weak branch of medicine: and the constant aim of those who would further and strengthen it is to apply to it the methods of scientific inquiry. If these result in encroachments on the area reserved for the art of medicine, and substitute assured knowledge for assumptions and intuitions, so much the better. This is not to deny the large part which compassion and human feeling must play in the care of mental disorder: its history attests that they will always be necessary; but they operate in a territory that must be explored and charted. Psychiatry in this is like the rest of medicine, combining moral and personal principles of action with those arrived at by the methods of science, and depending on the last for any increase in its power to prevent and control disease.

There is a large subcontinent of psychiatric research which is concerned with applying the methods of the natural sciences to morbid phenomena—biochemical and physiological investigations in mental disorder are obviously of this nature. Psychological and sociological inquiries are in another area, that of the social sciences. Many studies in psychiatry lie in both areas—because they are intermediate, as physiological psychology is, or because they are carried out through joint activities. Much controversy has centred on

This paper was delivered as the Bradshaw lecture in November 1957 before the Royal College of Physicians. It is reprinted from the *Lancet* (1958), **1**, 171–5 and 227–30.

differences between the methods of the natural sciences and of the social sciences, stressing the relative weakness of the latter. Weaknesses in the social sciences—immaturity in their technical procedures, laxity in their theorizing —will tell heavily against psychiatric advance. It is true that some psychiatrists distrust the social sciences so much that any excursion in that direction is for them tantamount to walking the plank. Nevertheless the part that psychology and sociology must play in the advancement of psychiatry is undeniable.

Though there is manifest convenience in distinguishing between the natural and the social sciences, fundamental difference between them cannot be discerned. The slower tempo of development in the social sciences, and the immense difficulties in the way of measuring and controlling the phenomena they study, cannot be gainsaid; but the social, like the natural, sciences depend on sense-data, are nourished on hypotheses, and ask to be continually corrected through experiment and enlarged through further observation. If psychiatry were to put all its hopes in the application of the natural sciences and were to claim exemption from the discipline of the social sciences, it would be aligning itself, along a large stretch of its front, with dead philosophies and cults in which doubt is repudiated for the sake of a limited and spurious inner consistency.

*   *   *

The scientific method, which has been so closely studied of late by philosophers, is not, of course, the preserve of the natural sciences (though to them it owes its enormous prestige). Whether in the physical, the biological, or the social sciences, there is the same essential passage from untested guess to tenable, unfalsified conclusion—which may be, rather loosely, called a confirmed conclusion or a certainty, in the sense in which the circulation of the blood is a certainty. The initial hypothesis is arrived at by diverse routes, about which on the whole little is known: deductions from it entail predictions which are put to the test of direct observation or contrived experiment: and when enough evidence in support of the hypothesis has accumulated, it is given provisional acceptance. In time statements are thus arrived at which embrace and order very many facts; these statements have always started as hypotheses, plausible guesses.

It is a commonplace that hypotheses are indispensable for scientific activity; and that hypotheses must be judged by their heuristic as much as by their veridical importance: inadequate or false hypotheses may have value in provoking further observation and experiment. 'Even mistaken hypotheses are of use in leading to discoveries', wrote Claude Bernard. 'It seems indeed a necessary weakness of our mind to be able to reach truth only across a multitude of errors and obstacles.' De Morgan put it in a telling paradox—'Wrong hypotheses, rightly worked, have produced more useful results than unguided observations': the phlogiston theory or the corpuscular theory of light illustrates his point. It is equally a commonplace, however, that hypotheses are an impediment to knowledge when they are so loosely formulated that we

196

cannot deduce their logical consequences and therefore cannot make predictive statements which could be verified or refuted; the systematists of the eighteenth century exemplified this in medicine. Moreover, it is a poor recommendation in favour of a certain hypothesis to say that it explains all we know; for, as Karl Popper emphasizes, it is only by testing it on seemingly contrary instances that we can carry out that determined effort at refutation which is what we really mean when we speak of verifying a hypothesis. Interpretations which explain the phenomena only too readily, lead to a feeling of certainty which closes the mind to further inquiry and makes the believer hostile to any breath of scepticism.

I mention these familiar considerations because they have a direct relevance to some puzzling features in the development of psychiatry. In spite of the sophistication apparent in its literature, psychiatry is in some important respects struggling with problems which beset the physical sciences three hundred years ago. The word 'hypothesis' was a bad word in the seventeenth century.

'Hypotheses non fingo', said Newton. 'Hypotheses, whether metaphysical or physical, have no place in science.' (Quicquid enim ex phenomenis non deducitur hypothesis vocanda est; et hypotheses seu metaphysicae seu physicae seu qualitatum occultarum seu mechanicae in philosophia experimentali locum non habent.) Indeed, Newton lost no opportunity to belittle them, as in a letter to Oldenburg in 1672 where he wrote 'I do not think it needful to explicate my doctrine (of colours) by any hypotheses at all . . . You see therefore how much it is besides the business in hand to dispute about hypothesis. For which reason I shall now proceed to abstract the difficulties involved in Mr Hooke's discourse, and without having regard to any hypothesis consider them in general terms.' It is a little odd that the most illustrious scientist whom England has produced should have spurned what men now regard as an essential element in the process of arriving at truth. Surely a semantic misunderstanding. but a widespread one. Let us look at a great medical contemporary of Newton's. Thomas Sydenham wrote, in the Preface to his Observations, that hypotheses should be laid aside, in the study and description of diseases, 'for 'tis difficult to give a detail of the errors that spring from hypotheses, whilst writers, misled by these, assign such phenomena for diseases as never existed but in their own brains', and similarly, in his letter to Dr Paman, he speaks sharply of the many authors whose 'writings are founded upon Hypotheses which are the result of a luxuriant imagination; and the symptoms of diseases (wherein their true history consists) as described by them, appear to be deduced from the same source; and the method of cure, also, is derived from the same fictitious principles, and not from real facts, and thus becomes most destructive to mankind; so full of specious reasoning is every page of the writings of such superficial men, whilst the directions of nature are overlooked.' A hundred years later Pinel was still writing in the same strain, rejecting 'toute discussion métaphysique, toute hypothèse sur la nature des fonctions intellectuelles ou affectives, sur leur génération, leur ordre, leur enchaînement réciproque'.

It is plain that in those days hypotheses had a bad name because they connoted speculative propositions, so tenaciously held that conclusions derived from observation were rejected if they conflicted with them. It might be assumed that hypotheses no longer carry this taint. Yet in the introduction to a recent English textbook the authors review the requirements for a scientific approach and then say:

'It is embarrassing that such basic ideas of scientific method should have to be repeated and discussed in a textbook of psychiatry; but not one of these requirements is met by a very large part of the contributions which are made to contemporary psychiatric literature ... Hypotheses are reared in a vacuum without logical basis, and are expressed in imprecise phraseology in terms which have not been defined. They are often so vague that it is impossible to draw logical consequences, but even when that can be done critical investigations are not made. ... (Workers') hypotheses serve the single aim of providing a framework for interpretation' (Mayer-Gross, Slater, and Roth 1954).

These strictures echo the complaints from the 17th century: and are voiced, from a more detached standpoint, by a medical historian reviewing the theory of psychoanalysis:

... 'a "system" explaining in logical sequence the origin, nature and treatment of all disorders of a given class is suggestive—within the mental field—', says Richard Shryock, 'of those general medical systems which were so typical of the eighteenth and earlier centuries. If, like the latter, psychoanalysis cannot be checked one way or the other, it represents a reversion to the system-making stage in medical methodology, and may be expected to reproduce the various features and developments typical of that level. It is suggestive that this is indeed just what has happened. Once more, within this particular field, one hears of master and disciples, of divergent "schools", of scientific controversies, in which there is an "attack" or a "defence" of a given system, with more or less feeling on both sides.'

A more recent censure, by outspoken psychiatrists, is that of Lemkau and Pasamanick, who, contemplating the preventive powers at our disposal, wrote in 1953:

'The flashes of insight that have characterized the great leaders of our field in the past must be documented painstakingly with proof, a type of scientific discipline of which psychiatrists are perhaps more derogatory than appreciative.'

Whether these severe judgments are unfair is less important than that they repeat a pattern of criticism which is neither unfamiliar, nor confined to psychiatry and psychoanalysis. Historians have similar hard things to say about Professor Arnold Toynbee. Sociologists note such frailties in other sociologists. And in the most entrenched and assured branches of medicine critics sometimes discern them too. As an unsparing observer of loose thinking in medicine noted, the dividing wall between an unconfirmed hypothesis and a valid explanation often disappears, especially in therapeutics, because autistic aims prevail over rational thought (Bleuler 1927). This is nothing new: 'the human understanding resembles not a dry light, but admits a tincture of the will and the passions ... for man always believes more readily that which he prefers ... his feelings imbue and corrupt his understanding.'

*   *   *

It would be easy to pile up instances showing that psychiatry is not the only branch of medicine—or of knowledge—to be pilloried for lax thinking and complacent dogmatism. It has, however, troubles which seem peculiar to itself, and some ministrants who seem peculiarly indifferent to the scientific method as understood by the rest of the world. Nevertheless, I doubt if these are special characteristics: psychiatry's troubles are those inherent in the study and improvement of human behaviour; psychiatrists are for the most part bent, like other doctors, on doing their best for patients according to current methods and theories, without stopping to pick up and examine the little hedgehogs of doubt that sit by the therapist's path. There is nothing specially psychiatric about that. Besides those undoubting psychiatrists engaged mainly in treatment, there are in many countries psychiatric investigators fully alive to the rigorous demands of research but equally alive to the extreme complexity of their problems.

This complexity can be well seen when the value of treatment is reviewed. It has been said that 'psychotherapy is where organic medicine was in the days of Paracelsus': this gross exaggeration attests the gloom which some feel when they try to judge the present position of psychotherapy, and indeed of psychiatric treatment in general. Has the psychiatrist culpably failed to observe elementary principles of trial and evaluation, or has he attempted the task but found it too formidable? The question is not a rhetorical one. To answer, it, the evaluation of psychiatric treatment has to be looked at more closely.

*   *   *

The aims of medical treatment are ordinarily to remove or lessen disabilities and pain, to put an end to morbid changes in the patient's body of which he may not be aware but which must sooner or later cause disability, and, thirdly, to enable him to live as satisfying a life as possible, in spite of persistent disability and morbid process. Applied to mental illness, all this becomes equivocal. The patient will often be unaware of disturbances very plain to others; he may not complain of his symptoms; he may even cherish them. He may lead a less satisfying life when his symptoms have been got rid of than when he had them. The morbid process often has no physical substrate that we know of: and the psychopathology may be obscure and inaccessible. The criteria of recovery are therefore hard to specify, and, like the criteria of improvement, depend on an assessment of the patient's happiness, competence, and well-being which involves moral and social values as well as plainly medical ones. It must moreover be a comparative assessment, since if the patient was a poor creature—an inadequate psychopath, as people now say —before his attack of anxiety and depression came on, it must be counted as recovery if he reverts to his previous state, free again from manifest anxiety and depression, though in another man, previously better equipped to fulfil his social role, an illness that subsided leaving him in a state of inadequacy and social malaise would be rightly regarded as having a bad outcome.

A rather silly but often repeated truism says that the aim of psychiatric treatment is to promote mental health. It is hard to tell what the latter phrase means. Mental health is an invincibly obscure concept. Those who have attempted to define it in positive terms have twisted ropes of sand, telling us, for example, that a man's mental health consists in '(a) active adjustment or attempts at mastery of his environment as distinct both from his inability to adjust and from his indiscriminate adjustment through passive acceptance of environmental conditions; (b) unity of his personality, the maintenance of a stable, internal integration which remains intact notwithstanding the flexibility of behaviour which derives from active adjustment; and (c) ability to perceive correctly the world and himself.'

This clutter of words is groping towards an ideal, a sociobiological ideal: but much of it can have no operational referents and it abounds in terms which are undefined and at present undefinable. Most of those who state criteria of mental health follow the lead of the World Health Organization in refusing to take the absence of disease or infirmity as the characteristic feature; they do not say a man is well when he is free from manifest illness but speak instead of 'optimal growth and happiness of the individual', 'full maturity', 'adjustment to the world and to each other with a maximum of effectiveness and happiness', using quantitative words like 'full' and 'maximum' to qualify immeasurable states like happiness.

*　　*　　*

Mental health, we may conclude, is an abstraction which is very loosely interpreted. We cannot in every case decide, by comparing the degree of mental health after an illness with that before, whether the patient has recovered, or whether his illness has improved, or is stationary, or worse.

It is of course true that in many instances such a difficulty hardly enters anybody's mind, since there is an undeniable change for better or worse in the patient's condition, and everybody entitled to express an opinion—the patient, his relatives and intimates, his doctor—will concur. But these cases are not, I think, the majority. With an illness such as schizophrenia, or still more perhaps with many neurotic disorders, the issue is not clear cut; there may be sharp differences of judgment about outcome. One psychiatrist can report a rich harvest of recoveries in a series of patients whom another, equally sincere and observant, would describe as partial failures of treatment.

This is indeed an obstacle which will persist so long as we have no satisfactory measures of clinical change. There is another, worse obstacle—uncertainty as to what would have happened if the treatment had not been administered. 'We cannot judge the influence of a remedy on the course and outcome of a disease if we do not previously know the natural course and outcome of the disease.' The course of a mental illness is affected by so many factors, within the patient and in his environment, it is so subject to unforeseen turns of fortune that a change cannot safey be attributed to therapeutic intervention unless it is frequently and regularly produced or comes prompt on the heels of the treatment. This is of course a common difficulty in therapeutics which can be overcome by rigorous trials using, as controls, patients closely comparable to those who are treated. But matching psychiatric groups for this purpose is a daunting business, since they should at least be alike in the distribution of sex, age, intelligence, duration of illness, form and severity of illness, and previous treatment: alike also in the physical, and still more the psychological, circumstances of their medical and nursing care, except for the particular therapeutic procedure that is on trial. It is an exacting affair to match for form and severity patients with illnesses whose somatic pathology is not known and the symptoms of which can be elicited fully only with the patient's concurrence—a requirement often unfulfilled. The therapeutic zeal of psychiatrists, now as great as was once their nihilism, militates also against painstaking trial and provisional judgment of various methods of treatment: a difficulty in other branches of medicine, too.

The delay caused by these impediments is evident in the confused verdict on hypoglycæmic treatment of schizophrenia with insulin. Here is a method that has been before the world for over twenty years, widely employed in all civilized countries, and the subject of hundreds of experiments and technical reports. Yet it is still in such a dubious state that one can read responsible statements declaring on the one hand that it is 'the only effective method of treating early schizophrenia' and, on the other, that 'there is no significant difference in the outcome of treatment (of schizophrenia) whether unconsciousness has been induced by insulin or by barbiturates'. Leucotomy is a rather similar case, and the medley of 'tranquillizing' drugs may pass, though more rapidly, into the like chiaroscuro of approval and rejection.

*   *   *

But the doubts which attend physical methods of treatment are dwarfish alongside the giant misgivings and disputes which envelop psychotherapy in dust and fog. The trouble is of long standing, and has divided psychiatrists bitterly. In the Bradshaw lecture of 1936, the psychiatrist who delivered it said:

'There is practically no evidence in existence as to the efficacy of psychotherapy which is guarded against fallacy in such a way as would entitle it to serious consideration in a court of law. Among those 'cured' by any novel remedy are those who have never had the disease, those who still have it, those who have never had the treatment, and those who would have recovered equally well without it. All these classes are generously represented among those cured by psychotherapy.'

After this pungent and uncompromising passage, Professor Mapother went on to express his qualified belief in the usefulness of psychotherapy:

... 'it is time to recognise', he said, 'that the hard-boiled disbeliever in psychotherapy is as dead as Queen Anne. The real division is between those who are contented and discontented with the fumblings at present enjoying the name. . . . It would be absurd to deny a certain limited efficacy to psychotherapy.'

Since then belief in the efficacy of psychotherapy has become much more general among psychiatrists, and valuable systematic observations like those of Whitehorn and Betz have become available. But the same note, with modifications, can be heard in the following passage from a recent paper by two prominent American psychiatrists:

'We do have the firmest kind of conviction that psychotherapy carried on under the aegis of medicine provides . . . a type of help which is of the first order of importance. . . . But while admitting the importance and efficacy of psychotherapy in its many forms, we cannot emphasise too strongly the necessity for being as rigorous as possible when we make scientific judgments about the methods, goals and effectiveness of psychotherapy' (Bowman and Rose 1954).

This attitude, moreover, is found among psychiatrists who are constantly engaged in pyschotherapy. Thus a veteran psychoanalyst, C. P. Oberndorf, acknowledged the many obscure aspects and unpredictability of treatment, about which psychoanalysts themselves were not agreed, and urged the need for a planned investigation of the results of psychoanalysis.

The psychiatrists I have referred to—and, I should think, the great majority of psychiatrists everywhere—are convinced that psychotherapy is beneficial. But which patients it will benefit, what changes it will effect, whether one form of psychotherapy is more effective than another and if so for which types of illness—these are questions they ask themselves with varying insistence and frustration, distrusting their personal opinions on a matter of this kind, and distrusting the consensus of their fellow experts equally or more— since they know enough of the history of medicine and of human illusion to be aware that what most people are convinced of at a given time is not necessarily true.

Psychiatrists have not yet succeeded in investigating the efficacy of specified forms of psychological treatment for specified mental disorders in a way which satisfies the customary requirements of scientific evidence.

Besides the reasons I have been mentioning, there is the difficulty of accumulating a sufficient number of treated and untreated patients and of withholding treatment which patients desire and which their doctors think would benefit them. Psychotherapy, in its most widely known form—i.e., psychoanalysis—may go on for years, and is more often than not carried out in private practice. To collect the requisite number of comparable patients entails the cooperation of a number of psychiatrists engaged in psychotherapy and requires that their patients should be willingly available for independent examination at various phases of their treatment.

Psychotherapists are seldom sceptical or, as one might say, ambivalent about the treatment they give, and 'philosophic doubt' is not in keeping with their métier; many of them would desist from psychotherapy if they ceased to be sure that it is effective. It is therefore asking a great deal to invite them to cooperate, at this time of day, in trying to find out whether they may be deceiving themselves as to the usefulness of their life's work. In my own experience, it has not proved possible to get groups of psychotherapists committed to an adequate planned investigation into the results of their treatment.

Among the main problems to be solved if such an investigation is to succeed are how to measure mental change and how to predict mental illness. Now the measurement of mental functions is an enterprise to which psychologists have addressed themselves with brilliant success, and the prediction of behaviour on actuarial lines has been developed by psychologists also, as the names of T. R. Sarbin, Philip Vernon and Paul Meehl remind us. It would be natural therefore for psychiatrists to have prayed in aid of psychologists here for flattening the major obstacles and designing the whole investigation with that scientific detachment which psychologists may be supposed to possess in high degree.

Detachment is not always evident in psychologists when they concern themselves with psychotherapy. Some immerse themselves in it wholeheartedly as practitioners, on the American pattern. Others sedulously contemplate the pretensions of psychotherapy, shudder, and denounce its hollowness; they are drawn to it by a fascination like that which God has for atheists. But even if psychologists are sometimes emotionally involved, just as psychiatrists are, there is no doubt that they can contribute notably to the elucidation of a problem which everyone must wish to see solved. They have in fact tackled it, if C. R. Rogers' 'client-centred' counselling is to be reckoned as a form of psychotherapy. Their skills are relevant, and in my view indispensable, if we are to emerge from the existing morass—as indispensable as the skills of the psychiatrist. By emergence from the existing morass I mean not just a warranted conclusion that psychotherapy is or is not effective for such and such conditions—though that would be much—but a discriminating set of unrefuted propositions which would define attainable goals appropriate to categories of illness or of personality, classify forms of psychotherapy in terms that could be applied without ambiguity to the practice of any psychiatrist, and provide a more 'objective', more public and uncontaminated analysis of the therapeutic process than any now offered.

These may seem overweening hopes, in the light of what we have had for so long: but, even if they were fulfilled it would still be only an instalment, largely empirical, of what is needed to free psychotherapy from clogging uncertainties. Current methods of psychological treatment are, or seem to be, legion; they doubtless include procedures that can do harm, at any rate in irresponsible hands; and for some of them the connexion between theory and practice is tenuous, the connexion between what is preached and what is done so remote as to be discreditable. Besides these infirmities, there is of course much strength and much achievement. How could it be otherwise when there are so many psychiatrists of great ability and intellectual integrity, broadly trained, and gifted in handling complex relationships with others, who devote themselves without reservation or misgiving to psychotherapy as their main business in life? It is in no sense derogatory of their work to want psychological treatment put on a firmer basis of confirmation and precision than it now has. A fair-minded and illuminating review of psychotherapy in 1955 included the following declaration:

'In our present ignorance it is practically certain that clients are treated by methods of varying inappropriateness, largely as a function of which therapist they happen to get to. Also it is practically certain that many hours of skilled therapists are being spent with unmodifiable cases, or in the use of techniques which are effective but unnecessarily time-consuming.' (Meehl 1955).

This is true, and it has a moral—a moral that can be drawn with special force in a Welfare State like ours, under obligation to provide its citizens with all the approved medical treatment they need. To withhold psychotherapy from any neurotic invalid, or any delinquent, or anyone with psychopathic personality—once it had been demonstrated properly that such treatment would lead to recovery or much improvement in these people—would be indefensible. It would be indefensible, within a comprehensive national health service, even if elaborate treatment were shown to be requisite for many patients: practical objections would be raised, of course, on grounds of cost and the availability of doctors, but the issue turns essentially on whether there is convincing evidence of the value of treatment. The United States Department of Health recently published a book on *Evaluation in Mental Health* which listed and abstracted 980 relevant articles. It concluded: 'an obvious finding is the thinness of the efforts at evaluation.'

Here, then, is a great domain of psychiatric practice in which there has been an excessive proportion of guesswork and rather a lot of subjective certainty. More doubt might have been salutary, for the reason that Bacon stated: 'if a man will begin with certainties, he shall end in doubts; but if he will be content to begin with doubts, he shall end in certainties.' The remedy lies in the hands of psychiatrists and psychologists working together. It will demand a considerable effort of reorientation, and indeed sacrifices, from those psychiatrists who devote most of their time to systematic psychotherapy; and from psychologists it will demand an intimate understanding of the conditions of clinical practice and, indeed, some reorientation likewise.

An effect of growing, but excessive, confidence in the power of psychiatric treatment is discernible in the changing attitude towards those who are delinquent or may become so. The recent Royal Commissioners on the Law relating to Mental Illness and Mental Deficiency assumed that doctors can tell which persons of psychopathic personality will benefit by treatment, and what treatment will be needed; consequently they recommend that compulsory powers to force a psychopathic patient into hospital should be used only when it is 'clearly established' that he needs a particular form of treatment, which the hospital in question can provide; they recommend more extensive compulsory powers over adolescents and young adults who show psychopathic personality, because 'it is generally agreed that treatment or training is most likely to be successful if it can be given at this stage'. It may well be that both these assumptions about the benefits of treatment for psychopaths will turn out to be warranted: but as yet they rest on the certainties or the clinical impressions of those who took part in the treatment and on unchecked appraisal of the association between outcome and treatment. No controlled studies, of adequate size, have been carried out, and many of the difficulties which have so far precluded this were demonstrated in the investigation of a cognate problem—whether juvenile delinquents and 'pre-delinquents' benefit from having a kindly older person to whom they can turn for friendship and guidance. Richard Cabot had supposed they would; an elaborate inquiry, with well-matched controls, was carried out to test his hope. This investigation had nothing to do with psychiatric treatment, nor were psychiatrists concerned in the analysis of its findings, but it afforded a model of honest, hypothesis-testing, longitudinal study of the effects of deliberate intervention. It exposed weaknesses in design and execution which can be foreseen now and guarded against; it demonstrated that social investigations concerned with human beings over a period of years cannot be carried out wholly according to plan, yet can be made to answer a correctly stated question; and it threw light on our ability to predict behaviour. Prognosis is more difficult in psychiatry than in other branches of medicine, as Kraepelin insisted: some psychiatrists, it is true, pride themselves on their gifts in this direction, but their complacency usually has weak foundations. Criminologists have been in the same boat.

In the Cambridge-Somerville study just referred to, three experts in criminology (one of them a psychiatrist) predicted what would be the later social adjustment of the 782 'difficult' or 'pre-delinquent' boys, aged about 9 years, who were reviewed for the study; a similar prediction was made by the children's teachers; and it emerged that there was a correlation coefficient of 0·48 between the actual outcome on the one hand and the predictions both of the experts and of the teachers on the other. In other words, the predictions were above what would occur by chance, but experts in juvenile delinquency were no better at predicting what would happen to these children than were their school teachers. Moreover, both the teachers and the experts predicted more delinquency than actually occurred; so if there had been no 'untreated' group for comparison they might have inferred—mistakenly—at the end of the investigation that the discrepancy between their predictions and the actual outcome was attributable to the benefits of the 'counsellor' scheme of treatment provided (Powers and Witmer 1951).

The most recent and sophisticated prediction study is Mannheim and Wilkins's inquiry into the effects of borstal training. Besides constructing prediction tables which they validated, they found it expedient, like others before them, to provide individual case-studies—i.e., to combine the clinical with the statistical method, in order to 'demonstrate the variety of factors which, combined, may produce the same statistical score; to work out a typology of cases related to the various score classes; and to make a special study of atypical cases, i.e., cases who, in spite of favourable statistical scores, actually become failures, and vice versa'. In their view the control technique, though in many ways indispensable, is insufficient as the only method of evaluating the diverse patterns and changes in the behaviour of individuals (Mannheim and Wilkins 1955). But Mannheim, in expressing this view apropos of the Cambridge–Somerville study, concluded that such investigations will have to be 'in keeping with the experiences of experimental social science rather than those of medicine' (Mannheim 1953).

This seems an innocuous conclusion. But it contains the chief elements of a vital controversy. Psychiatry is, like criminology, a form of applied social science: it is also a branch of medicine. If there is an intrinsic opposition or sharp difference, as Mannheim implies, between the methods appropriate to study of social experiments and those of medicine, psychiatry will be pulled hither and thither, in a bewildering zigzag. I do not believe there is such an opposition; but the literature might suggest it—and the progress of psychiatry does look a little indecisive and wobbly at times. The problem is to be found in the uniqueness, the singularity of each individual.

In the practice of psychiatry, attention must be concentrated on the individual. Because he is unique and extremely complicated, he does not seem wholly catchable within a scientific net. The succession of events which pertain to the medical, as to the social or psychological, course of an individual's life can, it is true, be predicted to some extent, and designedly influenced, by applying general principles to the historical and observational data we have about him: but there is still something over; consequently intuitive processes often play a large part in determining the physician's prognosis and treatment—especially in psychiatry. The doctor's procedure may hardly include at all the strict deductive application of a general theory to a particular, narrowly stated case, and it differs manifestly from that of the experimental biologist who does his utmost to get rid of uniqueness in his experimental animals. This difference applies to the practice of psychiatry. But it does not apply to the psychiatric investigator who must concern himself with what is common to human beings, or to classes and subgroups of human beings.

*   *   *

The controversy is not between medicine and the social sciences, or between medicine and the biological sciences, but between two schools of thought within the social sciences. Their debate has enlisted some notable disputants. There is guerilla warfare between the adherents of the 'nomothetic' school, which seeks general laws and employs the procedures of the exact sciences, and the 'idiographic' school, which endeavours to understand some particular event. Both approaches, as Gordon Allport has urged, have value in studying personality. But the proportion of idiographic to nomothetic study can be excessive: and there can be little question that this has been the case in psychiatry. Hence its weakness on the very ground where idiographic study should be most potent—the understanding of individuals to such a degree that their behaviour can be predicted.

Meehl, in a thoughtful monograph on this matter, collected all the published instances in which predictions arrived at by the skilled judgment of a clinician were compared, as to their correctness, with those arrived at mechanically by someone who had not seen the patients but who made appropriate calculations. In all but one of the twenty studies examined, the actuarial or cookery-book approach yielded results as good as those of the clinician, or better (Meehl 1954). It would be imprudent to draw from this the conclusion that clinical prognosis is a superfluous exercise, and that prediction had better be handed over to the clerks and computors: impartial judges like Vernon have pointed out that the clinical method—and in particular the clinical interview—has advantages which the actuarial method, based on psychological tests and biographical items, does not possess.

Informative as the idiographic approach has proved, and fertile as it will doubtless continue to be, it contains no built-in safeguard against persistent error. Such safeguards are essential; for, as Karl Popper puts it, 'if scientific objectivity were founded ... upon the individual scientist's impartiality or objectivity, then we should have to say goodbye to it'. Yet the safeguards contained in the scientific method are repugnant to some who devote themselves to psychotherapy, and their argument against it always harks back to the uniqueness of the individual. Thus C. G. Jung declares that:

... 'from matters of individual psychology science ought in fact, to withdraw. For, to speak of a science of individual psychology is already a contradiction in terms. It is only the collective element in the psychology of an individual that constitutes an object for science; for the individual is by definition a unique reality that cannot be compared with anything else.'

This is an obscurantist argument. Because an individual is a unique reality, it by no means follows that he cannot be compared with anything else: every individual plant, every individual animal is a unique reality but not therefore exempt from comparison and collective study. The argument is a reversion to the claim, so often voiced during the controversies about Evolution, that man is, by his nature, fundamentally distinct from all other creatures and an improper subject for comparative study. The opponents of the evolutionary theory refused to consider what human beings have in common with other living creatures: the argument put forward by Jung ignores what human beings have in common with each other. Psychology has in fact concerned itself with individual differences, and has had notable success. It may be that the difficulty is verbal, and that Jung means by the psychology of an individual the study of just that which is the essence of each person's total personality, something that would be shattered by analysis and resolution. I doubt, however, if his statement is merely a truism, as this explanation would suppose.

The dispute has many facets. For some, it can become a theological issue. For others, the distinction is between the generalizing sciences and the historical sciences. Popper, whose analysis has been so searching, put forward the view that whereas the generalizing sciences are interested in testing universal hypotheses having the character of natural laws, and in predicting specific events, the historical sciences are concerned in explaining past specific events by means of interpretations and specific hypothetical statements about 'causes'. This view, which is in keeping with Max Weber's, would put clinical psychiatry in the historical class, in so far as it is directed at understanding morbid behavior, trying to uncover what Jaspers in his elaborate exploration of the matter called 'verständliche Zusammenhänge'. It would be improper to put all psychiatry in this class, and I would not have laboured this issue if it were not again evident at the present time that there is a strong move away from the search for general laws, and towards preoccupation with the individual. Thus Manfred Bleuler, one of the most prominent of European psychiatrists, declared recently that the most essential feature in the recent development of psychiatry has been that the diagnosis of disease has given place to absorption in the personal tragedy of individuals: 'das Hauptaugenmerk richtet sich auf Einzelschicksale' (Bleuler 1957). The effect of this movement will, I submit, be retrograde.

*   *   *

I have dwelt so far on prognosis and treatment. There is another extensive but rather neglected territory in which few psychiatrists tread a confident path—the alleviation of chronic disorders, and especially chronic schizophrenia. The word 'chronic' has got a bad name, and many think they can dodge its terrors by submitting 'long-stay' for it. But changing names has always proved a futile game in psychiatry, and the chronic patients, whatever the euphemism applied to them, remain a vast reproach. The Chairman of the Board of Control lately reminded us that the number of chronic patients in England and Wales has remained fairly constant throughout the years, at about 130,000; 85 per cent of the patients in the mental hospitals have been there for more than a year, and 60,000 (i.e., two-fifths of the whole mental hospital population) have been there more than ten years; 50,000 of these patients suffer from schizophrenia (Armer 1957). Considered in relation to the general population, there are for every 100,000 people over 16 in England and Wales, 270 in a mental hospital suffering from schizophrenia, mostly in a chronic form. It is painfully clear that chronic schizophrenia is an outstanding medical and social issue.

Some therapeutic zealots believe that if appropriate treatment, especially insulin-coma treatment, had been administered early to these patients, many of them would not have become chronically ill. For this belief there is no adequate foundation. We must, unfortunately, reckon with the continuance, for decades at least, of this vast company of more or less incapacitated schizophrenics.

It is, however, necessary to distinguish between being chronically ill with schizophrenia and having therefore to be in a mental hospital. The attitudes of doctors and of society at large determine whether a person with a long-continued mental illness lives in a mental hospital or in the community. The practice of some countries has been towards increasing mental-hospital care, and of others towards keeping it at a minimum. Many communities have been readier to build and equip medical institutions—hospitals as we know them—than to provide hospitals in the older sense—asylums for the infirm and the indigent—and homes in which the patients could find friendly shelter, as at Gheel.

We are now entering a phase in which we shall be directing our efforts towards keeping patients in the community as long as possible, and if they have to come into hospital, towards returning them to the community quickly. The reasons for this are mixed—awareness of the deleterious effects a mental hospital environment can have however well ordered it may be and aptly designed for the patients' benefit; regard for favourable social influences which independent life in the community affords, even to the mental cripple; economic advantages for the patient, the taxpayer, and the nation; shortage of nurses; and perhaps some changes in the social ethos. The recent Royal Commission expressed this trend of opinion, in its broadest form, in their recommendation—'there should be a general re-orientation away from institutional care in its present form and towards community care'.

This is a hopeful change from that overcautious policy which regarded the mentally ill, especially the chronic schizophrenic, as debarred from society so long as delusions, hallucinations, or peculiarities of conduct were discoverable. But the new policy—I call it new but it was advocated as long ago as 1905—could go to extremes and do much harm. It could also lose its impetus and purpose. Reforms that rest on humanitarian impulse have been most powerful for good, especially in psychiatry, but their momentum has often been lost or their drawbacks been perpetuated when the generation of reformers passed away. The chief safeguard against this recurrent backsliding lies in the accumulation of more precise knowledge, permitting generous aims and lofty principles to be translated into regular procedures that will be applicable even when the reformer's driving force has slackened and gone.

* * *

How much do we know about the issues touching on community care for the chronic schizophrenic? As yet little. Shrewd empiricism and clinical intuition provided, so it was thought, all that we needed for the rehabilitation of the chronic psychotic. There have been preliminary sketches but no finished pictures of the effect of hospital environment upon such patients: few studies of how the patients may be selected, and how prepared, for satisfactory life in the larger community: and only tentative cartoons and inadequate blueprints of the domestic, social, and occupational conditions requisite if they are to keep their heads above water when they have left the mental hospital.

It has long been a commonplace of psychiatric thinking that for many patients there is a critical stage in their mental-hospital stay: if the turning-point is not recognized and the patient then discharged, he will subsequently react to his hospital life and surroundings by becoming worse and the chances of his ever leaving will be very small. What truth there is in this, how the favourable phase is to be recognized, what characteristics of the hospital regime need to be altered to make adverse effects less—regarding these questions there is much guesswork, sometimes ill-assorted with a feeling of certainty 'on the strength of my thirty years experience, I am absolutely convinced that . . .' A French psychiatrist, P. C. Racamier, wrote a few months ago that there is no creature in the world more sensitive and vulnerable to his human environment than a schizophrenic, and that a psychiatric ward is a two-edged weapon, potentially therapeutic and potentially 'le plus remarquable intrument d'aliénation qu'on puisse imaginer . . . surtout pour ces aliénés achevés que sont les schizophrènes'. He states the general proposition that autistic isolation is the only stable relationship which a schizophrenic can establish with another person, and declares that it is a 'law of sociopathology' that the hospital milieu tends to maintain this morbid stability. ('Le milieu hospitalier, l'hôpital tout entier, a tendance à maintenir le status quo stable acquis au prix de la chronicité des malades.') A generalization such as this, derived from a psychoanalyst's experience as doctor in a mental hospital having no unlocked wards, goes much too far, but it suggests some provocative hypotheses.

To state hypotheses and devise suitable experiments in this field of inquiry is a formidable business, as we and others have found. Social experiments in hospitals will seriously affect the daily care and the disposal of patients, put a strain on the attitudes and sense of security of nurses, and perhaps run counter to cherished clinical beliefs. Only those who would not have to carry out such experiments could be disposed to throw stones at doctors, sociologists, and psychologists for not having accomplished the feat yet.

In the investigations which the Social Psychiatry Research Unit has been carrying out, we have found it necessary at each stage to pass backwards and forwards from laboratory to ward and from ward to laboratory, and to pass from both to the outer world where relatives live and conditions of work and daily life may make or mar the chronic schizophrenic's chance of staying outside hospital for good.

First, there was the inescapable problem of ascertaining the patients to be studied, and then matching one group of them with another. Since there may not be agreement as to which patients are properly diagnosed as schizophrenic, some unambiguous and communicable criteria must be used. Psychologists have applied factorial analysis to rating scales of behaviour, and so worked out diagnostic patterns which can be applied uniformly; the use of these minimised the risk that others who replicate the experiments might obtain discrepant results only because their criteria of paranoid and catatonic schizophrenia differed from ours.

When the patients had been selected—they were men who had been in hospital for years—their mental state and their potentialities for life outside the hospital had to be assessed. Clinical data had to be reinforced by observations on the capacity of the patients to learn and to improve their performance at industrial tasks. The reaction-time of schizophrenics, and the effect of distractions and other extraneous stimuli such as noise had to be determined. Differences were found between paranoid and other schizophrenics which made further laborarory experiments necessary. The effect of incentives had likewise to be investigated under laboratory conditions.

Then there were the chronic patients who had left hospital and managed to stay in the ordinary community. For them methods of investigation and statistical analysis were needed akin to those used for prediction work in criminology. A close study of the family relationships of the schizophrenics and of the community's attitudes to mental illness was called for. Such a study is best pursued by the combined work of the anthropologist, the psychiatrist, and the social psychologist. The available techniques and theoretical models are not entirely adequate: recent work has shown that the methodological problems are still acute. It has been necessary from time to time to leave the more practical problems set by clinical observation and therapeutic intention, and to pursue issues of a more general nature, such as the learning curve of the chronic schizophrenic patients, or the methods of measuring change in mental state over a period of time.

The history of these investigations is an object-lesson in reciprocity—reciprocity between fundamental and applied studies, between clinician and social scientist, between laboratory and ward.

*   *   *

I have dwelt perhaps too much on the psychological and social side of the picture. Psychiatry is not just applied sociology and applied psychology. It has its roots deep in medicine, and most of its surest knowledge derives from the bedside and from physiology, pathology, genetics, and biochemistry. It has methods of treatment which are of the same stock as those which have proved themselves in other branches of medicine. Its only assured methods of prevention concern mental diseases and defects due to known organic causes. It is moreover a practical activity, instinct with humane intention: the psychiatrist cannot refuse to act in what he judges to be the most helpful way for his patient, even though the therapeutic procedure is empirical and its benefits still dubious. Only a detached spectator, god-like above the battle, could expect the psychiatrist to refrain from giving some form of psychological treatment to patients with distressful anxiety or conspicuous hysteria, though he cannot be certain that it will have effect. There are some awful warnings of what a craving for certainty can lead to. You may remember the philosopher Cratylus who, as Aristotle tells us, decided never to say anything but what was certainly true, and so he ceased to talk at all and confined himself to wagging his finger.

Psychiatry suffers much from hopeful illusions and clichés used as incantations, just as a few decades ago it suffered, even more, from pessimistic and resigned inertia. Bleuler's monograph on autistic thinking in medicine is a sustained diatribe against the former of these extremes (Bleuler 1927): Adolf Meyer inveighed against the latter of them. Into the stagnant bog of nihilism in treatment we are hardly likely to fall again soon, but we are not out of the other danger.

It is easy to lay failings like these at the door of psychiatrists, blaming their lack of scientific training, their loose habits of thought, their incuriosity, their passion for psychoanalysis or for physical methods of treatment, their preoccupation with the fascinating art of understanding other people. To think this seems to me facile and unjust. More important than the deficiencies of doctors are the inherent complexity of the problems, and, as I said at the outset, the fact that the solution of many of the most complex and important depends upon the social sciences, which are still immature. Their growth has been rapid, it is true; psychology in particular has moved from strength to strength: but they have not crossed some of the awkward hills and ditches that lie in their path and in the psychiatrist's.

One of the most distinguished of living sociologists has said that sociology has few formulae, in the sense of highly abbreviated symbolic expressions of relationships between sociological variables. Sociological interpretations therefore come to be highly discursive, 'the logic of procedure, the key concepts, and the relationship between variables not uncommonly become lost in an avalanche of words'. The sociological analysis of qualitative data does not reside, as some people assume, in a private world 'inhabited by penetrating but unfathomable insights.... The procedure of even the most perceptive of sociologists must be standardizable and the results of their insights testable by others. Science, and this includes sociological science, is public and not private.' These words of Robert Merton have a familiar ring. The study of human behaviour strongly invites private and discursive interpretations: the development of the social sciences, pure and applied, has been a struggle to resist the invitation. Psychiatry has made one gigantic effort to escape it, but hardly succeeded: psychoanalysis, for all its stimulus and scope, has remained rather private and rather discursive.

I have not enlarged on the attainments of psychiatry, its solid groundwork of detailed, minute, and orderly observations, its empirical successes, its accretions through application of the basic medical sciences to clinical problems. There are large textbooks and innumerable monographs, compilations, and symposia setting forth this stock of knowledge which stands to the credit of psychiatry. It is because of it that the psychiatrist, even the self-critical psychiatrist, feels no need to beat his breast and recite penitential psalms when he meets other doctors. There are however occasions, such as this lecture offers, when a review of important areas of ignorance and doubt, and of the reasons for them, seems appropriate.

Clearly we are a long way from certainty, and when we meet anyone who is sure that he knows how to tackle the problems of mental disorder and to remedy the failings of psychiatrists and psychologists, we may recall Lord Lansdowne's remark: 'I wish I could be as sure of anything as Tom Macaulay is of everything.' Guessing, too, has its perils and its ardours: it takes unkindly to the discipline which is good for it. Yet between those who are nearly certain and those who guess much there is the bond which Isaac Newton spoke of: 'I doubt not we have one common design: a sincere endeavour after knowledge, without valuing uncertain speculations for their subtleties, or despising certainties for their plainness.'

REFERENCES

ARMER, F. Lancet, 1957, 1, 1031.

BERNARD, CLAUDE, An Introduction to the Study of Experimental Medicine (translated by H. C. Greene), New York, 1949.

BLEULER, E. Das autistisch-undisziplinierte Denken in der Medizin und seine Uberwindung, Berlin, 1927.

BLEULER, M. Schweiz. med. Wschr., 1957, p. 113.

BOWMAN, K. M., and ROSE, M. Amer. J. Psychiat., 1954, 111, 401.

DE MORGAN, A. A Budget of Paradoxes, London, 1872.

JUNG, C. G. Collected Works, vol. VII: The Structure of the Unconscious, London, 1953.

LEMKAU, P. V., PASAMANICK, B., COOPER, M. Amer. J. Psychiat, 1953, 110, 436.

MANNHEIM, H. Brit. J. Delinqu., 1953, 3. 215.

— and WILKINS, L. T. Prediction Methods in Relation to Borstal Training, London, 1955.

MAPOTHER, E. 'The Integration of Neurology and Psychiatry', Bradshaw Lecture, 1936.

MAYER-GROSS, W., SLATER, E. T. O., and ROTH, M. *Clinical Psychiatry*, London, 1954.

MEEHL, P. E. *Clinical versus Statistical Prediction*, Minneapolis, 1954.

— *Annu. Rev. Psychol*, 1955, **6**, 357.

MERTON, R. K. *Social Theory and Social Structure*, Glencoe, Ill., 1949.

NEWTON, ISAAC. *Opera quae extant omnia* (edited by Horsley), vol. 4, London, 1779.

OBERNDORF, C. P., GREENACRE, P., KUBIE, L. S. *Int. J. Psycho-Anal.*, 1948, **29**, 7.

PINEL, P. *Traité médico-philosophique sur l'Aliénation mentale*, Paris, 1809.

POPPER, K. *Logik der Forschung*, Vienna, 1935.

POPPER, K. *The Open Society and its Enemies*, vol. 2, London, 1945.

POWERS, E., and WITMER, H. *An Experiment in the Prevention of Delinquency: the Cambridge-Somerville Youth Study*, New York, 1951.

RACAMIER, P. C. *Evol. Psychiat.*, 1957, **1**, 47.

ROYAL COMMISSION ON THE LAW RELATING TO MENTAL ILLNESS AND MENTAL DEFICIENCY. *Report*, H.M.S.O., 1957.

SHRYOCK, R. H., *The Development of Modern Medicine*, London, 1948.

SYDENHAM, T. *Works* (translated and edited by John Swan), London, 1742.

U.S. DEPT. OF HEALTH, EDUCATION AND WELFARE. *P.H.S. Publication no. 413*: *Evaluation in Mental Health*, Washington, 1955.

14

THE STUDY OF DEFECT

I BELIEVE I am the first Adolf Meyer Lecturer to have enjoyed the privilege of working at the Phipps Clinic in the days when Dr Meyer was its head. It was therefore with exceptional pleasure that I learnt I was to have this opportunity of recording my personal debt to him. Tributes to the outstanding man in whose name this Lecture has been established have taken many forms, and American psychiatrists know better than we who came to Hopkins from abroad, what his services have been to psychiatry in this continent. But it is right for us who carried back to our own countries what we had learnt, to say what we owe him: the example of his integrity—his moral and intellectual integrity—and his conception of the humane aims of our specialty. These exercised a force upon his pupils whose effect can still be discerned in the psychiatric developments of Great Britain and some of the Scandinavian countries. No doubt it is a mistake to look around in one's middle age and decide that in comparison with the great men under whom we served our apprenticeship we are a lesser breed of epigoni, busy in dotting i's and crossing t's: it would, however, be no mistake to say that for the progress we have seen in psychiatry during the last quarter century we owe much to the labours of predecessors, very notable among them Adolf Meyer, teacher and exemplar.

I have chosen to speak of the study of defect. This may seem a paradoxical choice, since of all the wide issues in psychiatry mental defect is the one which Dr Meyer least considered in his oral teaching and his writings. In his Salmon Lectures [32] he acknowledged the relative lack of plasticity and modifiability in defectives, and the passage might be taken to suggest that because of his melioristic passion, the intractability of this group of constitutional weaknesses put them outside the scope of his concentrated thought and effort. Such an inference would be, I think, mistaken. Dr Meyer was distressed by the common attitude of superiority and even contempt towards the mentally defective: he tried to counter it by emphasizing 'that there are perfectly good and useful imbeciles and that it is the use, and not only the quantity of the

---

This paper was read as the Adolf Meyer Research Lecture at the 116th annual meeting of the American Psychiatric Association, Atlantic City, N.J., in May 1960. It is reprinted from the *American Journal of Psychiatry* (October 1960), **117**, no. 4, 289–304.

assets which decides human desirability' [31]. But lacking clinical access and experience in these conditions, and having so much work to his hand in other areas of psychiatry, it is not surprising that he said and wrote very little about the intellectually handicapped.

The intellectually handicapped—in using such a phrase I am perhaps begging a question? At home I should almost certainly be told that I am, for this is a contentious issue with us. Because of it mental defect has become a murky concept. The most recent and outspoken inquirer [48] into this vexed matter concludes that

'the urge to get away from purely intellectual concepts of mental deficiency and to substitute the criterion of social competence, has thus left us with a situation which is fantastically complicated—or perhaps "muddled" would be a better word.'

I shall be returning to this cardinal issue: I mention it now, as a reminder— at any rate for us in England—of the fuzzy outlines and unsteady basis of the object of our studies in retardation, or defect (as I think we may still call it).

It has been until lately a neglected branch of psychiatry. But in research this is now happily untrue. The rate at which fresh knowledge about mental defect has been accumulated in the last 20 years contrasts strangely with the slowness with which public authorities and doctors have given up regarding it as an Ugly Duckling. In few countries does the care of defectives receive the administrative and financial support that is accorded to psychotic patients— extramural facilities for them are weaker than those offered to the neurotic who seeks help in out-patient departments and day hospitals; and, most disconcerting of all, the bulk of psychiatrists do not regard this branch of clinical work as lively and rewarding.

Yet its notable recent triumphs are surely the prelude to a wide advance. The doors are opening fast. At least five distinct metabolic anomalies have been detected, so that possible ways appear of aborting their ill effects on mental growth: the genetic peculiarity of mongolism has been disclosed in the extra chromosome produced, we may suppose, by non-disjunction; challenging evidence has accumulated on maternal conditions during early pregnancy which may retard a child's mental development; the capacity of imbeciles to learn has been found greater than we thought. These are advances, fit for application to treatment and prevention, which are as considerable as any made in the study of other forms of mental disability during the same period. Professor Böök [5] says that in the field of mental deficiency we can see some of the most brilliant contributions of genetics to psychiatry; that statement might be extended, I believe, to cover the contributions of biochemistry and perhaps of psychology also. In spite of this arresting efflorescence of research in mental deficiency, it remains the branch of psychiatry that seems least attractive to our recruits. For a vacant post in the mental deficiency hospitals competition is less keen than for posts of the same standing in the other mental health services. Yet the prestige of any subject commonly rises when it is known to be advancing in basic knowledge that can be applied to human affairs. It may be objected that though this sort of prestige impresses informed onlookers and attracts research workers it does not move doctors to take up the practice of a special branch of medicine. This I doubt: while recognizing, of course, that many other factors besides impressive scientific advance determine the choice of a particular career in our profession. Professor Merton's investigation [30] showed that the process begins early. The recent study by Professor Pasamanick and Dr Rettig [39] has confirmed that in the eyes of medical students psychiatry still ranks low among the specialties; and one may suspect that if subdivisions of psychiatry had been explored, work in the mental deficiency services would have been found near the bottom of the list.

Is this poverty of esteem because the study of defect is unimportant to modern society? Far from it. In England and Wales—to take the statistics best known to me—the expectancy of admission to a mental deficiency hospital is four for every thousand male births, and three per thousand female births: over a quarter of all the beds for mental disorder are reserved for mental defectives; besides the occupants of these 58,000 beds in mental deficiency hospitals, there were nearly 80,000 ascertained defectives receiving community care from local health authorities in 1955. In spite of many causes for divergence in prevalence estimates, there is substantial agreement between surveys carried out at different times and in different places during this century which indicate a prevalence rate of between 0·8 and 1·0 per cent of population, or 3 to 3·5 per cent of the population under the age of 18, exhibiting varying forms or degrees of defect. This figure proclaims the rough extent of the aggregate personal misfortunes, the waste and the socio-economic handicaps which widespread mental defect implies for a civilized community. It is true that these are crude statements. Defect is not a biological entity, or indeed a psychological or pathological entity, but rather a congeries of morbid conditions. Its prevalence is not an absolute, but a conditional estimate. The cultural values and attitudes of a society have much to do with its recognition and may determine how heavy will be the economic and social burden it creates. Moreover, here kindness may be cruel, and efficient provision a hardship: for in a wealthy, humane, highly organized society people who are poorly endowed may be set aside and debarred from living a normal life, so that they cannot contribute their self-respecting mite to the common stock or fulfill their side of the social contract, whereas in a ruder, less exacting society they might be integrated into the life of the community and be indistinguishable from the common run of its members. And the extent of the liability is mounting: the social and medical advances which permit mongols and other handicapped children to survive, lead to an appreciable increase in the prevalence of defect: a fourfold increase over the last 30 years in the prevalence of mongols in the population of children aged 10 years, as Carter [7] has recently shown. Such considerations reinforce the argument that here in defect we have an enormous social and medical issue—or rather network of issues. They

216

underline the disturbing paradox: mental defect is a challenging, insistent, promising branch of psychiatry, yet psychiatrists are not, on the whole, drawn towards it.

It is all the stranger when we consider that the study of defect promises to throw light not only on its own path but on some of the byways of the rest of psychiatry—byways so often traversed that they have become ruts leading into bogs. There are important and popular divisions of psychiatry in which the law of of diminishing returns is painfully evident, so that there is much cry and little wool. This cannot be said of the study of defect at the present time, nor of its potential relevance to cruxes that puzzle psychiatrists generally. Now that the ice has broken here in the streams of biological, social and psychological research, our understanding of mental illnesses stands to profit from advances in knowledge of the pathology—psychopathology and somatic pathology alike—of mental defect. Perhaps the paradox I have been dwelling on is only a matter of time-lag. Among psychiatrists in England at any rate there has been, I believe, a perceptible quickening of interest during the last two or three years in the practice as well as the study of mental deficiency: it can be attributed to their awareness of the scientific stirring in the subject, and its closeness to other psychiatric issues of moment.

The concept of defect has, of course, long been based on a simple dichotomy, that many would say has now served its turn. It was summed up by Esquirol [10] in an epigram—'The dement is a man deprived of the possessions he once enjoyed, he is a rich man who has become poor. But the defective has been penniless and wretched all his life.' Esquirol—who said also 'Defect is not a disease, it is a condition'—was herein making a distinction that had been firmly established in jurisprudence. The common law of England, from the thirteenth century, drew a line between the 'natural fool', witless from birth, and the lunatic who 'hath had understanding but by disease, grief, or other accident, hath lost the use of his reason'. Similarly in the early Brehon Laws of Ireland. It is an obvious way of dividing those who have never been, from those who have ceased to be, mentally normal. Yet this commonsense differentiation took a long while to achieve clinical sanction. At the end of the eighteenth century the medical distinction between dementia and defect was blurred, as we see very plainly in the writings of such leaders as Philippe Pinel and Johann Christian Reil:

'Insanity in one of these forms can go through a sort of transformation, emerging in another form, so that one sees melancholics pass into mania, some manic patients fell into dementia or idiocy, and sometimes even some idiots pass into a temporary attack of mania and then fully recover the use of their reason' (Pinel) [41].

Such being the jumble, Esquirol was rendering some service to clear thought by asserting the distinction he did, with sharp and authoritative precision. But it is significant of the whirligig on which our thinking about these matters seems to turn, that we are now veering back in some respects to the position which had been assumed by Esquirol's predecessors, and which seemed to have been abandoned more than a hundred years ago.

A few months ago a Committee of the Group for the Advancement of Psychiatry, in their brochure on basic considerations in mental retardation, wrote [15]:

'Historically the concept developed that deviant children could be classified accurately into clear-cut categories such as the psychotic, the neurotic, those with character problems, and the mentally deficient. More recent experience has underscored the difficulties inherent in differential diagnosis. In a substantial number of cases the diagnostic term attached to a given patient depends upon the orientation of the examiner rather than upon the presenting symptomatology or developmental history of the patient.'

Such subjectivism is an indictment of our discipline (if we may continue to call it a discipline, after that), but it shows the way the wind is blowing.

Classification is usually a jejune theme. In this instance it has the value of a signpost, betokening changes in the direction of our thought about the nature of defect. The latest swing is expressed in the 1957 report of our Royal Commission [42]:

'The basis for this (the traditional) distinction between the mentally ill and the mentally defective is practical rather than scientific. Broadly speaking, people who develop a mental illness in adult life and people who have been mentally retarded since birth or childhood need and receive different forms of care and treatment. On the other hand, the term "mental defectiveness" as well as the term "mental illness" covers a wide range of mental conditions, and there is a body of opinion which considers that it would be more suitable to treat some forms of mental deficiency in the same hospitals as the milder forms of mental illness than to accommodate all types of mentally defective patients together in one hospital. It is also a fact that some diseases which affect the brain, at whatever age they occur, result in a mental condition similar to that of a person whose mind has never fully developed, and general degeneration of the mental faculties in adult life sometimes has a similar result. One of the questions on which opinions differ widely is whether the term "mentally defective" should be confined to people who are subnormal in intelligence, or whether it should also be applied, as it sometimes is at present, to some whose intelligence is normal, being near or even above average, but who show serious lack of maturity in other aspects of their personality.'

After lengthy discussion of the question the members of the Royal Commission concluded that the general class 'mental disorder' should include disability from defect as well as illness; and in the Mental Health Act which became law last year their recommendation was adopted. Of course neither Royal Commissions nor Acts of Parliament can make us use for medical purposes categories which we do not think useful and apt; but the statutory changes were in fact the response of legislators to a strong trend of informed medical opinion. The implications of this trend reach far, and I shall return to it.

The revolutions of opinion about how defect should be classified and treated derive from historical influences more extraneous to medicine than is commonly supposed. Certain of these deserve closer regard.

In the first phase social issues—such as criminal responsibility, and capacity to control one's possessions—dominated systematic consideration of the

218

nature of defect. Men stressed its kinship to the limited capacity of children to reason, to judge moral or intellectual issues, and to act appropriately. Hence came feudal claims to wardship of the land of a 'natural fool', 'purus idiota', and the definition of

'an idiote or a natural foole is he who notwithstanding he bee of lawfull age, yet he is so witless that hee can not number to twentie, nor can he tell what age he is of, nor knoweth he who is his father, or mother, nor is able to answer any such easie question.'

At the same time influences of an older date caused defectives to be credited with guileless virtue, so that 'innocent' and 'crétin' (chrétien) were considered appropriate terms for them.

As we move through the centuries towards our own time, philosophers have more and more to do with the matter. Vives, the pupil of Erasmus, developed the principle that in education the process of learning is determined not only by the subject matter to be learnt but by the nature of the learning mind. And, concerned as he therefore was to adapt methods of instruction to the peculiar needs of the learner, he became a pioneer in urging the special requirements of the mentally defective and the deaf. A century later came Locke, insisting that all knowledge derives from experience, by way of sensation and reflection, i.e. introspection—a view half accepted by Condillac, with consequences that are still discernible in our methods of treating defect. Condillac, in his famous model or myth of the animate statue endowed only with one modality of sensation, illustrated his belief that from sensations all the mental operations, including desire and abstract thought, are genetically developed: hence it followed that anyone who would educate children who are handicapped from their earliest years must foster a dual process, training them in observation and training them in reasoning.

Everybody knows how these views, and probably those of Helvetius, determined the persevering experiment by Itard 150 years ago which, misguided though it was in aim, put an end to the long era of hopelessness and neglect for the imbecile. All that has since been done, and is still being done, for the education of the mentally defective harks back to that patient application of eighteenth century philosophy.

In the nineteenth century the extraneous forces came not from philosophy but from biology: and within medicine, from morbid anatomy.

The biological mould into which current knowledge about defectives was poured was at first largely anthropological, in the spirit of Blumenbach and Prichard—and of course Gall. Interest in the size and shape of skull became intense. Medical writings on defect in the first half of the nineteenth century are cluttered with cranial measurements. Esquirol devotes six or seven pages of his textbook to considering the value of such measurements; Griesinger likewise. But little was gleaned from all this craniometry. Thomas Fuller had put the matter in a nutshell—'their heads (those of naturals) sometimes so little, that there is no room for wit; sometimes so long, that there is no wit for so much room.'

Another illegitimate offspring of biology and anthropology was the long-lasting conception of mental defect as the last or the 'atavistic' stage in the degeneracy of a stock; it was in its heyday when propounded by Morel, it passed into its decline with Langdon Down and, last of all, Cruikshank: and was deeply involved in the pedigree-haunted terrors of those who told us about the Jukes and the Kallikaks.

In this century the dominant influences upon defect have come from more dispersed fields of knowledge—from metabolic studies, from epidemiology, genetics, and—in grateful mutuality—from psychology, which owes to mental defect the incalculable impetus given by Binet's brilliant development of mental tests between 1904 and 1911 [2, 3, 4]. In our time investigation into mental defect has been responsive—sometimes weakly, sometimes strongly—to every wind that blows through medicine: witness the sizeable output of papers on the effect of 'tranquilizing' drugs upon defectives, and the little series of reports a few years ago on what prefrontal leucotomy and hemispherectomy could do for some disturbed imbeciles. The Zeitgeist seems to have been quite busy, fixing the advances, and ensuring the periods of stagnation, in this branch of psychiatry.

There is, however, one tributary to the stream of progress that has received, I think, too little attention. For the last hundred and fifty years or more it has flowed powerfully though intermittently.

This is the study of language, and particularly its application to the work of teaching deaf children to speak. There are several curious themes which intersect the mesh of this story. I do not want to go too far back, so I shall remind you only of Lord Monboddo, the forerunner of Darwin. Lord Monboddo [6] maintained that speech is not performed 'naturally', but is acquired by custom and exercise, and in support of this quoted the 'wild men who had been reported from the fourteenth century onwards'—

'I say in the first place that of all those savages which have been caught in different parts of Europe, not one had the use of speech, though they had all the organs of pronunciation such as we have them, and the understanding of a man, at least as much as was possible when it is considered that their minds were not cultivated by any kind of conversation or intercourse with their own species . . . One of these was caught in the woods of Hanover as late as the reign of George I and for anything I know is yet alive . . . He was a man in mind as well as body, as I have been informed by a person who lived for a considerable time in the neighbourhood of a farmer's house where he was kept and had an opportunity of seeing him almost every day, not an idiot, as he has been represented by some who cannot make allowance for the difference that education makes upon men's minds; yet he was not only mute when first caught, but he never learned to speak.'

Here, in 1774, we have a topic familiar in the earlier history of defect—can a 'natural' or feral man be educated; we have also the prelude to the hotly argued debate as to whether these wild men are mute and brutish because they have been brought up away from human kind, or because they have congenital mental defect. You may be wondering whether Monboddo borrowed his ideas from the French philosophers then busy with such matters. I think not. He tells us that he developed his opinions without knowledge of Condillac's views (though he later read an extract from the *Essai sur l'origine des connaissances humaines*).

Lord Monboddo clinched his argument about the origin of speech by adducing a special case:

'What puts the matter out of all doubt, in my apprehension, is the case of deaf persons among us. And their case deserves to be the more attentively considered, that they are nearly in the condition in which we suppose men to have been in the natural state. For, like them, they have the organs of pronunciation; and, like them too, they have inarticulate cries, by which they express their wants and desires. They have likewise, by constant intercourse with men who have the use of reason, and who converse with them in their way, acquired the habit of forming ideas; which we must also suppose the savage to have acquired, tho' with infinitely more labour, before he could have a language to express them. They want therefore nothing in order to speak, but instruction or example, which the savages who invented the first languages likewise wanted. In this situation, do they invent a language when they come to perfect age, as it is supposed we all should do if we had not learnt one in our infancy? Or do they ever come to speak during their whole lives? The fact most certainly is, that they never do; but continue to communicate their thoughts by looks and gestures, which we call signs, unless they be taught to articulate by an art lately invented.'

Monboddy then describes the methods used by the Abbé de l'Epée in Paris and by Braidwood in Edinburgh, and continues:

'If it had not been for this new-invented art of teaching deaf persons to speak, hardly anybody would have believed that the material or mechanical part of language was learned with so much difficulty. But if we would get an Orang Outang, or a mute savage such as he above-mentioned who was caught in the woods of Hanover, and would take the same pains to teach him to think that Mr Braidwood takes to teach his scholars to speak, we should soon be convinced that the formal part of language was as difficult to be learned as the material. For my own part, I am fully persuaded that the minds of men laboured as much as first, when they formed abstract ideas, as their organs of pronunciation did when they formed articulate sounds; and till the mind be stored with ideas, it is a perfect void, and in a kind of lethargy out of which it is roused only be external objects of sense, or calls of appetite from within. It was this want of ideas which made the Hanoverian savage pass, in the opinion of many, for an idiot.'

The parallel here with Itard's [19] reasoning in the famous case of Victor is obvious: the education of the wild or natural man is to be modelled on that of the deaf-mute. For Monboddo the exponent of how to teach the deaf is the Abbé de l'Epée; for Itard, 30 years later, it is de l'Epée's pupil and successor, the Abbé Sicard. There were, of course, conspicuous differences between Itard and Monboddo; one was a young doctor of 25, the other an elderly judge, a busy Lord of Session at Edinburgh: and whereas one was enthusiastically occupied day by day with treating deaf children at the Institution Nationale des Sourds-et-Muets, the other was able only to speculate about them and about others deprived of a normal upbringing. But the line of thought was the same, and it brought lasting benefits to the defective.

Itard's example fired Séguin, who never faltered in his admiration for the man and his achievement. And like Itard—possibly because he had been Itard's pupil—he looked back in his efforts for the defective to the principles which underlay the successful education of deaf-mutes. But it was not to the principles of de l'Epée and Sicard, but to those of their brilliant rival, Jacob Rodriguez Pereira, that he turned for guidance. Whereas de l'Epée had been content to teach the deaf to communicate by signs and finger-spelling. Pereira taught them to speak. Séguin [43] drew an analogy between Pereira's basic principles and those which had enabled Séguin himself, as he believed, to solve the problem of treating defect.

'I am not unaware that the problem of educating deaf-mutes was attacked and even solved in the last century from a wider standpoint, that of Pereira, which is strikingly analogous to that which I have used to solve the problem of treating mental defect.'

This analogy bore practical fruits in many countries. When Séguin came to this country it was to Dr Samuel G. Howe, an expert in the treatment of the deaf and the blind, as well as of the feebleminded, that he first went. In Germany, at the same time, Dr Saegert, the head of the Asylum for Deaf-Mutes in Berlin, established his school for defectives (1842). Earlier in the century Albrecht Vering in Münster, Guggenmoos in Salzburg, K. F. Kern in Möckern, and Katenkamp in Oldenburg had conducted the education of mentally defective, deaf and blind children in the same schools, on the same broad principles.

There was, it is clear, a powerful and significant transfer from the theory and practice of educating the congenitally deaf, to the training of the mentally defective. This derived from recognition of the cardinal role that language and speech play in mental activity. Esquirol said that

'what determines the peculiar character of the different varieties of defect is the use of language, that essential attribute of man, given him to express his thought: it is the feature most clearly related to intellectual capacity in defectives.'

Fifty years ago Binet and Simon endorsed Esquirol's view:

'So one can distinguish the patients according to their ability to speak or to learn to read, because these are not inherent faculties but practical attainments which depend on the energy and level of certain faculties: and that is all measurable.'

The issue still has contemporary importance. In current research, when we talk of problem-solving and thinking, we are forced to consider how words enter into the formation of concepts, and facilitate generalizations. And since even the simple operations which imbeciles can carry out, may entail the solving of a problem, we have to regard closely the defective's way of attaining concepts, and of using verbal generalization to this end.

The dependence of concepts on words was stated in its most uncompromising form by Max Müller [34].

'What we have been in the habit of calling thought is but the reverse of a coin of which the obverse is articulate sound, while the current coin is one and indivisible, neither thought nor sound but word.'

We know from studies in aphasia, such as Head carried out, and from many experimental inquiries how untenable this extreme view is. But there is much convincing evidence that words aid thinking and are for some conceptual processes indispensable—what C. E. Osgood has called the 'representation level' of organization in cognitive processes.

Vigotsky, Luria and other Soviet psychologists [45, 25, 26] have emphasized the directive and adjuvant function of speech in normal mental development. Lublinskaya [24], for example, showed that children could differentiate signals much more quickly when verbal labels were attached to them, and that differentiations thus verbally reinforced were more stable and generalized than those elaborated without it. Similarly the Iowa workers—Spiker and his colleagues [44]—have demonstrated that when a child is given a common name for a set of stimuli, or a relation name (e.g., middle-sized), he learns more quickly to generalize and discriminate in an instrumental task: assigning a verbal symbol, or label, to approved stimuli may make it more likely that a child will be able to transpose his learning to a new situation.

To determine how far this adjuvant role of words is held good for imbecile children, two of my colleages in our Research Unit [16, 17, 18, 35, 36], Dr O'Connor and Dr Hermelin, devised and carried out during the last few years a series of experiments, some of which I should like to describe very briefly, though I fear that in doing so I shall rob them of their lucidity. O'Connor and Hermelin examined Luria's hypothesis that the significant deficit shown by poor verbal capacity is not so much an aspect of defective intelligence as an inherent difficulty in making the connexion between words and motor behaviour. They found that though imbeciles (mean I.Q. 40) did not differ from normal children of the same mental age in certain tasks requiring discrimination and transposition, they were more quickly able to reverse a response previously learnt (i.e., to move, for a reward, the larger of two black squares): whereas almost all the normal children could express the principle of discrimination in words referring to size, only one of the imbeciles did so. But when the reversal experiment was repeated with a group of imbeciles who were trained to state correctly in words that they had moved the bigger square each time that they did this, and then given the trials in which they were required to move the smaller square to obtain their reward, there was no longer a significant difference between the number of times they needed before they were successful and the number needed by normal children of the same mental age. It could be concluded that verbal reinforcement had made good a deficit in the imbeciles—a deficit which in other contexts we might regard as an advantage. They forsook a learned motor habit too easily, until a word—a concept —reinforced it, or, as we might put it, until verbal self-instruction induced a 'set' which caused negative interference when the opposite choice between stimuli was imposed on the task. Their behaviour was the antithesis of that which might be shown by an obsessional or by a patient with organic cerebral disease who perseverates. It is open to several theoretical interpretations. It might be, as Luria supposes, that defectives are handicapped by a failure (in

223

Pavlovian terms) to bring the second signalling system, which operates with words, fully into intimate and regulatory relation with the system that determines motor behaviour.

But whether the interpretation be along the lines of Pavlov's or Skinner's or Osgood's theoretical formulations, it is evident that the use of verbal symbols, and especially those which refer to connexions that have meaning, is the *pons asinorum* of defectives. If they can be helped to cross that bridge they have advanced considerably and may even be on the road to a modest literacy, such as Itard struggled so hard to attain in poor Victor.

In the next experiments imbeciles learnt to transfer a verbal response (a three-letter noun) from a pictured object to its written equivalent, and then to discriminate between each of the written words and two others with one letter different. Finally when they made ten correct choices of written words in succession, the subjects were presented with the four written words and asked to say what these were, so that their 'reading score' (the number of correct responses out of a possible twelve) could be assessed. Before the experiment these imbecile children had failed to pass Burt's scholastic reading test at the four-year old level; now they learnt to read and they retained to some extent what they had learnt. They improved further in their ability to discriminate between written words after they had traced the letters of the correct word with their fingers, thereby suggesting that the relation between motor and verbal modes of behaviour may still be one of weak reciprocal aid. The simple conditioning technique used in this experiment is, of course, a familiar if old-fashioned way of teaching a child to read: here its interest lies in the demonstration of what reinforcement and practice can achieve in this domain for severely retarded children. The experiment also demonstrated that the conditioned response could be very rapidly transferred to new material, when the task was changed—a potentially important finding.

In further investigations into discrimination of written words, O'Connor and Hermelin selected 24 children of I.Q. 30-39, mean I.Q. 33·7, and having trained them to discriminate a printed word from three others (each of four or five letters) varied the size of the letters (height between 3 mm and 10 mm) in a determined sequence, to discover whether changes in size helped the defectives to learn to discriminate shape, or hindered them in this, through being mistaken for the relevant attribute of the stimulus display. The result was in keeping with G. A. Miller's [33] findings. Shape discrimination was found to be easier when alternative discriminatory features in another category of visual stimulus, size, were also offered, provided that the ,subjects had not in their first discriminatory tasks been able to rely on constant size in the letters of the cue word whenever exposed. A learning set could be established in the first stages of the experiment which worked for or against the generalization that size of letters mattered in discriminating between words.

The same investigators found that when imbeciles (I.Q. 40) had learnt to repeat a number of unrelated words, it was significantly more difficult for them to learn an equal number of familiar words which were synonyms of the first; but if a second lot of words was given, related by sound instead of by sense to those first learned (e.g., rhyming with them, as in 'heel' and 'meal'), then learning the second lot was facilitated: if the two sets of words were not connected by sound or meaning, there was neither advantage nor disadvantage from having learnt the first set. In part this conformed with the learning behaviour of normal young 'children; similarities in sound help association between words. But it also indicated—contrary to Luria's findings—that in these defectives some semantic generalization takes place, and causes interference. Moreover when O'Connor and Hermelin asked their imbecile subjects three months later to give their first associations to the words contained in the original test set, and classified the responses, it was clear that those who had in the previous experiment been given synonyms to learn now gave a majority of meaningful associations (85 per cent), whereas those who had previously had sound-connected sets to learn, or sets unconnected either by sound or meaning, showed no significant preference in their associations and did not differ materially in this respect from a control group who had not taken part in the experiment three months earlier. The tentative conclusion is that in these imbeciles training in learning semantically connected words leads to an effective 'set' which is relatively stable, and educationally valuable.

You may interrupt at this point to ask what all this has to do with the medical aspects of mental defect. Very interesting to academic psychologists, no doubt, but clinically trivial, and unpractical. To this objection I would reply that studies which throw light on the defective's ways of thinking and learning can hardly be trivial, nor, if they further his use of language, are they unpractical. Consider the three great Frenchmen whom I have already quoted: Itard [19] thought it worth his while to struggle for four years to teach Victor to speak and read: Séguin [43] asked us to picture 'the difficulty, the weariness, the exhausting, heart-breaking efforts that these experiments entail for the teacher': he is referring to the experiments in which he tried to teach the hydrocephalic defective Amedée how to articulate words distinctly, and to read them; and Alfred Binet at the end of his joint Mémoire with Simon on the intelligence of imbeciles, pleaded eloquently for experimental study of the process of thinking and especially of generalization. If a more modern justification is called for, it is surely implicit in our therapeutic aims. We want defectives to lead as happy and socially normal a life as possible. A socially normal life in literate societies presupposes, even at a low level, some education. It calls for acts of decision, and even, in very simple terms, for discrimination between words: to take a crude example, the defective going about in a modern city needs to recognize the symbols which distinguish public toilets for men from those for women, or the numerical symbols which denote the particular bus he wants to use. If he is capable of engaging in some productive occupation, his ability to connect symbols with concepts, and concepts with motor behaviour, is of social importance—though occupational adequacy is far from being the whole of social adequacy. As Sarason and Gladwin [28] have lately emphasized, our culture makes demands on learning capacity in all those, severely subnormal or not, who are trying to live in society. This is no novel view; the most cogent declaration of our duty towards defectives in this regard was made by Binet and Simon in 1907 [2]. Reviewing the pedagogic and other reasons for retaining in special schools what they call verbal work, alongside the concrete manual tasks, they said:

'These reasons apply particularly to the school. There are other reasons, social reasons, which are still more imperious. Nowadays, especially in towns, it is necessary that people should be able to read, write, count and express themselves appropriately. It has been rightly pointed out that reading is the triumph of abstraction and that a defective may take two years to learn to spell words out even at the most modest level: never mind, if the thing is possible, with however great an effort, that defective ought to learn to read. What matters is not the level of his intelligence, but his social status, and there he will suffer if he is illiterate. In questions of this sort, psychological and educational indications should give way to the demands of ordinary life; necessity decides it.'

The indications of psychology and education now point in the same direction as the demands of daily life.

It would be appropriate here to turn aside from imbeciles, so limited in their capacity to learn and think, in order to consider the social adequacy of that much larger group, the high-grade defectives. But before looking at this tangled issue I should like to refer, cursorily, to other studies of imbeciles carried out by members of our Unit—studies that are complementary to those I have been describing. They examined particularly the effects of motive upon performance, in its social bearings.

In a series of laboratory and workshop investigations [8, 12, 13, 23] they demonstrated that the performance of imbeciles who had been given an external incentive improved significantly, when compared with that of a control group of imbeciles, in a variety of motor tests; moreover the imbeciles acquired a skill—folding cardboard boxes—which improved strikingly when the social conditions in the workshop approximated to normal, in that each imbecile worked alongside a high-grade defective who did the preparatory glueing and the two boys constituted a working unit; they could readily see their joint work and in most cases took pride in their attainment; this was true even of patients with an I.Q. of only 20 or so. Further experiments by Clarke and Hermelin [9] (which preceded Hermelin's studies of concept formation) showed that incentives act differently, as might be expected, upon imbeciles of diverse personalities: but an appropriate incentive brought the patients to the point at which they could perform repetitive tasks, of the sort industry requires, as well as high-grade defectives could. The imbeciles could thereafter partly support themselves through the payment they received, for work that gave them pleasure and satisfaction.

Since personality and personal relationships have been experimentally shown to have an effect upon the level which imbeciles can attain, we thought it desirable to examine the differences between severely subnormal children who remain in their families and those who have been committed to institutional care. In the ensuing survey by Grad and Tizard [14], there were 150 families with an idiot or imbecile living at home and 100 families with a similar defective child who had been in an institution for between one and 5 years. The children and their families differed in many respects, inevitably: and it is impossible to review briefly here the social and psychological characteristics of these two groups. The occupational data, however, bore out the experimental findings that there are considerable differences in the abilities of imbeciles which can not be attributed to differences in level of intelligence. A low intelligence score did not represent as severe a handicap as did a concomitant physical defect. Physical disabilities were, of course, common: half the patients, both those in the institution and those at home, had such disabilities, especially cerebral palsy and epilepsy. Gross multiple handicaps of this sort were, however, more frequent among the institutional patients. Although there were some almost untrainable and unemployable patients, burdened with an accumulation of defects, it seemed that with suitable training at least 10 to 20 per cent of imbeciles can be employed in useful remunerative work, provided there are economic conditions of full employment, and satisfactory care for them at home or in a hostel.

Defects of temperament were among the handicaps many of these imbeciles exhibited: some were restless and excitable, others torpid and apathetic. Among the 150 imbeciles over the age of 16 in this investigation, 13 per cent were judged to be over-active or almost uncontrollable, and 28 per cent sluggish and inactive, but of course these summary epithets do not convey the varied anomalies of personality. The investigation cast light, sometimes heartening and sometimes disconcerting, upon the interaction between doctors and welfare or other workers, on one hand, and the severely subnormal patients and their parents on the other. The social issues raised here were complex and crucial.

It is at this point that a British psychiatrist tends to leave the comparatively pure air of the field study and the experimental workshop for a sultrier atmosphere in which there is much contention about notions of sociopathy, and about enactments that seem to darken counsel. For in our recent Mental Health Act [29]—admirable in so many respects—there are, as I have mentioned already, some definitions which trail clouds of dubious nosology behind them. Please forgive me for saying more about them than I would if they bespoke only a national idiosyncrasy. I believe they reflect ideas about the nature of defect which are widespread and which are crowned with the nimbus of such adjectives as 'progressive', and 'dynamic'. I am not sure they deserve these epithets.

The new Act banished the term 'mental deficiency': henceforth officialdom does not know this category, it has been swept away to the limbo where 'idiocy' and 'insanity' and 'asylum' lie, waiting no doubt for the euphemisms that for the present have supplanted them. According to the Act the generic term 'mental disorder' is extended to include 'arrested or incomplete development of mind'. Three classes of mental disorder are defined—subnormality, severe subnormality and psychopathic disorder. So far so good: the decay that afflicts any word referring to an unpleasant reality has overtaken 'mental deficiency'; and Parliament and the World Health Organization urge us to say 'subnormality' instead—no great hardship. But there is another term defined in the Act—'psychopathic disorder'. The definition runs:

'a persistent disorder or disability of mind (whether or not including subnormality of intelligence) which results in abnormally aggressive or seriously irresponsible conduct on the part of the patient, and requires or is susceptible to medical treatment.'

This harks back to the recommendation of the Royal Commission, two years earlier, proposing that high-grade defectives and psychopaths

'should be recognised as together constituting one main group of mentally disordered patients, the other two groups being the mentally ill and severely subnormal.'

It is, of course, in keeping with the strong trend, both in Britain and in the United States, to shift the emphasis in high-grade defect (or retardation) from intelligence alone to other features of personality, to minimise inherited as against environmental causes, and to use as a main criterion of such defect social maladjustment and emotional insufficiency. This standpoint has much in common with the current view, expressed by Masland, Sarason and Gladwin [28] that

'cultural and environmental factors . . . through the establishment of unhealthy or inadequate patterns of intellectual response, may prevent the optimum function of the mind in a person whose nervous system is basically capable of normal activity [and that] "within certain broad limits one can distinguish those mentally subnormal individuals whose disability is attributable primarily to a demonstrable defect of brain structure or chemistry from those whose malformation is the result of hearing deficiencies resulting from unfavourable environmental influences.'

The advantages of this way of looking at the matter are manifest, but it is sometimes pushed so far that intelligence, about which we know a great deal, is played down in favour of emotional development and social fitness, about which, on the whole, we still know little. The approach can be a stimulating one for research, but over-zealously adopted it could have a retrograde effect upon administrative and clinical practice, in which the new legislation adjures us to follow it.

The distinction I am drawing is perhaps too sharp: scholastic and intelligence test performance is still the main criterion of diagnosis for subcultural defect or feeblemindedness, but the auguries point to its supersession. The *Manual on Terminology* [1] recently published by the American Association for Mental Deficiency lays it down that mental retardation is

'subaverage general intellectual functioning which originates during the developmental period and is associated with impairment in one or more of the following: (1) maturation, (2) learning, and (3) social adjustment [and states that] "social adjustment is particularly important as a qualifying condition for mental retardation at the adult level, where it is assessed in terms of the degree to which the individual is able to maintain himself independently in the community and in a gainful employment as well as by his ability to meet and conform to other personal and social responsibilities and standards set by the community.'

To use such concepts as these for purposes of research will be an arduous and slippery business. What its consequences might be when applied in epidemiological inquiries can be inferred from the instructive findings reported in the thorough and valuable Onondaga County Study. Dr Gruenberg and his colleagues [11] found that standards vary strangely, such factors as colour of skin and place of residence affected the ascertainment of children judged to be mentally retarded; mental retardation, Dr Gruenberg concluded, is 'a complex set of manifestations of some children's relationship with their immediate environment'. This is true, but such complexity cries out for heuristic simplification: otherwise confusion threatens. The conscientious inquiries into the effect of cultural background on the diagnosis of retardation which are reviewed in Sarason and Gladwin's comprehensive report seem to indicate that in this area

> 'Chaos Umpire sits
> And by decision more embroils the fray
> By which he reigns.'

While we struggle in this darksome realm, it is hazardous to put our trust in shifting semblances: or, to be more explicit, in social and emotional indices that vary with the observer and, more disconcerting still, vary with the environment. In her trenchant critique of psychiatric findings, which pillories many a lapse from logical and scientific rectitude, Barbara Wootton [48], herself a sociologist, takes up this weakness, states it in a clear proposition and explores its corollaries. Recognizing that mental defect tends increasingly, in Great Britain at any rate, to be diagnosed, not by an intellectual test but by the defective's inability to accommodate himself to the demands of a highly industrial society, she takes the next step—which is to recognize that

'if, as may be supposed, the capacity for social adjustment conforms to a more or less normal pattern of distribution, the cut-off point at which this defectiveness is held to be established must depend upon how exacting this demand for adjustment happens to be.'

so that it can come about that the criterion of defect may depend upon such completely adventitious factors as the state of the employment market.

'In a less sophisticated age we should have said that one of the merits of full employment was that it made it easier for mental defectives to obtain employment. Now apparently we have to say that it actually reduces the number of such defectives. To appreciate the full significance of this situation we may imagine what would happen if similar reasoning were applied to the analogous case of some incontestable physical disability, such as the loss of a limb. Full employment certainly makes it easier for legless persons to get jobs, but no one in his senses would take this to mean that under full employment there are fewer persons without legs. Similarily full employment makes it easier for ex-prisoners to get jobs; but that is not to say that full employment diminishes the number of ex-prisoners, as distinct from the number who are able to get employment. Such statements would be manifestly absurd; but their absurdity well illustrates the difference between a disability which is established by a criterion that is, and one established by a criterion that is not independent of current standards of social competence.'

And, Lady Wootton adds,

'so long as defectives are subject, as they are, to legal and other disabilities, the significance of this difference is much more than semantic. If defectives are deprived of full civic rights and responsibilities, and even in some cases of their personal freedom, and if the number of defectives varies with the state of the employment market, it follows that some people are liable to lose their status as fully responsible citizens or to be deprived of their liberty, merely because employment is bad.'

Lady Wootton's argument, thus lucidly stated, seems cogent. I say seems, for we psychiatrists, subtle-minded students of complexity that we are, distrust lucid arguments: convincing syllogisms, we suspect, are superficial, and what seems obvious is probably incomplete and over-simple. But surely in this instance we must concede something to the criticism: and we must admit that if we fall in with the tendency now to equate 'high-grade defect' with 'psychopathic personality' because of the relativity of the two concepts and their essential dependence on some standard of social competence or adjustment, it will widen unduly the social door of entry into a traditionally medical category. In Tredgold's well-known textbook of *Mental Deficiency* [45], we may read that

'it is probable that if the real nature of mental defect were more generally appreciated many, although not all of those who are called psychopathic personalities would be found to be certifiable under the Mental Deficiency Acts.'

Such an affirmation raises issues which far transcend the apparently diagnostic and semantic questions. It is pleasanter to consider Jastak and Whiteman's [20] conclusion that

'the retarded do not impose a disproportionate load upon community resources either in the form of legal infractions or excessive demands for social services . . . mental subnormality, it appears, need not connote an inability to fill an acceptable social role.'

I would like here to underline the distinction between social criteria, and social determinants, of defect. Nothing I have been saying is intended to minimize the manifest importance of the social factor nor the potency of emotional pressures and twists. Quite the opposite. A large part of the studies in defect by our Research Unit has been directed toward the social problem, as the title of O'Connor and Tizard's book [37] made clear. And as for the role of emotion, I would recall a passage from *Leviathan*

' Naturall wit consisteth principally in two things: celerity of imagining . . . and steady direction to some approved end. On the contrary a slow imagination maketh that defect, or fault of the mind, which is commonly called dullness, stupidity . . . And this difference of quickness is caused by the difference of men's Passions . . . And the difference of Passions proceedeth partly from the different Constitution of the body, and partly from different Education.'

It was the same Thomas Hobbes who said 'The Light of humane minds is Perspicuous Words.' In the psychiatry of defect our words will become perspicuous and the concepts they denote illuminating only if we probe further into how constitution, education, environment and emotion determine those differences of intelligence which Hobbes thought fundamental between man and man.

And so I finally come to causes. In psychiatry we seldom distinguish sharply between etiology and pathology; and in the network of preceding events it is profitless to insist on a strict hierarchy of causes, epidemiological, psychological, clinical and the rest. It is, however, plain that in the whole area of defect prospectors equipped with new tools can hope to 'strike it rich'. The vein has already been opened by metabolic studies, and by the genetic investigations that have revealed peculiarities in chromosome formation in mongolism— both, as Linus Pauling [40] lately reminded us, matters of molecular structure about which knowledge is decidedly on the move.

What is known and what is inferred about the etiology of defect has been critically reviewed within the last year or so by Professor MacMahon as well as by Dr Masland [27, 28]. Their masterly surveys make detailed consideration by anyone else superfluous for the present. However, among the diverse studies I should like to single out for reference those of Professor Pasamanick and Dr Knobloch and their associates [21, 22, 38], because of the care with which their data have been collected and analysed and because of the attractive explanatory hypotheses they offer. I need not recapitulate to this audience the arduous investigations through which they believe they have demonstrated that disturbance in the circumstances of pregnancy and birth can bring about a continuum of cerebrogenic anomalies, manifest as disorders of behaviour, reading difficulties, tics, defect of varying degrees, cerebral palsy, and epilepsy. The complications of pregnancy (such as toxaemia and bleeding), dietary inadequacy in the mother during the months of pregnancy, abnormal delivery, and premature birth were judged responsible for sub-lethal (as well as lethal) misfortune to the child. Mental retardation, according to their findings, is conspicuous among the sub-lethal consequences that may ensue when the reproductive process is deflected from its normal course. If retardation is accompanied by physical evidence of neurological damage, a relation of cause and effect is habitually and widely accepted, at any rate so far as perinatal damage is concerned: but the challenging conclusion of Knobloch and Pasamanick urges us to consider that lesser degrees of prenatal and perinatal cerebral damage may produce defects unaccompanied by detectable neurological signs, defects which are commonly attributed to heredity and post-natal influences. The body of evidence they have produced as warranty for these conclusions is impressive; and some of their more specific hypotheses are provocative, especially that which connects insufficient diet—perhaps of protein—during the critical early months of pregnancy with mental retardation in the child. Still more provocative are some recent developments of Pasamanick's views. Incorporating his continuum of reproductive casualty with Locke's and

Helvetius's *tabula rasa*, he supposes that men are conceived equal in intellect (apart from a few who inherit neurological defects), and that it is exogenous brain damage, 'life experience and the socio-cultural milieu influencing biological and psychological function', that make us differ one from another. This rather egalitarian hypothesis would exalt the power of environmental influences high above their wonted credit: if it proves correct—and no one can call it incorrect who has not examined with equal care Pasamanick's evidence and the contrary evidence which speaks for polygenic inheritance as the main determinant of human differences in mental ability—then the possibilities that open out do not merely concern the prevention of defect and other ills, but the raising of normal human capacity throughout the population. This would afford yet another instance of the wheel turning full circle. When Séguin devoted himself to experiments in educating idiots and imbeciles, he arrived at principles which had a larger scope than his medical obligations towards the defective. At the end of his book he wrote:

'But if by a turn of the wheel, in compensation as it were, it happened that the solution of a very small problem brought with it the solution of a very general one; if it happened that while working away to settle the modest question of how defectives should be educated, one had found a formula precise enough to be applicable to education generally . . . then not only would one have rendered some service in a relatively humble sphere, but one would have laid the basis for a scientific method of education.'

It is unlikely that Pasamanick shares all the St Simonian optimism of Séguin: but in such experiments in preventing defect as he now advocates, lies much hope of illumination.

Few of us psychiatrists can have a clear conscience about mental defect. We have given it less attention than it required, and research has only belatedly concentrated on the pitiful and involved problems which it thrusts upon the clinician's notice. Now that much serious inquiry is in progress, it seemed fitting that the Adolf Meyer Lecture should be devoted to a cursory glance into this large area of research and action. I have not tried to do in one lecture what 21 notable contributors aimed at accomplishing in the Woods School Conference [47] last year. Their survey and the current list of projects supported by your Department of Health, Education and Welfare show that the vineyard calls for diverse labourers to cultivate it in many places. I have referred to some work of which I have immediate knowledge, and to studies which illustrate the close interplay between developments occurring outside medicine and certain kinds of research that have been fruitfully prosecuted to elucidate and control defect. The work now in hand is inspiriting. It looks as if future lecturers who choose this theme may have a rich harvest to report.

REFERENCES

1 AMERICAN ASSOCIATION FOR MENTAL DEFICIENCY. *A Manual on Terminology and Classification in Mental Retardation* (ed. Heber), Am. J. Ment. Def. Monograph Supplement, September 1959.

2 BINET, A. and SIMON, T. *Les Enfants Anormaux*, Paris, Armand Colin, 1907.
3 BINET, A. and SIMON, T. *Ann. Psychol.*, 1909, **15**, 1.
4 BINET, A. and SIMON, T. 'L'arriération', *Ann. Psychol.*, 1910, **16**, 349.
5 BOOK, J. 'Genetical etiology in mental illness', in *Recent Progress in the Epidemiology of Mental Disorder*, Millbank Memorial Fund, N. Y. (in press).
6 BURNETT, J. (Lord Monboddo). *Of the Origin and Progress of Language*, vol. 1, 2nd ed., Edinburgh, Balfour, 1774.
7 CARTER, C. O., *J. Ment. Def. Res.*, 1958, **2**, 64.
8 CLARIDGE, G. and O'CONNOR, N. *J. Ment. Def. Res.*, 1957, **1**, 16.
9 CLARKE, A. D. B. and HERMELIN, B. *Lancet*, 1955, **337**, 2.
10 ESQUIROL, E. *Des Maladies Mentales*, Brussels, 1838.
11 GOODMAN, M. B., GRUENBERG, E. M., DOWNING, J. J. and ROGOT, E. *Am. J. Publ. Hlth.*, 1956, **46**, 702.
12 GORDON, S., O'CONNOR, N. and TIZARD, J. *Brit. J. Psychol.*, 1954, **45**, 277.
13 GORDON, S., O'CONNOR, N. and TIZARD, J. *Am. J. Ment. Def.*, 1955, **60**, 371.
14 GRAD, J. and TIZARD, J. *The Mentally Handicapped and Their Families*, Maudsley Monograph Series, London, Oxford University Press (in press).
15 GROUP FOR THE ADVANCEMENT OF PSYCHIATRY. *Basic Considerations in Mental Retardation: A Preliminary Report*, Report No. 43, N.Y., 1959.
16 HERMELIN, B. 'Concept learning and verbalisation in imbeciles', University of London, Ph.D. Thesis, 1958.
17 HERMELIN, B. and O'CONNOR, N. *J. Ment. Def. Res.*, 1958, **2**, 21.
18 HERMELIN, B. and O'CONNOR, N. *Qu. J. Exper. Psychol.*, 1960, **12**, 48.
19 ITARD, J. M. G. *Rapports et mémoires sur le sauvage de l'Aveyron: L'idiotié et la surdi-mutité*, Paris, Progrès Médical, Bibliothèque d'Education Spéciale, 1824.
20 JASTAK, J. F. and WHITEMAN, M. 'Prevalence of mental retardation in Delaware', in *Nature and Transmission of Genetic and Cultural Characteristics*, Millbank Memorial Fund, N.Y., 1957.
21 KNOBLOCH, H. and PASAMANICK, B. 'Distribution of intellectual potential in an infant population', in *Epidemiology of Mental Disorder*, Washington, Am. Ass. Adv. Sci., 1959.
22 KNOBLOCH, H. and PASAMANICK, B. *J. Am. Med. Ass.*, 1959, **170**, 1384.
23 LOOS, F. M. and TIZARD, J. *Am. J. Ment. Def.*, 1955, **59**, 395.
24 LUBLINSKAYA, A. A. 'The role of the word in the development of the child's cognitive activity', in *Psychology in the Soviet Union* (ed. B. Simon), London, Kegan Paul, 1957.
25 LURIA, A. R. *J. Ment. Def. Res.*, 1959, **3**, 1.
26 LURIA, A. R. and YUDOVICH, F. I. *Speech and the Development of Mental Processes in the Child*, (ed. J. Simon), London, Staples Press, 1959.
27 MACMAHON, B. 'Physical damage to the fetus', in *Recent Progress in the Epidemiology of Mental Disorder*, Millbank Memorial Fund, N.Y. (in press).
28 MASLAND, R. L., SARASON, S. B. and GLADWIN, T. *Mental Subnormality*, N.Y., Basic Books, 1958.
29 *Mental Health Act*, London, H.M.S.O., 1959.
30 MERTON, R. K., READER, G. and KENDALL, P. C. *The Student Physician*, Cambridge, Harvard U.P. for Commonwealth Fund, 1957.
31 MEYER, A. *Ment. Hyg.*, 1925, **9**, 673.
32 MEYER, A. *Psychobiology* (ed. E. A. Winters and A. M. Bowers), Springfield, Thomas, 1957.
33 MILLER, G. A. *Psychol. Rev.*, 1956, **63**, 81.
34 MULLER, M. *The Science of Thought*, vol. 2, N.Y., 1887.
35 O'CONNOR, N. and HERMELIN, B. *Speech and Language*, 1959, **2**, 63.
36 O'CONNOR, N. and HERMELIN, B. *J. Ab. Soc. Psychol.*, 1959, **59**, 409.

37 O'CONNOR, N. and TIZARD, J. *The Social Problem of Mental Deficiency*, London, Pergamon Press, 1956.

38 PASAMANICK, B. *Am. J. Ment. Def.*, 1959, **64**, 316.

39 PASAMANICK, B. and RETTIG, S. *Arch. Neurol. Psychiat*, **81**, 1959, 399.

40 PAULING, L. *Am. J. Orthopsychiat*, 1959, **29**, 685.

41 PINEL, P. *Traité Médico-Philosophique sur L'Aliénation Mentale*, Paris, Brosson, 1809.

42 ROYAL COMMISSION ON THE LAW RELATING TO MENTAL ILLNESS and MENTAL DEFICIENCY, 1954–1957. *Report*, London, H.M.S.O., 1957.

43 SÉGUIN, E. *Traitement morale hygiène et éducation des idiotes et des autres enfants arriérés*, Paris, Baillière, 1846.

44 SPIKER, C., GERYNOY, J. R. and SHEPARD, W. O. *J. Occup. Psychol.*, 1956, **79**, 416.

45 TREDGOLD, A. F. *A Textbook of Mental Deficiency*, 9th ed., London, Baillière, Tindall and Cox, 1956.

46 VIGOTSKY, L. S. *Psychiatry*, 1939, **2**, 54.

47 WOODS SCHOOL CONFERENCE. 'Approaches to research in mental retardation', *Am. J. Ment. Def.*, 1959, **64**, 227.

48 WOOTTON, B. *Social Science and Social Pathology*, London, Allen and Unwin, 1959.

15

AGENTS OF CULTURAL ADVANCE

THE HONOUR of delivering this lecture has not previously been bestowed on a psychiatrist. The reason may well have been L. T. Hobhouse's [1] known disapproval of those psychiatrists who tend to claim too large a kingdom for their science. He deplored such pretensions: 'people cannot even make discoveries —quite real and genuine discoveries—in morbid psychology without attempting to annex the whole realm of mind in their name'. I shall try to be more modest than the men he had in mind, but you will understand that I approach my task with more disquiet than a sense of personal inadequacy would alone account for.

My theme concerns two ill-defined concepts, 'culture' and 'advance'.

The culture of a given society I take to be the sum total of persisting values, ideas, and other symbolic systems that shape the patterns of behaviour. It has continuity, it is accumulated and transmitted: it is expressed in, and may dictate and enforce, patterns of social behaviour which the members of that society learn. It includes tangible tools and evidences of a mode of living, as well as institutions and codes, complexly interwoven. Into this cultural scheme new or extraneous ideas will normally be received and embodied only if they fit, or can be made to fit, into the pre-existing main pattern. Nevertheless in times of catastrophe or dire threat, utterly strange ideas, practices, or institutions may be accepted and perhaps incorporated, with resultant changes throughout the whole culture designed to make it an internally harmonious one again. An ideology may fight its way into an alien culture and transform it. There are thousands of distinct cultures in the world today: culture must be plastic to attain such diversity. It would seem that the tendency of any culture is to resist change, but that everywhere cultures are forced to change. Perhaps that is too loosely stated: what I mean is that the tendency of men organized in a social group is to resist change in their culture, but that everywhere they have had to make or accept changes and accommodate their culture to them.

This paper was read as the thirtieth L. T. Hobhouse Memorial Trust Lecture at University College London in April 1960. It was first published in booklet form by the Oxford University Press, 1961.

But cultural changes are not necessarily for the better. Whether they are advances, will be a matter of judgment: advance is a concept drenched in values, many-faced, constantly subject to revision. What in one aspect of a cultural change is applauded, in another is deplored. Of one of the great movements of change, Professor Polanyi [2] lately said: 'So it came about that the *philosophes* not only failed to establish an age of quiet enjoyment, but induced instead a violent tide of secular dynamism. And that while this tide was to spread many benefits to humanity, nobler than any that the *philosophes* had ever aimed at, it also degenerated in many places into a fanaticism fiercer than the religious furies which their teachings had appeased.' Whether the revolution to which he thus refers was a cultural surge forward is a question to which the answer cannot be a simple 'Yes'.

I shall not attempt to examine the familiar difficulties inherent in the idea of progress, so battered by some of the events of this century, nor presume to set one kind of progress above other kinds, as when intellectual and moral or economic and aesthetic progress are arranged in a hierarchy of approval. The nature of social development is a problem which Hobhouse [1] treated exhaustively, at a time when it was easier to be confident that 'unless some break of tradition is brought about by a catastrophe like war, the constant activity of mind operating through the tradition secures a slow but steady progress'. Still valid is the emphasis he put on mental activity as the fountain and origin of progress: 'the connexion between intellectual and social development is rough and indirect, but real and far-reaching': and he put forcibly the view 'which sees no cause of progress except in the human mind and will'.

It might be proposed that since cultural change is a response to changing external conditions or pressure, it represents an advance when the society in question succeeds in adjusting itself to these external conditions and reattains stability. This is commonly true, but has to be qualified: cultural change can be produced from within as well as from without; its new and stable form may express a less happy, less productive state of society; and the struggle of adaptation may have produced a social desert and called it peace.

The most acceptable criteria that have been laid down for cultural advance are three: first, it should satisfy the healthy psychological and physical needs of the individuals composing the society, more than did the culture it grew out of or replaced; secondly, it should promote to a higher degree the integration and stability of the society; and thirdly, it should favour collective survival more. This is the evolutionary view. It has, on the whole, less general acceptance than when Hobhouse powerfully examined and expounded it. Between processes of organic evolution and the social variations brought about by men's thought and conscious effort the differences are too profound for the biological concept to be used confidently to explain all the comparatively rapid changes through which society has passed. Nevertheless the broad notions of adaptive differentiation and of 'fitness' as capacity to survive in relative independence of the environment, serve as something more than analogies.

236

In applying them to cultural advance, emphasis can be put on the physical, material side of the matter, or on the psychological, spiritual side. The disparity between the two is notorious. We can point to the steadily greater command acquired over the world we live in, the growing technical mastery which makes men more and more independent of the immediate conditions of their environment; but can we—with confidence—point to moral, aesthetic, imaginative, and intellectual power distributed more widely, heightened in intensity, and cultivated more generously throughout society: or to greater control of the relations between people which would favour survival and stability?

'Excelsior' seems a mocking device on the cultural banner nowadays, and we may jib at distributing badges of cultural advance to highly organized, contemporary societies because of their achievements and physical control of their environment. But cultural advance need not be, and indeed seldom has been, all of a piece. Moral advance may have outstripped intellectual, or aesthetic may be ahead of technical advance. There may be, at a given period, retrocession and decadence in one direction, while brilliant progress is evident in another. 'The cultures of wider span may show some looseness and lack of unity.' On the whole, however, many vigorous and resourceful societies show a cultural outline, or profile, which, though uneven, is without recurring plunges from peak to trough.

Cultural advance, as many anthropologists have regarded it, derives from the need to adapt to environmental pressures and opportunities: and the resistance to it comes from the viscous minds of the multitude who like to stick together, to adhere to familiar ideas and practices, and to flow, if flow they must, along a sluggish track into another pool. But this antithesis between external pressures and resistances in men's minds is obviously too crude. It ignores the complexity of the relationship between the chosen environment and the men who choose it, or between the inescapable environment and the men who have through the generations learnt how to survive in it; between the adventuring minds which bring fresh developments in the culture and the steady toiling minds which prepare the way for new ideas and consolidate and integrate them.

I shall be very brief in what I say about the environmental pressures. They are the substance of the materialist theory of history. The means of subsistence, climatic conditions, the ecological balance, contact with other societies, and the changing physical milieu brought about by scientific and technical advances in communication, range of movement, and control of energy—all these conditions undeniably influence the culture of a particular society in a given place and time. If they were outside human control, and men were everywhere obliged to adapt to their unalterable surroundings or die out, it would be permissible to concede to the environment as dominant a cultural role as it seems to have, say, among Eskimos and in Tierra del Fuego. But this is plainly not so. We may, then, acknowledge the immensely important influence of environmental conditions, without supposing that they are responsible for those spurts and near-miracles which have occurred in the cultural history of many recorded societies.

The impulses to change that come from within the society are sometimes attributed to exceptional individuals—the Great Men conception of cultural initiative. This conception has been much disparaged, and is not what it was in Carlyle's day, or Nietzsche's: but it persists. Its persistence is due, I think, to its having some truth in it. But it ignores the contributions to cultural advance that are made by men of lesser capacity, who are not conspicuous innovators, creative artists, and thinkers. And it ignores the social factors that enforce or condition cultural changes.

An exceptional individual is, *ex vi termini*, abnormal in significant respects. One of the most distinguished historians of science, George Sarton, put this simply when he wrote [3]:

'The men who clinched the great [scientific] discoveries, who made or seemed to make the gigantic steps upward, were most of them outstanding personalities in their own right, not simply conspicuous or lucky men. Between their work and that of other scientists who were responsible for the smaller steps, there was in general not simply a difference in degree but also in nature. To put it as briefly as possible, the greater steps were generally synthetic, the smaller ones analytic. And for this reason also the history of science of the extreme biographical type and very simplified is not wrong, or at any rate is far less distant from the truth than would be a political history under the same circumstances.'

In thus identifying scientific achievements and their main architects, Sarton begs a question to which I shall come presently: but he is in agreement with many other historians of science in attributing exceptional influence, and qualities, to certain men who (as Butterfield says of Descartes) sprawl over their century.

Of course there have been many who dissent violently from the view that intellectual, moral, and political or social progress is due to a relatively small number of outstanding men. Herbert Spencer is, I suppose, typical of these dissenters. But in his bitter attack on the 'great-men theory of history' he made two significant points: (1) 'if it be a fact that the great man may modify his nation in its structure and actions, it is also a fact that there must have been those antecedent modifications constituting national progress before he could be evolved; before he can remake his society, his society must make him'. And (2) 'he is powerless in the absence of the material and mental accumulations which his society inherits from the past'. These two considerations concede the power of the exceptional man to shape and change society, but make all this dependent on the cultural state into which he was born. And Spencer (like Tolstoy in his famous Second Epilogue) finds his most telling arguments and illustrations in political leaders rather than in scientists and artists, in the fluctuations of national rise and decline rather than in literature and discovery.

This distinction accounts for much of the debate between the 'great-man' upholders and those who invoke the *Zeitgeist* or the social dynamic. It is a distinction often made in the past. Hume, you will remember, drew a sharp

238

division between soldiers, statesmen, and monarchs on the one hand, whom he regarded as mediocre figures, creatures of chance and opportunity, and, on the other hand, men who could shine in natural philosophy, poetry, and 'the higher parts of learning'.

'Were we [he wrote] to distinguish the ranks of men by their genius and capacity, more than by their virtue and usefulness to the public, great philosophers would certainly challenge the first rank, and must be placed at the top of mankind. So rare is this character that perhaps there has not as yet been above two in the world who can lay a just claim to it. At least, Galileo and Newton seem to me so far to excel all the rest, that I cannot admit any other into the same class with them. Great poets may challenge the second place; and this species of genius, though rare, is yet much more frequent than the former.' [4]

For him truly great men were relatively independent of their environment, the men of action very dependent on it.

More recent writers on the same theme have attempted to distinguish between the scientists on the one hand and the poets, musicians, and artists on the other; and have searched for differences between the two groups in their hereditary endowment, their personality, their modes of thought, the circumstances of their lives, and the cultural situation in which they developed. The problems raised invite speculation, reinforced by telling instances: but systematic attempts to solve them by psychological and social studies have had only limited success. They compel reflection about the relationship between abnormality that consists in outstanding achievement, and abnormality that we classify as mental disorder. Before considering this I should like to refer briefly to the conditions that seem to attend powerful contributions to cultural advance.

The individuals who have made these contributions have mostly been characterized by high and precocious intelligence, persistence of motive and effort, confidence in their own abilities, and 'force of character'. They have in many instances combined Don Quixote with Sancho Panza—rich in fancy, but severe and down to earth in checking and appraising its fruits. Their upbringing has included early encouragement, intensive instruction, liberal facilities for reading, and exposure to other means of stimulating and exercising their growing powers, teachers who were of such capacity and personality that they excited emulation or discipleship in the student, and the opportunity of intimate communication with others of like mind.

The cultures within which these individuals developed had no common pattern. The social heritage and the biological heritage of each society interact to produce extremely varied cultural states which may be propitious to the flowering of individual genius. Some forms of achievement, especially in science and invention, may depend on what has already been attained in a culture; others, such as the mathematical, may evidently be the expression of exceptional biological endowment. The contrast, however, is specious. Scientists, for instance, may be great mathematicians; exceptional mathematical abilities may be associated with equally exceptional linguistic gifts or

239

powers of memory; and no analysis of social conditions in relation to cultural progress has succeeded, in my view, in demonstrating what happy conjunction brings together the man and the culture that can combine to effect an advance. This is indeed the view of the most erudite of the historians of science [3].

'It is not possible to explain why a discovery was made by this man rather than by another, in Denmark rather than Italy, and strangest of all, at this time rather than a little earlier or a little later. To be sure there is a certain determinism in the sequence of discoveries, the best proof of this being the not uncommon occurrence of simultaneous ones. Yet this is only true in a rough way. Some discoveries are made too early, others are unaccountably delayed; their logical order is often reversed and their gradual adjustment and integration is sometimes very capricious. Why was the discovery of the circulation of the blood completed by an English physician and why was it deferred until the seventeenth century? External circumstances do not provide more than a part of the explanation, generally a small one.'

Neither, one must add, do internal circumstances, as Freud sadly acknowledged.

A considerable step, however, in the direction of systematic inquiry into the social conditions that favour scientific progress has been taken during the last three decades. An example of this is Robert K. Merton's well-known study [5] of the relation between the rise of science in seventeenth-century England and the Puritan ethos. Influenced primarily by Max Weber's studies of the connexion between the Protestant ethic and the rise of capitalism, Merton inquired into the reciprocal interplay of scientific activity with Calvinism, economic growth, technological development, the search for new means of transportation and communication, increase of population, and other social factors. The chief motive force, according to Merton's analysis, lay in the Calvinist spirit: the spirit of diligence, asceticism for the sake of this world, and 'seeing God in his works' which has been so vividly described by Tawney in a related context: 'The Puritan flings himself into practical activities with the daemonic energy of one who, all doubts allayed, is conscious that he is a sealed and chosen vessel. Once engaged in affairs, he brings to them both the qualities and limitations of his creed, in all their remorseless logic. . . . He has within himself a principle at once of energy and of order which makes him irresistible. . . .' This attitude Merton discerned plainly evident in the writings of such men as Boyle, Newton, and Ray—though of course the effect had not been intended by those who formulated the ethos (for example, Calvin); it became secularized with the passage of time, and specific discoveries aroused the antagonism of theologians. To test his hypothesis further, Merton examined the religious background of those in eighteenth-century Europe who contributed most to scientific progress. In the founders of the Royal Society in England and of the Pietistic Universities in Germany (Halle, Heidelberg, Königsberg), as well as in the promoters of a utilitarian, empirical type of education (Comenius, Locke), he detected support for his conclusion that Protestants constituted proportionately the overwhelming majority of the leading scientists in Europe. Whether Merton's conclusion is sustained or not, his inquiry, which was as systematic as the available material permitted, opened fresh territory in that he applied the methods of sociology and social history to the problem. Other studies of this kind, as by Knapp and Goodrich (origins of American scientists), C. C. Gillispie (genesis and geology), Ogburn, and Barber, also bespeak a more rigorous approach to the sociology of scientific advance. It serves to test the generalizations of historians and to establish more precise relationships between social conditions and cultural development. It may be hoped, for instance, that it will permit a more detailed restatement of Butterfield's view [6] that the scientific revolution was a

'creative product of the West—depending on a complicated set of conditions which existed only in Western Europe, depending partly also perhaps on a certain dynamic quality in the life and history of this half of the continent. And not only was a new factor introduced into history at this time amongst other factors, but it proved to be so capable of growth, and so many-sided in its operations, that it consciously assumed a directing role from the very first. . . .'

The language in which other historians seek to relate the dynamic of great artistic, religious, political, and literary creations to social conditions is similarly general and imprecise—or more so: and here too sociologists and psychologists and perhaps even psychiatrists may illuminate the problem with a more focused light.

Everyone who examines the history of cultural advances is compelled to note, and to try to explain, the antagonism with which they have been met. Samuel Butler [7] said that the characteristic of genius was not, as Carlyle put it, a transcendent capacity for taking trouble but a transcendent capacity for getting its possessor into trouble and keeping him there, as long as the genius remains. 'Genius points to change, and change is a hankering after another world, so the old world suspects it. It disturbs order; it unsettles mores and hence it is immoral. . . . The uncommon sense of genius and the common sense of the rest of the world are thus as husbsnd and wife to one another; they are always quarrelling and common sense, who must be taken as the husband, always fancies himself the master.'

It would be convenient to suppose that there is a common factor of conservatism or rigidity which makes most people cling to what is familiar and traditional in religion, art, and *Weltanschauung*, but which does not operate against acceptance of scientific advances except when these threaten a whole structure of beliefs. Psychologists have failed to produce satisfactory evidence of such a personality type or trait. But it is fairly clear that in the natural sciences and in biology there is now little evidence of that bitter, irrational denial of new knowledge which was once inescapable, and whose counterpart is still so plain in the reception of new artistic forms and conceptions. Scientific discoveries now arouse resistance not on the score of their truth or falsity but of their potential misuse, their revolutionary effects in overriding values which people put higher than those of knowledge. So far as the truth of a scientific discovery goes, it is as likely to be received with credulity as with cautious judgment or would-be refutation. The battleground has shifted and the contest is about how knowledge may legitimately be applied, not how far it is indeed knowledge.

Sometimes the obstacle to acceptance of scientific advances is some intellectual hurdle, such as that which Priestley and Lavoisier surmounted: sometimes it is the tangle of truths and errors in the new ideas—the mixture of dubious guesses and illuminating concepts—that stands in the way of their acceptance. But it is the strength of relevant habits that mainly determines the resistance to change, reinforced by fears of what the change may entail or lessened by the rewards which the change plainly offers. Envy, too, and injured narcissism may play a part: the defects of great men are the consolation of dunces, failure in a noble enterprise can give joy to the mean-spirited.

But the opposition to great discoveries can be exaggerated, and its effects unduly deplored. Though it may make the life of the discoverer arduous and bitter, it derives from mental processes which, on the credit side, make for stability and continuity in a society's culture, and partially protect it against the tendencies (especially in an unsettled or transitional society) to embrace new systems and practices irrespective of their worth. Cults and pseudo-sciences alike attest the force of this philoneism (if I may use the term), in past and in contemporary societies. It is not limited to the illiterate and the psychopathic, it may take admirable as well as silly and degrading forms, its effects must be judged in the long rather than the short run; but shocking psychological epidemics and aberrations would not have occurred, or at any rate been so severe, if there had been a greater reluctance to adopt new beliefs and ways without close examination of the claims made for them. Credulity is, of course, a product or symptom: it cannot account for the unwarranted acceptance by masses of people, or by certain groups, of new ideas and modes of behaviour; for this there are multiple social and psychological causes, as yet insufficiently explored.

This raises the general question whether scepticism is an attitude of mind harmful to creative thought and cultural advance. A psychologist recently wrote: 'higher education often seems to encourage an attitude—which may become habitual—of negation rather than receptivity towards the creative thought of others', and he instances Thurstone's description of two types of student, the one critical and rather destructive, the other receptive and rather gullible. Obviously the most productive thinkers have both: they are ready to generate and examine new ideas, and to exercise discriminating criticism. The latter may be their chief concern. This was what Descartes aimed at, and perhaps achieved:

'tout mon dessein ne tendait qu'à m'assurer et à rejeter la terre mouvante et le sable pour trouver le roc ou l'argile. Ce qui me réussissait, ce me semble, assez bien, d'autant que, tâchant à découvrir la fausseté ou l'incertitude des propositions que j'imaginais, non par de faibles conjectures mais par des raisonnements clairs et assurés, je n'en rencontrais point de si douteuse que je n'en tirasse toujours quelque conclusion assez certaine, quand ce n'eût été que cela même qu'elle ne contenait rien de certain.'[8]

The influence of Descartes' policy of 'methodical doubt' was in the long run to be most significant on the destructive side; and who shall say it was not revolutionary and powerful in freeing men's minds for the scientific advances of the ensuing century.

The unqualified proposition—that men resist change—and the unqualified comment—that they should not—are both extremely dubious. Some men at some times resist change, others welcome it, and no one has succeeded in casting up the full account. 'Advance is not always nor necessarily in the right direction. . . . After all, mankind has a perfect right to distrust novelties and to exact abundant proofs of their value before accepting them.' Where moral and aesthetic judgments are in question, however, such proofs may be impossible to come by, unless there has been agreement about the criteria of value.

It is seldom, of course, that all the members of a society, except a few illuminati, deny the truth of some scientific discovery. Between the masses who may understand the issue crudely or not at all, and the men of genius who have originated the new ideas and advanced evidence in their support, lies a large group of people of talent, informed, judicious, and many of them also creative (though less conspicuously and powerfully so than the Darwins and the Galileos). In the acceptance if not the initiation of moral and aesthetic advances too, men commonly show a gradient, rather than the dramatic contrast of a percipient handful isolated amid teeming Philistines and Panglosses.

When the history of science is presented as an abstract account of the history of scientific ideas, it is apt to be simplified into a series of logical developments. The false starts and blind alleys hardly figure in the schema, which concentrates on the approved highways. From such accounts it might be supposed that the progress of science has been effected through the ways of thinking and experimenting characteristic of the great pioneers. This is implied in the passage I quoted earlier from George Sarton, and it is broadly true. But it omits humbler yet essential workers in the tradition and the discipline. A physicist, H. K. Schilling [9] has recently stressed the probable differences in intellectual strategy and tactics between what he calls 'common-man science' and 'great-man science'.

'Historical analysis would probably reveal that much of the growth of physics is the aggregate effect of the interests, attitudes, professional habits, and contributions, of the lesser men of physics. In all probability the meandering onward flow of science is determined helpfully and positively—and to a large extent—by the rank and file who, because of their persistent interests and preoccupations, carry exploration and exploitation in particular fields to their logical conclusions long after the geniuses have lost interest and turned to other more enticing problems. It may show also that progress is aided greatly by the damping and filtering effects of the intellectual inertia and scepticism of the ordinary man of physics upon many of the exuberant, free-wheeling and less useful ideas of the great or near-great. Finally the sum total of the relatively less important research endeavours of the very large numbers of individual mediocre scientists is tremendous and probably accounts for most of science as measured by both input of energy and output of results.'

Scientists, he holds, constitute a community with characteristic attributes, deeply embedded in the larger community, and made up of people with very diverse abilities, thought processes, and motives. Much of this is pretty obvious, but often hidden behind the stereotyped picture of the scientist—or, for that matter, of the artist or the musician. It is a view not particularly dissimilar (though expressed in more sober and contemporary language) from that of Henry Maudsley [10], a nineteenth-century psychiatrist who wrote in 1865:

'It is by the patient and diligent work at systematic adaptation to the external by the rank and file of mankind; it is by the conscientious labour of each one, after the inductive method, in that little sphere of nature, whether psychical or physical which in the necessary division of labour has fallen to his lot—that a condition of evolution is reached at which the genius starts forth. Tiresome, then, as the minute man of observation may sometimes seem while he exults over his scattered facts as if they were final . . . it is well that he should thus enthusiastically esteem his work. . . . Whosoever, in a foolish conceit of originality, neglects the scattered and perhaps obscure labours of others who have preceded him, or who are contemporaneous with him . . . may rest content that he is . . . more or less an abortive monstrosity; the more extreme he is as a monstrosity, the more original must he needs be.'

Cultural progress depends on favourable conditions and the thoughts and deeds of people of exceptional gifts, the so-called geniuses; it depends also on sufficient training and stimulus being given to men and women of talent to enable them too to make contributions to the general stock of discovery and advancement. Awareness of this is now a political issue, and self-conscious societies are striving—if only for the sake of power—to give full scope to talent, especially in science and the application of science. Modern bureaucratic societies, with their intensive technological concern and institutional organization, are trying not only to give full opportunities to talent but to 'enable ordinary people to accomplish extraordinary undertakings'. And in the United States superior endowment is being searched for: perhaps that is putting it too strongly—at any rate the need for intensifying the search is being vigorously proclaimed and means to carry it out are being explored. Thus at Columbia University since 1950 there has been a continuous study of the 'conservation of human resources', directed at this end, and the Social Science Research Council carried out, between 1951 and 1955, an investigation of how talent might be recognized; their elaborate report, published two years ago [11], showed the complexity of the methodological problems. The results of an English inquiry, carried out during the last ten years with the support of the Nuffield Foundation, will shortly be available. One of the major areas of ignorance is in respect of the qualities other than intellectual which enable talented people to make appreciable contributions. In the well-known California study by Lewis Terman this was the chief gap: the intellectually very gifted schoolchildren whom he followed up had in many instances outstanding achievements to their credit in adult life, but the factors of personality and motivation that differentiated them from others of equal intellectual endowment who had made little use of their superior ability could not be sufficiently determined. It was, however, a noteworthy finding that those who had a strong educational tradition in the family, were persevering and emotionally stable, and made satisfactory marriages, achieved much more in their adult careers. Terman held that as such talented children are potentially a nation's most precious asset, it is all-important to find out the environmental factors that favour or hinder the expression of such talent and the emotional compulsions that give it dynamic quality. He added, with good reason, that we should know too the personality distortions that make it dangerous.

Among Terman's gifted subjects it was the emotionally stable who made the best use of their intellectual gifts. This raises a question that has often been asked—a question to which Terman could not give the answer, for he says:

'It is conceivable that the personality factors which make for ordinary achievement under ordinary conditions are different from those which make for eminence of a superlative order. The two approaches agree in the conclusion that beyond a certain high level of intellectual ability success is largely determined by non-intellectual factors and that the number of persons who are endowed with abilities equal to great achievement is immensely greater than the number who will attain eminence'. [12]

The question at issue was posed in an extreme form, and sometimes dogmatically answered, in antiquity: nullum magnum ingenium sine mixtura dementiae (as we are told Aristotle believed). It has been of perennial interest, and is still a matter of controversy, especially among psychiatrists.

In the last century Moreau de Tours in France and Lombroso in Italy gave currency to the view that genius and insanity have common origins. In this century Kretschmer [13] has maintained that men of genius

'show in their psychological structure an unusual instability and hypersensitiveness, together with a very considerable liability to psychoses, neuroses and psychopathic complaints. . . . The loosening of mental structure, the plasticity, the hypersensitiveness to fine distinctions and remote relations, the frequently bizarre play of contrasts in the inmost parts of the personality—all these things, conditioned by the passionate quality of genius, its restless internal production, and its immense intellectual range, are part of the daemonic element which is identical with the psychopathic structures in the personality. . . . For some types of genius, this inner dissolution of the mental structure is an indispensable prelude.'

Now Kretschmer is one of the most distinguished of living psychiatrists; his views are based on an extensive review (akin to that of Lange-Eichbaum who arrived at similar conclusions); and they are entitled to respect—but not, I think, to approval and consent. They lead him to the conclusion that

'were we to remove the psychopathic inheritance, the daemonic unrest and mental tension from the constitution of the man of genius, nothing but an ordinary talented person would remain. The more one studies biographies, the more one is driven to the viewpoint that the psychopathic component is not merely a regrettable, non-essential accident of biological structure but an intrinsic and necessary part, an indispensable catalyst, perhaps, for every form of genius in the strict sense of the term.'

This widely held but erroneous opinion can be espoused at very different levels. Perhaps the lowest is that which regards 'psychopathic' or 'neurotic' as a derogatory term, and believes that if mental disorder is attributed to men

245

of genius they are being pulled down from their pedestal. It was in this way that Diderot made Rameau's nephew talk: as an adherent of the view that men of genius are a little mad, and great troublers of the *status quo*, he says in his shameless, cynical way, 'I have never heard any genius praised without its making me secretly furious. I am full of envy. When I hear something discreditable about their private lives, I listen with pleasure: it brings me closer to them; makes me bear my mediocrity more easily.' There is ample evidence that many of those who harp on the eccentricities or insanity of outstanding men get similar comfort from what they consider a pejorative statement. The matter is expressed a little more charitably by Slater and Meyer [14]: 'If, however, we find [the great man's] personality strange or difficult to understand, then we may only be able to bear the comparison by trying to cut down the man or his work to our own scale. We can do this more easily if at some point we are able to look down on him from above, from a superior level of sanity, or social competence, or moral integrity.'

At a more factual level, the intrinsic nexus between genius and mental disorder is affirmed by those who have considered, superficially or profoundly, the mental constitution and mental health of famous contributors to civilization. Many lists have been drawn up, recording casual or expert judgments as to which of the great had manifest mental illness of one sort of another. Such lists usually include Goethe, Fechner, Mill, and Nietzsche; Luther and Swedenborg; Comte and Rousseau; Isaac Newton, Pascal, and Robert Mayer; Van Gogh and Blake; Hölderlin, Tasso, Coleridge; Strindberg, Dostoevsky, Gogol, Maupassant, Gérard de Nerval, Lamb, Swift, and Ruskin; Donizetti, Robert Schumann, and Hugo Wolf.

It is easy to see from this and other more extensive lists that there are enough instances of the concurrence of mental illness and great creative achievement to account for, though not to justify, the widespread and inveterate tendency to identify them in some measure.

But it is necessary to remember that mental illness is a common affliction, and that unless it occurred with greater frequency in men of genius than in the general run of people of comparable age, sex, and nationality, its occasional appearance in the former could not be regarded as indicating similar roots for both genius and illness. Two analyses have been carried out, to see if indeed this is the case. Before discussing them, it is relevant to point out that in many of the people whom I mentioned just now, their mental disorder became manifest long after they had done their best work, and that in some of them it was an acquired disease (syphilis of the brain) or a senile process that occasioned their mental breakdown.

The first of the statistical analyses was made by Catherine Cox, working in conjunction with Professor Terman [15]. Following in the footsteps of Galton (in his *Hereditary Genius*), William James (*Great Men and Their Environment*), Havelock Ellis, Ostwald and Cattell, she collected full biographical data about three hundred of the most eminent people who have lived since 1450 (eminence being judged by the space accorded them in encyclopaedias and biographical dictionaries). Their presumptive I.Q. was estimated, and the philosophers topped the list with I.Q.'s of 170: next came the poets, dramatists, novelists, and revolutionary statesmen (160); then the scientists (155), and the musicians (145). There are many most interesting findings that emerged from this analysis—the great men's versatility, for example—but it is only possible here to record that the majority of them were above the average in force of character and social attributes, and did not differ materially from the normal run of people in their emotional balance and control.

A more restricted group of eminent men was analysed by the late Dr Adele Juda [16]. She collected the most eminent scientists and artists of the German-speaking countries since 1650. There were 113 artists (made up of painters, sculptors, architects, musicians and poets) and 181 scientists (among whom, in the German usage of the term, she included, besides 112 in the Natural Sciences, 51 theologians, philosophers, historians and jurists, and, rather oddly, 18 Field-Marshals, statesmen and inventors).

Taking the artists separately she found that more than two-thirds of them were entirely free from psychological abnormalities: an eighth had had a psychosis, but in all but three cases this was a late-appearing organic disease of the brain; and neurotic or psychopathic disorders of personality had been detectable in less than a third (28 per cent). In their parents, 3 per cent had endogenous psychoses, and 13 per cent some psychopathic disorder. Only a third of their brothers and sisters showed any kind of psychological disturbance. Among their children, there were 4 per cent with an endogenous psychosis, and 14 per cent neurotic or psychopathic; and among their grandchildren 4·6 per cent had an endogenous psychosis, but only 6 per cent seemed psychopathic. Altogether, the data indicate that artists and their families are mostly free from mental disturbance.

The scientists were even more plainly a mentally healthy group on the whole. Three-quarters of them were free from any mental abnormality; such psychoses as occurred in the remainder were manic-depressive (4 per cent). Neurotic symptoms or personality disorders occurred in 14 per cent of the group (mostly the philosophers and other *Geisteswissenschaftler*). Creative activity was lessened or suspended during the manic-depressive attacks, as one would expect, but fully restored after recovery. Studies of their parents showed a lesser incidence of all kinds of mental disorder than in the parents of the artists; and among the children of the scientists there was less psychopathic disorder than in the artists' children.

A comparison was also made with an intermediate group of talented people, mostly professional men. The proportion of psychopathic persons among them was much the same as in the genius group: endogenous psychoses were slightly less frequent than in the latter.

The general conclusion reached by Juda is that 'there is no definite relationship between highest mental capacity and mental health or illness, and no evidence to support the assumption that the genesis of highest intellectual ability depends on psychological abnormalities. . . . Psychoses, especially schizophrenia, proved to be detrimental to creative ability.' Milder mental abnormalities, of the neurotic type, seemed to exert in some instances a stimulating influence.

In contrast to this genetic statistical approach, there have been a large number of clinical studies of the psychopathology of individual men of genius who had some variety of mental illness. The inquiries had as their aim to discover how far the mental disorder provided either a necessary condition, or an adjuvant, of the creative process. It would be impossible here to review the methods and conclusions in all these 'pathographies', of which the most distinguished and penetrating is Jaspers's study of Strindberg, Van Gogh and Hölderlin. The issue has been in a few instances illuminated, but in far more clouded and confused, by reference to the artistic and literary productions of mentally ill people of average ability.

Just as in Juda's study, it has been observed—by Kraepelin and others—that in these biographical analyses a clear difference can be discerned between the creative activity of great poets and artists and that of great scientists, mathematicians, or historians. In the artists, composers, and poets a psychotic illness may remove inhibitions, especially at the beginning of a manic attack; or a schizophrenic change of experience, in its early phases, may provide rich material for poetic expression and plastic representation. An attack of depression may provide deeper understanding of suffering, disclosing the Dark Night of the Soul. None of these, however, can result in a work of genius unless the illness occur in a person of exceptional capacity: the illness may facilitate, or provide, some of the mood and content of a great work, but cannot beget such a work and alone bring it to birth.

When the illness is schizophrenia, its effects are anything but uniform and predictable. In Swedenborg a schizophrenic illness gave rise to new content for his mystical fantasy, but did no detriment to his eventual productivity: in Hölderlin on the other hand it conspired to bring about a new creative burst, different in essential style from what he had hitherto produced, but this was the prelude to decay and creative incapacity. Manic-depressive illnesses may have more dramatic but less radical effects: the three-year-long melancholia of Fechner, for example, gave a fresh turn to his interests which persisted for the rest of his life, but it did not alter his fundamental 'style', his way of thinking and of presenting his thoughts: 'das Leben bleibt eine große einheitliche Gestalt; wenn ein Bruch da ist, liegt er nicht im Tiefsten, sondern in einem mehr Aeusserlichen' [17].

A philosopher-psychologist like Fechner stands midway between the religious thinkers and the scientists. Scientific work will almost inevitably suffer through an illness which weakens the formative, structuring powers of the mind. Such an illness may conceivably favour a brilliant intuition, but is hardly likely to promote that laborious process of conscious wrestling with a problem which Helmholtz and Poincaré so emphasized in their introspective accounts of creative scientific thought; as Graham Wallas put it, and as subsequent psychological inquiries have corroborated, creative scientific thought requires preparation, incubation, illumination, and verification. A psychologically disturbed mind is ill equipped to meet these demands. Where, however, the work of preparation and incubation has gone on over a long period, in a mind of the highest quality, a transient toxic disturbance may favour illumination, as when Alfred Russel Wallace suddenly saw the answer to his long questioning, during a bout of malarial fever.

Psychotic illness has, in English-speaking countries, attracted less attention than neurotic conflict as the requisite for artistic creation—a conception to which Edmund Wilson brilliantly drew attention in *The Wound and the Bow*. Psychoanalysts, literary critics, and psychologists have written much on this. But it is pretty well recognized now, I think—as indeed it was by Freud— that though artistic productions can be regarded as substitute gratifications, and the genesis of certain features in them can be traced back just as symptoms can be, this tells us nothing about the distinctive quality in them which makes them valuable, nor about the conditions of its realization. The shaping of the material and the mastery of the creative process elude reductive psychological analysis. Lamb, who has the right to be heard on the matter, said of the poet that 'where he seems most to recede from humanity he will be found the truest to it. From beyond the scope of Nature, if he summon possible existences, he subjugates them to the law of her consistency. He is beautifully loyal to that sovereign directress even when he appears most to betray and desert her.' These paradoxes the psychologist cannot yet resolve and restate in the language appropriate to psychopathology.

That the value of notable work cannot be raised or lessened by considering the medical condition of the man or woman who created it, is strikingly evident in the field of religion, where such diagnoses as 'hysteria', 'epilepsy' and 'catatonic ecstasy' are often freely applied. William James commented on this with customary directness. 'St Teresa might have had the nervous system of the placidest cow, and it would not now save her theology if the trial of the theology by these other tests should show it to be contemptible. And conversely if her theology can stand these other tests, it will make no difference how hysterical or nervously off her balance St Teresa may have been when she was with us here below.'

It is, of course, true that a neurotic conflict may mirror conflicts in our culture. But what is distinctive and lasting in a work produced by a neurotic genius is not the conflict but the manner and form of its expression. It is also true that though we cannot adequately explain artistic and other sorts of mental achievement by reference to psychological sickness in the achiever, we can so explain defects and misguided aims. The artist's or scientist's abundant power to conceive, and develop, and conclude his work is healthy, no matter what mental disabilities he may also have: but these disabilities can invade his creative functions and lessen them.

I have several times referred to men of outstanding gifts and achievements as abnormal. By this I meant literally or statistically abnormal, without implying a value judgment about health or other desirable abstractions. The departure from the norm may be most rare and wonderful. While preparing this paper I have many times thought that the powers of some outstanding men pass beyond what most of us would suppose possible of human attainment. Perhaps the most telling evidence of how far they excel the general run of mankind is their intellectual precocity. Such men as Leibniz and Grotius seem preternatural in their performance in this regard, as indeed in many others. To conclude, may I somewhat irrelevantly tell you about a little boy who died before he could ever do anything to advance culture or make any lasting impact on the world: but his story is not without a moral, close to my theme.

This poor little boy, Christian Henrich Heineken, was born in Lübeck in 1720 [18]. When he was nine months old his startling ability to speak and to memorize what he was told caused his parents to entrust his education to a tutor, von Schöneich. By the time he was thirteen months old he knew most of the events recorded in the Old Testament, and before long he had acquired a good knowledge of Latin and French, church history, the Code of Justinian, and much other mental lumber. By the time he was three years old we have unquestionable evidence that he had a vast and correct storehouse of geographical, historical, legal and astronomical information at his disposal. When he was presented to the King of Denmark, he made a long speech and submitted to an examination of his knowledge and reasoning powers, lasting several hours, which he passed with honours. (He was at this time not yet weaned, and the examination had to be suspended for a few minutes while his wet-nurse fed him.) He was ill and made a comment in Latin, as he often did, saying 'Oh I am so sick. In rebus adversis melius sperare memento.' This little prodigy died when he was four years old—four years and four months to be exact. Just before he died he made long speeches, parading his knowledge: he listed fifty places along the Rhine where famous grapes were cultivated, recalled all the heroes of antiquity by name, and, as always, conversed only in French and Latin except when he was talking to his wet-nurse. He never learnt to walk.

I said there was a moral. The moral in this pathetic cautionary tale is that we commonly underestimate the range of intellectual power possible in human beings; we concentrate too much on its minus variants—on disorder and defect—leaving those with maximum potentiality to develop this as luck and the educational system may determine; and though we are not so besotted and unfeeling as the tutor and mother of the wonder-child of Lübeck, we still do not know whether we go the right way to work with our treasury of very exceptional children, capable of so much as agents for the furtherance of society and its culture.

Neither do we know whether we do the best for those less remarkably gifted, who are likewise potential agents of progress. Part of the problem, and the paradox, were stated by Hobhouse [1]: 'there is no progress without passion, and neither order nor progress without the subdual of passion.' We can translate that easily into a contemporary idiom. How to attain the desired 'synthesis of opposites' and promote the mental development of individuals

250

so that it would conduce to social and cultural development, is an area of uncertainty still. As Gardner Murphy [19] put it in the concluding paragraph of his recent book:

> The realization of human potentials lies in studying the directions in which human needs may be guided, with equal attention to the learning powers of the individual and the feasible directions of cultural evolution. The last thousand years have created a level of scientific and aesthetic satisfaction which has already made human nature different today from what it was in the Middle Ages; yet this is merely a beginning. Even this much of an evolution has hardly commenced in the area of interpersonal relations, where modern psychology, including psychoanalysis, has shown us more about the roots of conflict and destructiveness among people than about the development of positive social feeling. If we cannot make rapid gains in the control of conflict, there will be no human future. But if we can, the future extension of scientific and aesthetic interest, together with the evolution of greater capacity for satisfaction in relations between people, will not constitute a goal or a Utopia, but will define a widening theatre for the development of new potentialities.

—and a richer culture. The predicament is there: it is a predicament which Hobhouse recognized, with fluctuating gloom and confidence. Today we are more insistently reminded of the problem than when Hobhouse examined it, and are more urgently aware of the necessity for investigating it, and solving it, in the interests of our survival.

REFERENCES

1 HOBHOUSE, L. T. *Social Development*, London, Allen & Unwin, 1924.
2 POLANYI, M. *Beyond Nihilism*, Cambridge University Press, 1960.
3 SARTON, G. *The History of Science and the New Humanism*, Harvard University Press, 1937.
4 HUME, D. 'Of the middle station of life' in *Essays Moral, Political and Literary*, 1742.
5 MERTON, R. K. *Puritanism, Pietism and Science in Social Theory and Social Structure*, Glencoe, 1949.
6 BUTTERFIELD, H. *The Origins of Modern Science*, London, Bell & Sons, 1949.
7 BUTLER, S. *Notebooks*, selections edited by J. Keynes and B. Hill, London, Jonathan Cape, 1951.
8 DESCARTES. *Discours de la Methode*, Troisième Partie, London, J. M. Dent & Sons, p. 36.
9 SCHILLING, H. K. 'A Human Enterprise', *Science*, 1958, **127**, 1324.
10 MAUDSLEY, H. 'The distinction between genius and work', *J. Ment. Sci.*, 1865, **52, 289**.
11 McCLELLAND, D. C. *et al. Talent and Society*, Princeton, Van Nostrand, 1958.
12 TERMAN, L. M. (ed.). *Genetic Studies of Genius*, vol. 3: *The Promise of Youth*, Stanford University Press, 1930.
13 KRETSCHMER, E. *Geniale Menschen* 5th ed., Berlin, Springer, 1958.
14 SLATER, E. and MEYER, A. 'Contributions to a pathology of the musicians' *Confinia Psychiat.*, 1959, **2**, 65.
15 TERMAN, L. M. (ed.). *Genetic Studies of Genius*, vol. 2 (C. M. Cox): *The Early Mental Traits of 300 Geniuses*, Stanford University Press, 1926.
16 JUDA, A. *Hochstbegabung: Ihre Erbverhältnisse sowie ihre Beziehumgen zu Psychischen Anomalien*, Munich, Urban & Schwarzenberg, 1953.

ADDRESSES

17 JASPERS, K. *Strindberg and Van Gogh*, Bremen, Strom Verlag, 1949, p. 171.
18 LEHNDORFF, H. and FALKENSTEIN, L. 'Christian Henrich Heiniken: the miracle baby from Lübeck, 1720–1724', *Arch. Pediat.*, 1955, **72**, 360.
19 MURPHY, G. *Human Potentialities*, London, Allen & Unwin, 1960, p. 329.

16

EBB AND FLOW IN
SOCIAL PSYCHIATRY

I WOULD like to begin by expressing my sense of the honour done me by the invitation to deliver this Lecture, instituted in memory of a brilliant investigator of social psychiatry. Wherever psychiatrists meet to discuss the social aspects of their subject, the outstanding contributions of this school are certain to be quoted. Need I say that these contributions are embodied to a large extent in two books—Hollingshead and Redlich's *Social Class and Mental Illness* [1], and the companion work by Jerome Myers and Bertram Roberts [2], in which the family and class dynamics in mental illness are so thoroughly explored.

In the beginning of their book, Dr Roberts and Dr Myers explained that the New Haven study grew out of 'that body of theory and research of the past half century indicating that the social environment in which men live is related in some way, not yet fully explained, to the development of mental illness'. A footnote to this passage refers us to Professor Dunham's well-known summary of the development of research in social psychiatry. In that summary likewise the emphasis is heavily, and rightly, on work done in the last half century. Since scientific progress during any period cannot be appraised without considering the state of the subject at the beginning of the period, it seemed worthwhile to devote this lecture to a cursory review of where social psychiatry had got to by the end of the first decade of the twentieth century.

The title I have chosen for the lecture suggests that the tide of social psychiatry has ebbed as well as flowed. This is open to question: some of you may think that its development is always onward:

> Like the Pontic sea
> Whose icy current and compulsive course
> Ne'er feels retiring ebb; but keeps due on
> To the Propontic and the Hellespont.

This paper was originally delivered as the fourth Bertram Roberts Memorial Lecture at Yale University in May 1960. It is reprinted from *The Yale Journal of Biology and Medicine* (August 1962), **35**, 62–83.

It may be so. I doubt it, but I would not press the point, being more concerned to recall men and ideas now unjustly overlooked.

It would be strange if we found that instead of discussion and inquiry there was, fifty years ago, only indifference or denial of the social issues which are raised by mental illness. Sociology had been launched by men of the stature of Comte, Leplay and Herbert Spencer in Europe, and in this country Lester Ward, Summers and Veblen. Around the turn of the century its study was being pursued by men like Dürkheim, Weber, Simmel, Hobhouse and Cooley. Psychiatrists, on their side, had, as we shall see, been showing alert awareness of certain social problems from the middle of the nineteenth century onwards—some of them problems peculiar to mental illness, others general to medicine as a whole. It will be best, because of the range of the subject, first to take a look at the systematic expositions of psychiatry. Three of these were published approximately fifty years ago: there was the section on mental diseases in Allbutt and Rolleston's *System of Medicine* [3]; the elaborate and comprehensive *Handbuch der Psychiatrie* edited by G. Aschaffenburg [4]; and the *Traité International de Psychologie Pathologique* edited by Auguste Marie [5].

The English *System* is the least informative. Beyond a few paragraphs regarding the influence of occupation and upbringing, and some expert reflections on the genesis of criminal behaviour and society's ways of dealing with it, there is very little in it to suggest that in 1900 or thereabouts the compatriots of Pritchard and Burrows were alive to the fact that the mentally ill do not each live marooned on an unpeopled island or emerge from an anarchic jungle. But the scantiness of the English survey was due to the limited vision of the editor, Savage, and the narrow horizons of his contributors rather than to the real bareness of the land.

When we come to the Aschaffenburg *Handbuch* [4]—a much more ambitious and workmanlike undertaking—the coverage is ampler, the volume of relevant study impressive. It is most discernible in the section on etiology. The topics include occupation, cultural environment, and catastrophies, especially war; each is reviewed in detail. The author of the section on etiology, Voss [6] of Griefswald, had a close interest in these matters and contributed the chapter on 'Einfluss der sozialen Lage auf Nerven- und Geisteskrankheiten' in Moose and Tugendreich's manual on social medicine (1913). I should like to survey his treatment of these themes in a little detail.

First, the occupational problems of adolescence are considered—choice of job, psychopathic hesitations, the stress of disappointment when there are frequent changes of career; then the effects of unemployment, with emphasis on the psychiatric causes and significance of vagrancy or 'nomadism'; here Voss recalls the classical study by Wilmanns [7], published in 1906, and Bonhoeffer's [8] (1900) and Mönkemöller's (1908) contributions to elucidation of the matter. The next occupational question to be considered is the frequency of certifiable mental illness in different occupational groups; the English statistics of 1909 are adduced, as are Austrian data on economic groups. He pays special regard to general paresis and alcoholism, taking note of the then recent studies by Marie and Martial (1908), statistical data by Jolly (1910) and Pandy (1908), and Hellpach's report on occupational psychoses (1906). An occupational group thought to be especially at risk was the nursing staff of mental hospitals, investigated by Förster; he considered them prone to develop 'psychic infections'. Not surprisingly in the Germany of 1910, many studies are reviewed which deal with military service and its psychiatric problems. Bennecke (1907) had looked into the apparent causes of dementia praecox in volunteers, stressing the factor of selection as more important than the pressures of the military situation. Schultze (1906), like Pactet (1908) in France, reported that the incidence of hysteria had risen steeply among soldiers in the previous decade. E. Meyer had shown that the incidence of psychiatric illness was higher in the Navy than in the Army, and other writers examined the perennial question of the high suicide rate in the German Army.

Voss then turns to a question which, as he puts it, 'strongly engages the interest not only of psychiatrists but of wider circles too': viz., what influence does the general culture of a people have on mental health? He enters upon it by a survey of the evidence for and against assuming an increase in the incidence of mental illness, including neuroses. He concludes that there has been an increase and that Kraepelin [9] is justified in regarding the neurotic disabilities that follow accidents and the various forms of obsessional neurosis as typical products of western civilization. He accepts Dürkheim's [10] conception of anomie in society, links it to the decline of authority, especially in religion, and sees it as a potent cause of mental illness and suicide. Voss compares incidence rates of mental disease between different peoples, pointing out that study of 'racial psychiatry' was then of very recent development, and that because of the obscurity of the concept of race he would prefer the term 'ethnic psychiatry' ('Völkerpsychiatrie'). Most of the recent publications which he reviews deal, it is true, with general paresis and the factors determining syphilitic infection, but there are also studies, such as that of Revesz (1911), which examine the whole question of frequency and form of mental illness among diverse peoples. Voss gives unquestioning credence to crude differences based on dissimilar methods of ascertainment, but he is cautious and judicial in weighing up the relative influence of constitutional predisposition in each ethnic group, and the climatic and other environmental conditions to which it has been exposed. He agrees with Kraepelin and other authors that there are no psychoses specific to particular peoples, but that national character puts its stamp on the manifest clinical pattern, and on the relative frequency of the different psychoses. The cultural stage a people has reached partly determines the content and form of neuroses: hysteria in particular reflects cultural development. Ideas of demoniacal possession and religious ecstasy have given way to hypochondriacal forms and complaints developing after an accident.

Voss also considers the effect of wars and other major misfortunes. Stierlin

(1911) and Italian writers had reported how populations were affected by earthquakes, tidal waves, and volcanic eruptions (like the then recent one in Messina). The frequency of mental illness in contending armies had been reported, after the Russo-Japanese war, to have been only moderately higher than in peace time; from numerous Russian reports it emerged that depressive states were prominent, and that physical stresses—head-injuries, lack of sleep, infectious fevers—played at least as large a part as psychological ones. Data collected in England during the Boer War are somewhat naïvely supposed to show that reverses brought about a lessening of detected crime and a temporary abatement in the rising trend of mental disorder.

There is much more in this Aschaffenburg article regarding psychological stresses of social provenance, but it is sufficient to mention here the thorough exposition of induced or communicated disorder. In France, Marandon de Montyel (1906) had classified the varieties of folie-à-deux—folie simultanée, folie communiquée, and folie imposée. In Germany, Weygandt (1905) had performed a similar service, distinguishing between 'psychopathic transfer' and 'psychopathic release' of symptoms. Partenheimer and other contributors to this topic were specially concerned with the question of whether someone perfectly healthy could catch a mental illness through close and constant association with an affected person (usually a person with paranoiac delusions) and most of them concluded that only those with a hereditary predisposition could succumb. These psychiatrists were, like Dr Gruenberg in our day, led to consider psychic epidemics, especially those occurring in hysterical subjects in schools and convents, as well as the mediaeval outbreaks of tarantism, flagellation and convulsions. Such mass phenomena and the formation of eccentric sects and 'crack-brained' political parties were put down to suggestion and imitation: they were aligned, in this respect, with panics and other signs of collective emotional upset, and the resonance of mobs to the tunes of hate, enthusiasm and fear played by psychopathic leaders received much attention as instances of the psychopathology of suggestion. It may fairly be said that in the first decade of this century more analysis of these group phenomena occurred than in the ensuing thirty years—the thirty years that preceded our current strong, and by no means detached, interest in them.

So much for the section in etiology in Aschaffenburg's *Handbuch*. There are, of course, in that extensive compilation sections on therapeutics and other issues of a social nature; and the large branch of preeminently social psychiatry dealing with crime is very thoroughly explored in a 300-page section.

When we turn to France and Auguste Marie's *Traité* we are again left in no doubt of the interest our predecessors took in social and cultural aspects of psychiatry. The massive third volume, published in 1912, deals with applied psychopathology. In its ample pages all the matters which I have mentioned as covered in the Aschaffenburg section are exhaustively reviewed, as well as much else that could nowadays be regarded as epidemiological. Beginning with a wide sweep, Dr Cullerre looks at the historical changes that have occurred in the forms of mental illness, and in mankind's approach to their understanding and control. How they have been manifest in religion, and have waxed or waned with the cultural movements that accompanied great shifts of religious attachment; their responsibility for such events as took place in the Ursuline Convent of Loudon or around the remains of the Deacon Paris in 1727; and their occurrence in men who lead revolutions or attain power—all these matters are systematically expounded in the light of the writings of French psychiatrists and social historians. There is no dearth of factual material or social interpretation. Auguste Marie himself then presents the state of knowledge of ethnic psychopathology in his time. He acknowledges the factors which preclude simple comparison, or summation, of estimates of incidence, in different peoples:

'We are still unable to compare the geographical variations in the number of admissions and discharges, cures and deaths in the different mental disorders, because of differences in the law, differences in material facilities, in the number of mental hospitals and the amount of therapeutic activity in them, as well as because of the repercussions brought about inside the mental hospitals by the swings of endemic and epidemic disease, and by social and international upheavals.'

Then he collects the scattered data. Migration and industrialization make demands on adaptation which some precariously healthy people cannot meet; hence the higher rate of mental illness when a rural community is invaded by factories, or a rural population moves into the city, or citizens of European countries emigrate to North America, the Argentine, or Brazil. In an interesting analysis he undertakes to show that when the figures for admission to a Paris mental hospital are analysed by occupation, those for agricultural workers are much higher than expected; when the individuals are scrutinized as to place of origin, the overwhelming majority of them come from the country and have either migrated at the beginning of their mental illness because of restlessness, desire to escape from persecutors, or need to be looked after by relatives living in Paris, or have moved to the city to better themselves and found that, uprooted, they could not keep their heads above water.

Marie tackles the irrepressible question: is mental illness on the increase in our troubled times? With praiseworthy caution he states and partly demolishes the evidence that purports to demonstrate this, but leaves the main issue unsettled. Like many before him and since, he incriminates the rapidity of social change. 'The more thorough and sudden changes in social circumstances brought about under modern conditions go beyond the limits of what the average vulnerable person can adapt to.'

In this he is chiefly addressing himself to the effects of western civilization upon mental health. He is, however, well aware that stresses and strains are not the prerogative of civilized communities. He is closely tied to the anthropology of his period and, very naturally, to the theories of Levy-Brühl. But attractive though he finds these in unravelling the psychopathology of preliterate societies, he is always close to the observable facts and on his guard against facile inferences. Examining in turn the available data about the peoples of Asia, Africa and Polynesia, he has given full weight to the role of physical disease and drugs in producing mental illness. The statistics of mental hospital admissions, reported by diverse authorities and classified by diagnosis, lead him to conclusions not far removed from those set out today in books on cultural psychiatry. He recognizes beri-beri, pellagra, trypanosomiasis, malaria, bilharzia and other infections as epidemiological problems bearing directly on the prevention of mental disorders, but gives as much weight to opium and hashish addiction, and to animistic beliefs and magic rituals, especially among the indigenous people of Africa. His general standpoint however, is in favour of the uniformity of the types of mental illness everywhere. Thus he says, 'Among the black people of Africa and the offspring of mixed black and white parentage we find all the mental and physical diseases of the white races, with variations solely attributable to the local milieu.'

As one reads on in Marie's review of the literature of the subject, it becomes more and more plain that in 1910 people were asking much the same questions we ask and were as aware as we are that institutional statistics, however scrupulously classified for epidemiological purposes, could not give a safe answer to questions about causes or ethnic differences.

Qualitative differences, however, were thought to lie in the geographically limited disorders known variously as Amok and Latah, Myriachit, Malinali and Baktachi; and to be possibly discernible among offspring of marriages between peoples of European stock and Africans or South Americans (especially Brazilians). But Marie, resuming the evidence, concludes that these people were not, as had been maintained often, 'degenerate' and more prone to breakdown.

'The results of our investigations show conclusively that the defects of people of mixed blood are the outcome of the false position we put them in, and our neglect of them . . . There is no doubt that their uncertain social situation affects the development of psychiatric troubles, acting both as a powerful cause and as a means of making them manifest: it is only another instance of how the environment can evoke antisocial reactions when adaptation becomes too difficult . . . Aspirations checked by a sense of inferiority and by cultural deficiences show up in their mental illnesses. The Negroes generally have low aspirations. When the struggle for existence drives them to greater efforts than they ordinarily would make, and they encounter obstacles, the direct result may be a breakdown. The mental illness they thus develop can reflect its special origins.'

In the next section of Marie's *System* he collaborated with Bagenoff, of Moscow, in reviewing the genesis and psychopathology of collective or communicated mental disorders. Like Voss he devotes much space to the problems of psychic infection, and as might be expected of the countryman of Gabriel Tarde and Gustave Le Bon, he stresses the tendency to imitate and to respond to suggestion as a powerful factor in generating these shared disorders. The literature he adduces is extensive, and it confirms the impression that at that period psychiatrists and sociologists in many countries (especially France, Italy and Russia) were keenly alive to the obscurities, and the dangers, of collective mental illness, whether outwardly mild or severe, whether limited to two people or embracing a group or nation. Marie and his colleague, Halberstadt, had themselves made careful observations and distinguished the psychopathologically disparate forms of such disorder. On the manifest issue of how much is attributable to individual predisposition and how much to influences from the environment in these cases, Marie adduces familial and twin evidence from the time of Lasègue and Marandon de Montyel onwards supporting the role of heredity in the 'communicated' and 'concurrent' forms, but not in the 'imposed' form. In the latter, where one 'active' person dominates another, Marie shrewdly insists that the active agent can effect his control only because he expresses and stimulates morbid tendencies latent in his 'passive' partner. He by no means minimizes the effect of cultural and personal environment. Illustrating his argument by cases and interpretations in the literature, especially those in which religious features are prominent, he enumerates characteristics of the environment in which such phenomena may appear: isolated localities where superstitions and fanaticism flourish; physical misery, such as famine, and fanatical austerities; illiteracy; and animistic cults. The extraordinarily widespread condition, mostly familiar under the name of Latah, is documented fully and attributed, like some other epidemic or endemic disorders of conduct, to hysterical mechanisms. Marie, however, sees no difference between collective hysteria and mass behaviour: 'There is a collective, or social, form of hysteria: the best examples of it are in the great religious and mystical movements.' This follows from his acceptance of Cabanis' principle:

'Between the normal and the morbid psychological phenomena of crowds, the differences are only of degree: the general laws governing them are the same . . . From research into the genesis, course of development and mutual interaction of such associated psychoses, general principles can be deduced which are equally applicable to the normal psychology of groups.'

It would be tempting to compare Marie's full analyses and conclusions on this whole matter with those of such recent writers as Helene Deutsch, Gralnik, Cantril and Gruenberg. I am inclined to think that we should not find that there has been as substantial an advance as we might wish, though of course modern views are expressed in rather different language and in greater detail. The data now available are more elaborately documented, but the essentials and the alternative explanations are much what they were in 1910.

In a final section on general etiology, Marie resumes the studies that had been made in France, especially in the mountainous département of Tarn-et-Garonne, attempting to relate the economic, demographic and cultural changes in given areas to the apparent increase in incidence of neurotic disorders. He likewise considers the grounds for supposing that revolutions, wars and calamities such as destructive earthquakes and cyclones directly bring about an excess of mental disorders. Here he draws on Russian literature, chiefly relating to the war with Japan and the 1906 revolution, as well as on Italian, South American and Swiss observers to document the psychological effect of natural disasters. He incriminates as psychogenic factors social disturbances, such as France underwent at the time of the Dreyfus case; large movements of population, as by emigration; and class movement up or down, with its attendant frustration and exactions. In this connexion he recalls that in 1910 at the International Congress in Berlin psychiatrists (including Kraepelin, Tamburini and Clérambault) from many countries had debated the ways in which civilization appeared to be related to mental disorder. On the questions raised by statistics of marital state, occupation, age, confinement in prison, and alcoholism, Marie offers concise and cautious judgements. He does not, however, approach in critical thoroughness Bumke [11], whose monograph, published in 1912, on 'Degeneration' as shown in nervous disorder, and its relation to culture, is a brilliant analysis of the problem, the evidence, and the permissible inductions.

I have dealt at some length with the contributions of Marie, not because he was a major figure in French psychiatry, nor because his own investigations and findings are of special importance, but rather as a telling witness to the breadth and the intensity of inquiry into social and epidemiological problems made by French psychiatrists, and indeed by European psychiatrists generally, at a time which some writers of today seem to think of as the Dark Ages.

The same range of interest is found in every comprehensive work of the period one picks up. Kraepelin, for example, in his textbook deals with the familiar social factors contributing to mental illness: isolation and restriction; wars and cataclysms; religious movements and political upheavals; welfare measures of the state; the affected person's age, sex, ethnic source, cultural status, kind of occupation or lack of occupation, upbringing, and social frustrations. Kraepelin's citation of relevant studies ranges widely; his review of such a matter as ethnic (Volksart) influences on mental disorder is terse, admirably critical, and still up-to-date in essentials. Besides these general themes there are a few topics that receive special attention, either because of the circumstances of the time, or because a prominent figure gave an impetus to the study.

One such timely topic was migration. The United States had recognized, as far back as 1874, that many mentally handicapped people were coming to that country from Europe. In 1891 a Federal Law was enacted excluding immigrants with mental disease and defect, and empowering the Government to see that they were returned to their country of origin. Then alarmist predictions began to be made. William A. White [12] said in 1903, 'the offscourings of all Europe are hastening to our shores', and he added dire predictions of the deterioration this would bring about in the collective mental health of the American people. It was a time when American psychiatry was particularly rich in Cassandras. A few years later James V. May [13] and T. W. Salmon [14] uttered similar warnings. 'When the enormous volume of the new immigration is taken into consideration,' wrote Salmon, 'and the vastness of the sources of population in Russia and south-eastern Europe, one can foresee the dimensions which the problem of the care of mentally diseased may reach twenty years hence.' These ill-grounded prophecies, which assumed a high incidence of psychoses and defect in immigrants on evidence which did not take into account their different age-distribution from that of the native-born, were in part countered by more prudent analyses, like those of Arthur Kilbourne and George H. Kirby [15] (Kirby called his paper, 'A study in Race Psychopathology'). The two official surveys, by Koren [16] in 1904 and by Hill [17] in 1910, put the matter in perspective, and not only made valid comparisons of incidence of mental illness between native-born and immigrants but paid regard to the difficulties of adjustment to life in an unfamiliar country, and the varying social factors which determine whether a mentally ill or defective person is admitted to hospital in different states. The general discussion of the problem, however, was not free of the prejudices of the time, nor uninfluenced by the political forces then brought to bear upon the issue of unlimited immigration. Dr Ødegaard [18] has reviewed the developments at this period and has recalled how immigrants deported because of mental illness often did not reach their original countries, but had to be admitted to mental hospitals near the French ports where they were dumped by the returning steamships.

It must be admitted that the accuracy of recording, the method of investigating, and the interpretation of the psychiatric phenomena in migrants at that time fell far short of what has been achieved in this field of late years; but then consider how insistent and cruel the problem has become for many in our time, and how the volume of involuntary immigration has been swollen by refugees and displaced persons. The studies published by Ødegaard, Malzberg [19], Murphy [20], and most recently Gillon, Duchêne and Champion [21], attest the complexity of the migration problem, its humanitarian aspects, and its significance in understanding the interplay between social conditions and psychiatric disturbance. The very extensive literature reviewed by the French authors in their recent Encyclopaedia articles is a reminder that the movement of population in all the continents, and between them, is reponsible now (as often before on a less world-wide scale) for maladjustment, misery and illness.

Isolation has often been held accountable for some of the psychological troubles of people transplanted from their homes. Forty or fifty years ago writers (e.g. Herschmann [22]) paid attention to linguistic isolation, which might have effects akin to those occurring in deaf people. Although migration within a country does not usually entail the risk of being cut off from speaking and being spoken to intelligibly, this barrier to communication can bring about profound and shattering upheavals in people who have moved to a strange country and, in their loneliness, are slow to learn its language. Interior migration, of course, has its problems too. In 1909 Karl Jaspers [23] wrote a thesis on, 'Homesickness and Crime', which illuminates another aspect of isolation—that of the rural worker, simple and perhaps stupid, who moves to the town and is overwhelmed. The exposition he offers is instructive but his ideas are not, I think, often consulted in the English-speaking countries. Isolation had its defenders, as well as its detractors. Most prominent of these was Pierre Janet [24]. In an elaborate review of its merits and defects he advocated isolation for neurotics, especially hysterics, because it temporarily withdrew the patient from an irritant human environment; but he emphasized that it must be only a brief withdrawal. And he adds: 'We have to take into account something that is ordinarily overlooked: namely that treating a neurotic who is living with his family almost always means treating several other people too.'

Fifty years ago there was also concern about the differing rates of mental disorder in parts of a single country—ecology in its rudiments. Perhaps the best example of this is the Presidential Address delivered to the Medico-Psychological Association of Great Britain and Ireland by W. R. Dawson [25] in 1911:

'We must study all the circumstances and conditions of life, past and present, in their relation to insanity in order to determine how far they each may have a bearing upon it. . . . I have therefore decided today to place before you certain data of more or less interest concerning the relative local prevalence in Ireland of certain social conditions such as density of population; poverty (as shown by the incidence of pauperism and by the rateable value of property, together with the number of emigrants from each district); disease incidence, as shown by the general death-rate and that from tuberculosis; and last but not least, the prevalence of criminality and alcoholism; the whole being considered in relation to the distribution of insanity, so far as this is indicated by the numbers from each county in the asylums and workhouses at the beginning of the present year. Unfortunately the figures showing the numbers outside institutions, which will appear in forthcoming census returns, are not yet available, but this is the less regrettable that such numbers possess, in my opinion, very doubtful value.'

He quotes the 1905 Report of the Commissioners in Lunacy for England and Wales, in which maps showing comparative density of population were set alongside similar maps about the distribution of insanity and of drunkenness in the different counties. His own findings are set out in a series of histograms indicating the rank order of the 32 counties in respect of frequency of the variables I have quoted. The results ran counter to many widely held beliefs: for example, no appreciable relation was apparent between the insanity-rate on the one hand and the density of population, the death-rate, the amount of poverty or drunkenness on the other. It is to be admitted that the basis on which these rates were calculated was very weak: thus poverty was determined by considering the rateable valuation of the counties and did not correspond to the 'pauperism' rate; the 'insanity rate' was in terms of the number of patients resident in public mental hospitals on a given day per 1,000 of total population, although Griesinger [26] in the middle of the previous century had pointed out that this calculation is quite unsatisfactory as a measure of prevalence. Griesinger's remarks have a modern ring:

'Of scarcely any country in the world do we possess quite trustworthy statistics.

Where more exact reports are presented, they are often rendered comparatively useless, owing to their not being collected according to the same method, and especially—a great source of difference of numbers—owing to the mixing of the states which ought naturally to be separated—insanity proper, and idiocy and cretinism. Of many districts our knowledge is limited to an average calculation of the number of the insane in asylums, so various in different countries. The unsatisfactoriness of this is self-evident . . . It will be well, therefore, to accept the following figures with great reservation.' (1845)

It is clear that those, like W. R. Dawson, who made topographical surveys and comparisons without heeding the warnings or dodging the pitfalls in their way, were liable to censure, but they could not be accused of indifference to the social aspects of mental illness. Their failing lay in the then common medical disregard for close inquiry into social data and for statistical analysis of them: indifference, in short, to what men like Quetelet, Villermé, Panum, and William Farr had taught and accomplished.

This criticism cannot be levelled at the author of one of the most durable contributions to social psychiatry in the last hundred years—I mean Emile Dürkheim. Dürkheim was, of course, not medically expert: he was a sociologist inspired by Comte and he brought to the investigation of suicide no medical knowledge but a brilliant combination of theoretical insight and rigorous method. We still drink at the waters which he caused to flow. But, as always, the outstanding innovator built on the achievements of his predecessors: in this case Lisle, Bertrand, Brierre de Boismont and Morselli. Their studies had been largely empirical, devoted to statistical fact-finding, and set in a very meagre framework of theory. Dürkheim came along with his novel concepts of social morphology and dynamic, and produced a study of deviant behaviour which, as Hanan Selvin [27] has said, is still a model of sociological research sixty-one years after it first appeared: 'Few, if any, later works can match the clarity and power with which Dürkheim marshalled his facts to test and refine his theory.' Set alongside Dürkheim's contribution, the investigations made by his contemporaries who were psychiatrists are a painful reminder that social studies of abnormal behaviour require the grasp and skills of the social scientist as much as those of the psychiatrist—perhaps more so. Happy the place, and excellent the fruits, when social scientist and physician combine as they have in this university in our time.

Dürkheim was himself acutely conscious of some of the hindrances to research, whether 'pure' or applied, in the social sciences. He wrote in 1904:

'Thus the specialization of which sociology has need in order to become a truly positive science, is already a well established movement but one very imperfectly organized. "Amongst the more conspicuous of existing imperfections may be mentioned (1) the want of a sufficiently wide and effective recognition of the interdependence and unity of all social phenomena, as a necessary working hypothesis; (2) the tendency of the specialists to needlessly multiply entities . . . and satisfy themselves with facile explanations and naïf simplicist formulas . . . and (5) the tendency of specialists to move at random without adequate conception of a definitive purpose, and hence not only to waste effort but also to leave important areas of the sociological field uncultivated.'

The more amateurish excursions of psychiatrists into social investigation, or social speculation, at the time Dürkheim was writing, attest to the gulf between them and him, and their unawareness of the sophistication, in theory and method, which had been attained not only by Dürkheim but by other contemporaries also, like Simmel and Weber.

  This is not to say that these psychiatrists and their predecessors had been indifferent to the social problems of etiology, pathology and treatment which their branch of medicine thrust upon them, or that they were obtuse in making the broad generalizations that seemed to fit the observed phenomena. They were aware, too, that in this area of our concern there are 'sturdy doubts and boisterous objections, wherewith the unhappiness of our know-ledge too nearly acquainteth us'. No one exemplifies this better than Henry Maudsley [28]. At the risk of bombarding you with quotations, I recall what he wrote in his *Pathology of Mind* in 1879: 'It seemed proper to emphasize the fact that insanity is really a social phenomenon, and insist that it cannot be investigated satisfactorily and apprehended rightly except it be studied from a social point of view.' And, as an example of his interpretation of what was going on in his day:

'It may be anticipated perhaps that the time will come, though it is yet afar off, when the feelings of anger and retaliation which are now roused by criminal and vicious doings will be extinct, and when those who perpetrate them will be thought so irrational as to be looked upon with the same feelings with which lunatics are looked upon now. In this relation it is instructive to take notice how complete a revolution in the feeling with regard to the insane has taken place within the last half century, with increase of knowledge of what insanity is: their irrational beliefs and turbulent deeds roused indignation formerly, and were dealt with by harsh measures of punishment, as if they were voluntary; now, however, since better knowledge of insanity has been gained, those who have to do with the insane look upon their delusions with curiosity or compassion, and are not moved to anger by their perverse and violent deeds; however much annoyed or distressed by them, they would no more think of getting angry and retaliating by punishments than they would think of punishing an unwelcome rainy day; but it is instructive also to note that the old sentiments still linger in the breasts of ignorant people.'

In this, as in many other eloquent passages in his writings, Maudsley was partly expressing *idées reçues* among enlightened late Victorians, and partly deceiving himself, as even disillusioned sceptics like him can do, about the changes occurring in the public attitudes pertaining to the recognition or the understanding of mental aberration.

  But when incisive scrutiny might puncture a bubble, these sceptics could be shrewdly destructive. Consider two fashionable notions which I have referred to—that civilization as it advances brings about more mental disorder, and that degeneracy is a well-attested biological phenomenon manifested in suc-cessive generations by more and more disabling mental handicaps. To the second of these notions Maudsley unhesitatingly subscribed because he relied on clinical impressions and a misleading biological analogy, but the former fallacy he saw through because he recognized how inadequate were the

statistics alleged to support it. Similarly in the preceding year (1878) Daniel
Hack Tuke [29] had concluded, after a painstaking review of the evidence:

'... that the increase of recognized insanity in this country during the last half
century has been enormous; that the great mass of this is easily explained by the
attention of the public and Parliament having been directed to the care and treatment of the insane; by the consequent provision of asylums; by the lower rate of
mortality; and by the increased stringency of the Commissioners in regard to certi-
fying patients. ... Lastly, looking not at the accumulation of lunatics in asylums
but at the admissions, and making every possible allowance for their considerable
rise beyond that of the population, it is impossible to deny that there is reason to
fear some real increase of occurring insanity.'

Profitless discussions about degeneracy and the effects of social change
largely usurped the place of impartial research during the nineteenth century
and the first decade of the twentieth. As Professor Rosen's [30] recent survey
indicated, much acumen was shown, and much sceptical good sense brought
to bear on the examination of popular beliefs concerning the price paid for
advances in civilization. But the painstaking business of collecting data and
making systematic inquiries was not pursued. In some crucial ways, the
situation was like that now prevailing in respect of socially ill-favoured
deviations of personality: whether 'psychopathic' or 'deviant' personality
is specifically related to certain changing features in our society, whether it
is on the increase, whether it can be prevented or mitigated by social measures,
whether it is part of the price we pay for rapid transition resulting from new
technologies, the application of scientific discovery, and great political and
cultural changes—these issues seem very familiar if one has been reading the
nineteenth century psychiatrists who interested themselves in the effects of
the industrial revolution and what was then called progress: one has only to
substitute 'degeneracy' and 'insanity' for 'psychopathic personality', and
perhaps read 'social instability' instead of 'progress in civilization'.

Here, we are, of course, close to the problems of crime and drug addiction
which attracted much attention from earlier generations of psychiatrists.
The social and moral questions raised when defective or insane people commit
a crime had been so sedulously conned by many of the best minds, in psychiatry that it is surprising to find how repetitive the arguments were, how
scanty the amassed data: they followed forensic rather than medical lines of
thought, and were fortified by clinical rather than social observations.
Though this is broadly true of all countries, there was in Germany fifty years
ago a particularly lively interest in the marginal groups—tramps, beggars,
prostitutes, juvenile delinquents—which anticipated later studies. Prominent
among those who investigated these groups were Wilmanns, Bonhoeffer [31],
Stelzner [32], Gruhle [33], Isserlin [34], and Schneider [35]. Their interest
led to a search for the *via media* between comprehensive statistics such as the
official figures provide on a national scale, and the 'Persönlichkeitsstatistik',
as Gruhle called it, which can be based on detailed and thorough investigation
of the history, psychological type and characteristics, social milieu, and interplay between milieu and disposition of the individuals on whom the statistic

is based. This familiar crux, and the compromises it necessitates, was at once more troublesome and less fully recognized fifty years ago than it is by us today in the light of statistical advances and advances in the social sciences. But it is still instructive to look at the studies published by these psychiatrists of the last generation—or perhaps I should say the last generation but one; I heard the the teaching of three of them, and think them now undeservedly neglected.

A social aspect of psychiatry to which these writers and their immediate contemporaries paid relatively little heed was the one concerned with the aims of treatment. A few years later, however, in the early nineteen-twenties, Arthur Kronfeld [36] examined this question. His standpoint was the following. The difficulties inherent in adapting to economic and social conditions may in a given community or a given epoch be insuperable for a large section of the population: we then concentrate on bettering the adverse external conditions, rather than on bettering the patient's state directly. Adaptation to surroundings is not the criterion of normality and health, nor is it necessarily the aim of treatment. If we accept the thesis that the aim of medical care for mental illness is to squeeze the patient into conformity with the conditions and demands of his actual social setting, we do so only at the price of disregarding the individual and his distinctive personality. 'Es würde eine grosse schematische Domestikation geben, ein Mensch würde aussehen wie der Andere.' The physician, and especially the psychotherapist, is not, Kronfeld insisted, the unquestioning agent of social institutions and norms, ensuring and enforcing them. The value of a human being may be evident in his capacity to adapt to these, but his fundamental quality, which gives him dignity, does not lie in such adaptation.

'Every age distills a new standard of human value out of its total economic and psychological trends, and is inclined to make it general and absolute. So our period has equated what is socially useful with what is intrinsically valuable: and increasingly we find working capacity made the criterion not only of usefulness but also of health, morality and goodness.'

We have all travelled a long way since Kronfeld wrote that, and it may seem to you that we are no longer in any danger of equating a man's mental health with his capacity for adapting to his surroundings, working, and conforming. But I doubt if this issue has really been clarified; all of us who have struggled to understand what we really mean by mental health have cause to hesitate, and it is often hard to say whether we overvalue the social acceptability of behaviour in judging whether the behaviour is morbid, and in assessing the degree of its morbidity. Behind this, as behind the relationship between choice of treatment and social class, lie prejudices and values which are too seldom made explicit.

I have referred particularly to Kronfeld because he is an outstanding representative of a regrettably transient school of psychiatrists who were keenly alive to the social implications of mental illness, rigorous in analysing the relationship systematically, and protected against untethered theorizing by

266

their daily contact with raw clinical material. Kronfeld, in the chapter on 'Sociology of the Mentally Abnormal' in his classical work on the *Perspectives of Psychotherapy*, and Karl Birnbaum [37] in his many writings on 'Culture and Psychopathology', furnished blueprints for the great argument which has held, and will long hold, the psychiatric stage. Dividing the problems into those which treat of how social forces contribute to mental illness on the one hand, and on the other those which trace the ways in which mental abnormality affects the well-being, the structure and development of society, these psychiatrists showed the influence of philosophers such as Husserl; of sociologists, like Weber and Dürkheim; and of psychopathologists, notably Freud and Adler.

The views these men (Kronfeld, Birnbaum) expounded in the nineteen-twenties were neither heterodox, nor hidden in obscure journals, nor embodied in pretentious and repellent language. They were readable and persuasive; men who had great authority, like Jaspers, subscribed to them: yet the average textbook of psychiatry in the English language, and the average practicing psychiatrist, paid them little regard. Psychiatric social workers, it is true, came to be regarded as essential members of a psychiatric staff; but often, as it emerged, their functions came to be exercised more in psychotherapy of the family than in the larger society of which the family is a nidus and microcosm.

In the thirty years since Kronfeld and Birnbaum and the rest flourished, there have been great advances in the social sciences and in their application to psychiatry, but psychiatrists, on the whole, have been dilatory in keeping up with them. It was still the case, five years ago, that Professor Hollingshead [38] had to describe the position in this way:

'In commenting upon the areas of acceptance (between schools of thought on causation) I would suggest the following order: first, the organic, because it is most firmly entrenched within the institution of medicine; second, the psychological, because it also is well accepted in medicine, though perhaps to a somewhat lesser extent; third, the social because it has been even less completely adopted; and finally, the dynamic, which I put at the end because I think that it would bring together and integrate the other three.'

It seems strange that psychiatrists, of all people, should be slow to accept the full implications of the thesis that men live their mental lives in and through society.

Fifty years ago sociology was emerging from its grand theory stage parented by Comte and Herbert Spencer. In 1904 Dürkheim had said, in an address to the Sociological Society of London:

'Most subsequent sociologists have continued the Comte-Spencer tradition of seeking to discover the general laws of social evolution by speculative rather than observational methods. And yet it is evident that the multitude of facts which are called social can only be studied in a scientific manner by disciplines equally multiple and special. It cannot suffice to survey the complex social world with general views prematurely unified, and hence confused and vague.'

And a year later, addressing the same society, Hobhouse said that the ambitious attempts at a great sociological system like Comte's having failed, the dwelling-place of sociology had been swept and garnished, and 'into this home have come the seven devils of sciolism. You have people prepared to dogmatize on social affairs from no knowledge at all, or from a little reflection on the popular literature of the day, or finally, you have the attempt to deal with the science of society as if it were a department of the science of biology'. The fears thus expressed were understandable but excessive. It may be that for a period the swing away from grand systems and sweeping theories went too far, and that empirical fact-collecting about irrelevant or trivial issues was carried to extremes, justifying Gunnar Myrdal's comment that 'more and more effort is devoted to less and less important problems'. But it is hardly seemly for a psychiatrist to enter into the jousts where Professor Wright Mills is laying about him, or to offer an opinion on the present conflicts. The psychiatrist sees, nowhere better than here in New Haven, that sociologists work mainly with theories of the middle range, within a relevant, limited socio-cultural context, testing these theories by empirical research. He sees that by collaboration the questions the psychiatrist asks can be formulated so that a significant problem, amenable to investigation by sociologist and psychiatrist jointly, emerges, and that its prosecution yields illuminating results. If the psychiatrist, turning as he can here from the demonstration of what such collaboration can achieve, examines the present state of social psychiatry in general he finds some cause for disappointment at the slow rate of progress; he may also conclude that progress takes a strangely cyclical course. 'For, as though there were a metempsychosis, and the soul of one man passed into another, opinions do find, after certain revolutions, men and minds like those that first begat them.'

Fifty years ago Bleuler's [39] arguments against indiscriminate admission of schizophrenics to hospital, and against retaining them in hospital until their symptoms had cleared up, were accepted and acted upon in many places. The pros and cons of community care for patients with residual symptoms—delusions, hallucinations, catatonic anomalies of motility—were debated, and serviceable principles were enunciated, notably by Hans W. Maier [40], Bleuler's successor at Burghölzli. But as time went on, particularly in the English-speaking countries, the surge of therapeutic optimism and of ambitious hospital programmes diverted attention to intra-hospital care. Nowhere is this better shown, I think, than in William A. White's *Outlines of Psychiatry* [41]. In the 1921 edition he devotes a page to the treatment of schizophrenia. He reminds the reader that many patients with this disorder will have to spend most of their lives in a mental hospital, and 'it is therefore desirable to educate them as early as possible in good habits'. To this end he advocated 're-education through the agency of industrial training. If this is to be done intelligently, however, it is essential that the patient be not merely put to work in a haphazard way, but that a sufficiently careful analysis of the psychology of his particular condition be made so that it will appear what is the best method of approach to arouse his interests and fix his attention. It is also necessary to bear in mind the motor disturbances, more especially of the catatonic group.' Here we have what was for the times a progressive standpoint, in which it is however, taken for granted that the aim is to make the patient's life more agreeable and normal within the institution; Bleuler's bolder plea for taking risks in restoring the still crippled schizophrenic to the general community is not entertained, even in passing. But since the war we have seen Bleuler's policy reasserted and developed. In Great Britain the development has followed two not quite consonant lines. The first is succinctly enunciated in the recommendation of the Royal Commission, which reported in 1957, 'There should be a general reorientation away from institutional care in its present form and towards community care.' The second line of action in Great Britain is a little different: it is less ready to accept the 'consensus of informed opinion' as *vox Dei*, and is experimental rather than reformist in temper. It labours to test hypotheses regarding some cardinal issues:— the indications for hospital admission and discharge; the effects within the hospital of various sorts of human environment, regime and occupational training, socializing measures and incentives; the prognostic and socio-therapeutic value of hostels, Industrial Rehabilitation Units and sheltered workshops (Remploy); and the favourable or adverse influences in the home and living conditions of patients with continuing schizophrenic illness. For this second approach, in which action-research and laboratory experiments are both required, there is everything to be said: naturally I think so, because that has for some years been one of the main activities of the Research Unit in Social Psychiatry of which I have the honour to be Director. As for the more confident policy, of which the Royal Commission were the very powerful spokesmen, there is of course immense advantage in a reformist movement which is consciously directed against the abuse of letting patients languish and moulder in a sterile, indifferent or neglectful milieu and which makes relatively normal community life the aim and the criterion of therapeutic success of patients who will never recover. But along with the advantages go risks of detriment—not to the patients, necessarily, but to those with whom they come in contact in the community: especially their families and those with whom they work. An overzealous fulfillment of the policy of turning away from institutional to community care can bring its own abuses in its train. The philosophers thought it proper to put not one but two mottoes on the temple at Delphi: one, the better remembered, was 'Know Thyself', but the second, equally imperative, enjoined 'Nothing in Excess'. It might be worth inscribing that over the temple of psychiatry.

This, however, is a digression. I have wanted only to recall that in this area of social psychiatry, which considers schizophrenia, we are today doubling on our tracks, reverting to a broad principle enunciated and acted on fifty years ago; but we are dealing with it now in a rather different way from that of Bleuler and his contemporaries. On the one hand we are accumulating our statistics of the increasing number of patients kept in the community, and we contemplate these with the satisfaction and fervour that attends a manifest effort towards progress; and on the other hand we investigate rather laboriously the social, clinical and psychological problems that must be solved before it is certain that the satisfaction and fervour are fully warranted. In its cyclical course psychiatry has come round to where it stood in 1910 on this matter, but today it has greatly enhanced opportunities for analysing and resolving the problems—especially those in the family—that underlie the socio-clinical issue affecting chronic schizophrenics. I believe the same could be said of many other socio-clinical issues in psychiatry.

The moral of this tale, it seems to me, is that we do ill to think lightly of our predecessors in social psychiatry. The ablest among us need not be so humble as to say, with Bernard of Chartres, that we are dwarfs sitting on the shoulders of giants; but neither need it be supposed that we are giants sitting on the shoulders of dwarfs, or sitting on nobody's shoulders at all. In fifty years there has been a great forward move, in which empirical generalizations from experience have been submitted to the chastening tests of experiment, quantification and reference to more refined theoretical concepts and systems of ideas. In the same fifty years psychiatrists, and I think sociologists too, have sometimes cultivated diverse plots in the psychiatric estate without counting the harvest reaped by the insight and the admittedly cruder methods of the men who were tilling the same areas around the turn of the century. The work of these men was not negligible. But in their day the extra-medical forces that influence the lines of psychiatric research were less consciously and powerfully directed towards social problems than in 1960. As Sigerist has said, the development of medical science is largely determined by non-medical factors—Weltanschauung, technologic invention, philosophy, religion, economics, advances in the physical and biological sciences. In our time advances in the social sciences, too, contribute an impetus to research and social action which perhaps owes something to psychiatry and which certainly promises to enrich it.

REFERENCES

1 HOLLINGSHEAD, A. B. and REDLICH, F. C. Social Class and Mental Illness: A Community Study, New York, Wiley, 1958.
2 MYERS, J. K. and ROBERTS, B. A. Family and Class Dynamics in Mental Illness, New York, Wiley, 1959.
3 SAVAGE, G. H. 'Mental diseases', in Allbutt, T. C. and Rolleston, H. D. (eds.) A System of Medicine, London, Macmillan, 1899.
4 ASCHAFFENBURG, G. (ed.) Handbuch der Psychiatrie, Leipzig, Deuticke, 1915.
5 MARIE, A. (ed.) Psychopathologie Comparée. Traité International de Psychologie Pathologique, Vol. III, Paris, Alcan, 1912.
6 VOSS, G. 'Die Aetiologie der Psychosen', in Aschaffenburg, G. (ed.) Handbuch der Psychiatrie, Leipzig, Deuticke, 1915.
7 WILMANNS, K. Zur Psychopathologie des Landstreichers, Leipzig, Barth, 1906.
8 BONHOEFFER, K. Ein Beitrag zur Kenntnis des groszstädtischen Bettel- und Vagabundenthums, Berlin, Guttenberg, 1900.

9 KRAEPELIN, E. *Psychiatrie*, 8te Auflage, Leipzig, Barth, 1909.

10 DÜRKHEIM, E. *Suicide: A Study in Sociology* (trans. Spaulding, J. A. and Simpson, G.), Glencoe, Ill., Free Press, 1951.

11 BUMKE, O. *Ueber nervöse Entartung*, Berlin, Springer, 1912.

12 WHITE, W. A. 'The geographical distribution of insanity in the United States', *J. nerv. ment. Dis.*, 1903, **30**, 257.

13 MAY, J. V. 'Immigration as a problem in the state care of the insane', *Amer. J. Insan.*, 1912, **69**, 313.

14 SALMON, T. W.'Immigration and the mixture of races in relation to the mental health of the nation, p. 241 in White, W. A. and Jelliffe, S. E. (eds.), *Modern Treatment of Nervous and Mental Diseases*, vol. I. New York, Lea & Febiger, 1913.

15 KIRBY, G. H. 'A study in race psychopathology', *N.Y. St. hosp. Bull.*, 1909 (New Series), **1**, 669.

16 KOREN, J. *Insane and Feebleminded in Institutions*, U.S. Bureau of the Census, 1904.

17 HILL, J. A. *Insane and Feebleminded in Institutions*, U.S. Bureau of the Census, 1910.

18 ØDEGAARD, Ø. 'Emigration and insanity', *Acta psychiat. (Kbh.)*, 1932, Suppl. No. 4.

19 MALZBERG, B. *Social and Biological Aspects of Mental Disease*, Utica, N.Y., State Hospitals Press, 1940.

20 MURPHY, H. B. M. *Flight and Resettlement*, U.N.E.S.C.O., 1955.

21 GILLON, J. J., DUCHÊNE, H. and CHAMPION, Y. 'Pathologie mentale de la mobilité géographique', pp. 37730 C.30, in Ey, H. (ed.), *Encyclopédie Médico-Chir.*, Vol. III: *Psychiatrie*, Paris, Editions Techniques, 1958.

22 HERSCHMANN, H. 'Verfolgungswahn der sprachlich Isolierten', *Z. ges. Neurol. Psychiat.*, 1921, **66**, 346.

23 JASPERS, K. 'Homesickness and crime', *Arch. Krim. Anthrop.*, 1910, **36**, 1.

24 JANET, P. *Les Médications Psychologiques*, Vol. III, Paris, Alcan, 1919.

25 DAWSON, W. R. 'The relation between the geographical distribution of insanity and that of certain social and other conditions in Ireland', *J. ment. Sci.*, 1911, **57**, 571.

26 GRIESINGER, W. *Mental Pathology and Therapeutics* (trans. Roberstson, C. L. and Rutherford, J.), London, The New Sydenham Society, publication no. 33, 1867.

27 SELVIN, H. C. 'Dürkheim's *Suicide* and problems of empirical research', *Amer. J. Sociol.*, 1957–8, **63**, 607.

28 MAUDSLEY, H. *Pathology of Mind*, London, Macmillan, 1879.

29 TUKE, D. H. *Insanity in Ancient and Modern Life, with Chapters on its Prevention*, London, Macmillan, 1878.

30 ROSEN, G. 'Social stress and mental disease from the 18th century to the present. Some origins of social psychiatry', *Milbank mem. Fd. Quart.*, 1959, **37**, 5.

31 BONHOEFFER, K. *Z. Strafrechtswiss.*, 1902, **23**, 106.

32 STELZNER, H. F. *Die Psychopathischen Konstitutionen*, Berlin, Karger, 1911.

33 GRUHLE, H. *Die Ursachen der jugendlicher Verwahrlosung und Kriminalität*, Berlin, Springer, 1912.

34 ISSERLIN, M. 'Psychiatrische Jugendfürsorge', *Z. ges. Psychiat.*, 1913, **12**, 465.

35 SCHNEIDER, K. *Studien über Persönlichkeit und Schicksal eingeschriebener Prostituierter*, 2te Auflage, Berlin, Springer, 1926.

36 KRONFELD, A. *Perspektiven der Seelenheilkunde*, Leipzig, Thieme, 1930.

37 BIRNBAUM, K. *Grundzüge der Kulturpsychopathologie*, Munich, Bergmann, 1924.

38 HOLLINGSHEAD, A. B. 'Areas of acceptance', in Kruse. H. D. (ed,) *Integrating the Approach to Mental Disease*, London, Cassell, 1958.

39 BLEULER, E. 'Frühe Entlassungen', *Psychiat.-neurol. Wschr.*, 1905, **6.** Abstract in
   Neurol. Centralblatt, 1906, **25,** 226.
40 MAIER, H. W. 'Die Frühentlassung der Schizophrenen', *Zbl. ges. Neurol. Psychiat.,*
   1929, **53,** 662.
41 WHITE, W. A. *Outlines of Psychiatry,* 8th edn., Washington, Nerv. Ment. Dis.
   Publ. Co., 1921.

17

MEDICINE AND THE AFFECTIONS
OF THE MIND

WHEN A man is chosen Harveian Orator it sets him thinking about his fitness for this signal honour, considering the notable roll of those who have had it before him and the quality and value of what they said. Many of his predecessors chose to speak of those problems in medicine which they had long pondered and which were the chief concern of their professional lives. Few have been psychiatrists—two in the last hundred years—and it seems, therefore, timely and suitable to my competence that I should speak particularly of those secrets of nature which lie behind the morbid affections of the mind.

In this College it is taken for granted that psychiatry has its place within the medical family—a wayward member perhaps, a prodigal who has taken his journey into a far country—but still one of the family. In spite of all differences in approach and subject-matter, the study and the care of psychological ills are as much a medical concern as is somatic disease. This seems obvious to us: but it has not always been obvious, nor outside this College is it everywhere conceded.

AN OPEN ISSUE

In the Middle Ages and well into the seventeenth century abnormal conduct was often construed as due to demoniacal possession, witchcraft, and sorcery: consequently the clergy played a large part in dealing, by exorcism and otherwise, with those whose mental illness brought them under suspicion of traffic with the powers of evil. As late as Harvey's time the issue was still open. 'It is a disease of the soul on which I am to treat,' wrote the author [1] of the *Anatomy of Melancholy* in 1621, 'and as much appertaining to a divine as to a physician.' Conversely, Sir Thomas Browne [2] declared, 'I can cure vices by physick when they remain incurable by divinity.' While there was

This paper was delivered as the Harveian Oration to the Royal College of Physicians of London in October 1963. It is reprinted from the *British Medical Journal* (December 1963), **2**, 1549–57.

this uncertainty about the due province of physician and priest, many divines put out treatises on insanity and nervous affections which differed in emphasis rather than in substance from those of medical writers. So intertwined were medicine and religion that in 1634 Harvey himself was required by the King to direct a search for 'devil's marks' on the bodies of four women who had been convicted of witchcraft in Lancashire.

There were some physicians contemporary with Harvey, and many in the generation that preceded him, who shared the general credulity regarding a diabolical origin for aberrations of conduct and belief: but the mental climate was changing. The change affected attitudes to rational explanation and scientific inquiry; it hardly touched treatment. During Harvey's two years at Padua the guides to practice were Dioscorides and Avicenna, Galen and Hippocrates [3]; all illness, mental and physical alike, was interpreted in terms of humoral mythology, and treatment was what it had been in the Middle Ages and before. But alongside this repose in the old ways there was a quickening, inquiring spirit, of which among universities Padua, and among doctors Harvey, were the great exemplars. A habit of mind was being cultivated which, in time, accustomed physicians to seek for natural causes and to give up deferring to past authority. It armoured them in the latter part of the seventeenth century against accepting too readily supernatural explanations of abnormal behaviour. And the contrast to which attention has been drawn [4], between the critical penetration and brilliance of Harvey the scientist and the antique medicinal treatment used by Harvey the physician —this contrast reminds us that therapeutics has always had its own imperatives, more conservative at some times and more audacious at others than those of scientific inquiry; and that, in Harvey's day at any rate, treatment, whether of mental or physical illness, was irrational, unenlightened, and largely ineffective, depending greatly on what Sydenham called 'the immense stock of much acclaimed medicines that we have so long been pestered with'.

MORAL FORCES

What chiefly distinguished the treatment of the mentally ill then and later was the harshness which made their lot as degraded as that of the criminals with whom they were often herded in a common misery. But towards the end of the eighteenth century two powerful moral forces came to bear on psychiatry. The one, humanitarian in its impulse and as much lay as medical in its origins, strove with fluctuating success to put aside stripes, threats, and humiliations as ways of coping with abnormal behaviour and aimed to substitute for these established abuses a form of treatment which took account of the patients' claim on compassion and understanding, and their need of considerate regard for their feelings. The new regime concentrated on influences which would allay the harm done by environmental hurts and intemperate passions. Although the passions were held responsible for much

274

mental disorder, it was not as evidence of moral obliquity that their excesses were viewed by the reformers but as signs and effects of misfortune. Sydenham [5] had put their standpoint a century earlier: 'I conceive that there would be very little room left for charity, unless the misfortunes which the inconsiderate bring upon themselves by their own fault, were to be alleviated with humanity and tenderness. It belongs to God to punish the offence, but 'tis our duty to assist the distress'd, and relieve the diseased to the best of our power, and not to make too strict an inquiry into the cause of the evil, and irritate them by our censures.'

Pinel and Chiarugi and Tuke were the standard-bearers of the movement for humane treatment; unlike in many ways, they had this essential in common, that they did not sit in moral judgment on the patients, nor treat outrageous and dissolute conduct as a culpable fall from grace.

There developed, however, almost concurrently, a school of medical thought, especially in Germany, which can also be called 'moral': a school which insisted that mental disorder is a consequence of sin. 'Madness,' wrote George Man Burrows [6], 'is one of the curses imposed by the wrath of the Almighty on his people for their sins.' Heinroth, and other psychiatrists who minimized the physical causes of mental disorder, maintained that it was invariably the outcome of moral transgression, the voluntary pursuit of evil. From this Pelagian sort of psychopathology the conclusion was drawn that the patient's will must be curbed, his physical movements restricted by fetters and coercion used, not capriciously but of set purpose, to bring the erring guilt-laden patient back to right conduct so that he will use his free will to keep clear of pride, greed, and other sins which are the prelude to insanity. Heinroth [7] even wanted to deny the mentally sick man who committed a crime that exemption from penalties which all societies have in varying degree allowed him because of his impaired judgment and self-control.

These moralistic vagaries of medical thinking, which could have ended by taking psychiatry out of medicine altogether, were countered by extremists of the somatic school, and as the century advanced the confused equation of sin and illness lost ground and came to be discredited as a mediaeval regression. The necropsy room and the microscope told about the pathology of many sorts of psychosis; and even neurotic and psychopathic disorder, in spite of the provoking symptoms displayed—moral insanity, as Prichard called it—nevertheless remained a medical problem, to be studied by the physiological and clinical approach of Charcot and others like him.

By the end of the nineteenth century, however, the concepts of virtue and mental health were again being interwoven by some influential exponents of psychotherapy, chief among them Dubois [8], and there have been ample evidences since then that the medical view of mental illness is apt from time to time to be strongly tinctured with moral values which the physician imports into his assessment of the causes and nature of neurotic illness, in particular.

There are degrees of this propensity to moral judgments on patients. The majority of psychiatrists, aware that 'no other specialty of medicine deals with diseases whose initial signs can be so easily confused with moral lapses', regard moral approbation or disapproval as irrelevant, medically speaking; they prefer to draw as firmly as they can the distinction between vice and illness, sin and morbid feelings of guilt. But there is a notable minority who still deny the distinction. They are not only psychiatrists: some psychologists, too, men of authority like Gordon Allport [9] and Hobart Mowrer [10], believe that neuroses have a large element of sin in them, that they cannot be properly called illnesses, and that only through confession of past stupidities and errors, and attempts at restitution, can the neurotic sufferer hope for relief. However, these psychologists have a declared bias, and a low opinion of psychological medicine: 'authority and power ought to go with demonstrated competence, which medicine clearly has in the physical realm, but equally clearly does not have in psychiatry' [10]. Some psychiatrists, too, come disconcertingly close to this antimedical position; in their eyes mental symptoms are inextricably tied to the ethical context in which they develop, and it is misconceived and futile to attempt to solve what are really ethical and social problems by medical methods. Carrying the issue to an extreme, they characterize mental illness as a myth and allow the term 'illness' only when the disabling mental symptoms arise from brain disease: all the rest is a matter of 'problems in living'.

So outright a rejection of customary medical theory and practice in regard to psychological anomalies provokes a strong dissent. But the persistence or revival of this train of thought in successive generations suggests that there is here a significant and possibly basic issue. It has arisen in the courts and in the schools of philosophy. Immanuel Kant [11] maintained that expert opinions as to the mental abnormality of people who had committed crimes should be obtained not from physicians but from philosophers; and it must be conceded that the debatable ground of free-will and moral responsibility with which courts are so often concerned is not an arena in which the psychiatrist is happy to be a gladiator. Nevertheless he is often called on, and often also has his *locus standi* questioned by social inquirers. A formidable critic of our forensic activities has lately said that she failed to discover 'either in the records of court proceedings or in literature, any convincing demonstration that an intelligible distinction between psychopathy and wickedness can be drawn in terms of any meaningful concept of moral or criminal responsibility.' [12]

Here we have then, in contemporary form and a particular context, a long standing charge against us: psychological medicine is accused of exceeding its proper bounds, and confounding moral with medical considerations.

PROPER SPHERE OF THE PSYCHIATRIST

What, then, is our proper sphere? The question is not one for psychiatry alone: it affects all medicine, for it turns on the concepts of health and disease.

A robust demonstration of our ability to define these two concepts would either dispose of the psychiatric difficulty, *a fortiori*, or change it to a dispute about professional scope, a lowlier but more tangible issue.

Health has long been regarded as consisting in freedom from discomfort or disability and from objective disturbances of function. A strict interpretation of this definition has hardly been possible since it became clear that a pathological change can be insidiously present without producing discomfort or lessening capacity; and a further crux is afforded by lifelong non-progressive abnormalities, like pentosuria, which can be harmless. As long ago as the days of Aulus Gellius people disputed whether a man with a congenital weakness, or a eunuch, or a pregnant woman, could be called healthy. Their interest, it is true, was focused on economic and social implications such as the price to be paid for a slave in this condition, but the philosophers spotted the basic problem. When it comes to defining mental health and disease, including mental defect, the area of uncertainty broadens. Distress and disability alone are hardly sufficient criteria; for distress may be normal and healthy, as in mourning, and disability may depend on external conditions and attitudes towards aberrant behaviour, which vary from place to place. Many efforts at finding more durable criteria for mental illness have therefore been made, usually with a strong propensity towards letting social adaptation, or even social approval, serve the purpose. But if success in adapting to the demands of society is to be a criterion, the same man will be judged healthy in one country and ill in another. Anyone who has reflected on the many definitions of health, and of mental health in particular, will, I think, conclude that there is no consensus, and he will see that when moral or social values are invoked there are scarcely any limits to the behaviour which might be called morbid. Medical criteria are safer; that is, criteria essentially concerned with the integrity of physiological and psychological functions.

Evidently we cannot fix the due confines of psychiatry by allocating to it a strictly prescribed field. We can, however, agree that the practice of psychiatry should be limited to illness and its prevention, and that illness occurs broadly when there is disabling or distressing interference with normal function. But in the last thirty years the impatience and perhaps the credulity of public opinion has pressed upon the psychiatrist requests that he treat people who are not ill and advise on problems that are not medical. It needs no logician to detect the fallacy in the syllogism which runs: psychiatrists are experts in mental disorder; mental disorder is a form of abnormal behaviour; therefore psychiatrists are experts in abnormal behaviour of every sort. Yet in matters touching on misbehaviour in children, vocational selection, troubles in marriage, crime, and many other tribulations, the psychiatrist has sometimes assumed responsibility, or had responsibility thrust upon him, beyond the range of his medical functions; and this has led him into a predicament in which he hears it said, in tones shrill with disappointment or mordant with derision, that he can give no useful service at all in matters of human conduct. Unwarranted detraction is as damaging as overweening aims. Psychiatry has suffered from both. There is no other branch of medicine which finds it so difficult to say 'no'; and is so often blamed when it says 'yes'.

Lord Adrian [13] has recently stated the temperate, rather generous view of this matter: 'now it is certainly the province of the doctor to detect and, if possible, to remedy the organic defects which may distort the personality and, if he can, to unravel the emotional web which may be leading to neurosis or crime. But this does not mean that we ought to shoulder the whole responsibility for producing agreeable and useful citizens. Training the mind to stand up to all the hostile experiences of childhood and adult life involves problems outside the sphere of organic or of psychological medicine, problems for parents and teachers and for the society which has set the standards of behaviour.'

DOCTOR'S ROLE

In our kind of society—and indeed in many societies very different from ours —the doctor's role is determined not only by the problems of ill-health upon which he is expected to use his skill, but also by the methods he is supposed to employ, the ethical and social obligations he assumes, and the privileges conceded to him. Today the privileges are many, the obligations correspondingly heavy; and the methods those of scientific inquiry reinforced by clinical experience and empirical art. They do not include passing moral judgment on his patients, nor taking political action for the better ordering of society. The doctor, of course, exercises moral judgment and takes political action as every other citizen does, but it is not part of his medical approach to his patients' disabilities to decide whether they are ethically good or bad.

If a child with behaviour-disorder is referred for medical help it is tacitly assumed that the methods of investigation and treatment will be mainly derived from the doctor's scientific training, and will, within the limits of present-day knowledge, be rational and specialized: specialized, that is, in so far as they will not be those of the teacher, the clergyman, the magistrate, or the educational psychologist—all of them people with a respected professional role and a discipline of their own to which their methods conform— but will be those of the doctor. If the psychiatrist steps out of his medical role and uses the methods of the clergyman, say, or the magistrate, he is in a small way infringing his implicit contract with society: a venial infringement, since his object is the betterment of the child's mental state, but an infringement of the sort which, greatly multiplied, brings on his collective head the reproach of exceeding his powers.

What is true of the psychiatrist's dealings with a disturbed child applies to many of his other practical activities in diagnosis and treatment. But besides diagnosis and treatment there is research and experiment. Here no such restrictive covenant can be implied. The doctor, as Harvey said, shall search out and study the secrets of nature; he has in the exercise of his clinical functions special opportunities for observation and insight; and he is free to use whatever methods seem appropriate and justified. He would, on the other hand, be guilty of a monopolizing and stupid hubris if he claimed that he alone can study and elucidate the phenomena of illness. The doctor's debts to the physiologist, the biochemist, the pathologist, the pharmacologist, are the largest part of the history of medical progress: and in the case of the psychiatrist there is a debt to psychologists also.

It is beyond dispute that whoever can advance knowedge of the problems inherent in human conduct and increase the means of remedying its defects must be given maximum opportunities for doing so. If any group of people were capable of relieving some form of illness better than the doctor can, they would be entrusted with its treatment, once their superiority had been demonstrated. But when comparable situations have occurred in the past, recognized deficiencies in medical education were presently made good, so that doctors acquired the therapeutic skill and knowledge that previous generations had lacked. It would probably be so in psychiatry. It seems unlikely that the doctor will be displaced from his traditional role in dealing with mental illness, any more than in other branches of medicine.

MEDICAL STANDING OF PSYCHIATRY

Fortified and transmuted by scientific advances of many kinds, medicine has shifted its areas of concern. The environmental causes of disease receive more attention; chronic and mental anomalies move closer to the centre of the stage; and psychology, with other sciences of behaviour, takes its place alongside the sciences long accepted as basic to medicine, though it is admittedly unequal to them in maturity, assurance, and exactitude. Psychiatry is at some disadvantage because its technical language sounds obscure and sometimes a trifle absurd in medical ears, its therapeutic achievements are still a subject of controversy, and its most characteristic means of investigation and treatment is talk—the clinical interview. These are not serious handicaps, nor are the first two peculiar to psychiatry; and it has many successes and advances to set against them. But the medical standing of psychiatry is sometimes more darkly overcast by those psychiatrists who belittle diagnosis as futile labelling, and who hold that treatment is to be judged successful by its effect on the freedom of the patient's personality and on his self-realization, rather than by whether he has become free from symptoms. Such departures from the ways and discipline of clinical medicine recall the disputes between the School of Cnidus and the School of Cos, long ago at the dawn of scientific medicine.

It is often said that psychiatry has had three revolutions—the first when humane measures and natural explanations replaced neglect, harsh repression, and animistic myths; the second, at the end of the nineteenth century, when Freud introduced a dynamic theory of human motives and conflicts; and the third, in our own time, when the assumption that the best treatment is individual treatment, preferably in hospital, has been dethroned in favour of community care, reinforced by group therapy, and sustained by newly synthesized drugs. This is too simple and too sweeping. The changes in our day have been notable, but hardly revolutionary: entrenched ideas have not been overthrown, power has not passed into new hands, opinion has swerved and wobbled rather than taken a new course. Many of the changes now in evidence have had precursors. In the forties of the last century there was a strong movement towards giving patients in mental hospitals maximal freedom to come and go, avoiding locked doors and imposed discipline, discussing with them their emotional and social difficulties, assisting them to resume family life as soon as possible; today we have a revived emphasis on these things which we describe as milieu therapy, the open-door policy, the therapeutic community, and rehabilitation. Our approach is more sophisticated and self-conscious; we use more systematic measures and more trained collaborators; we apply the findings of recent research: but in the main we tread closely in the footsteps of our predecessors of a century ago.

SCIENTIFIC STATUS OF PSYCHIATRY

There have likewise been periods which resembled our own in that some voices appealed for maximum objectivity in psychiatry, to be attained through measurement, systematic observation, and experiment, as in the natural sciences, while others cried down such strivings and maintained that objectivity in these matters can be achieved only at the cost of mummifying the mind, and sealing up the essential phenomena in so many canopic jars— tidy, docketed, and dead. This recurring dispute raises the vexed question of the scientific status of psychiatry.

Some would put this question aside as one of no importance except in the eyes of those who want to acquire for psychiatry the prestige that attaches to scientific pursuits. But the question is surely relevant and inescapable if we are considering the place of psychiatry in the household of modern medicine. The scientific method is not the only instrument for discovering truth, but it has proved so powerful that bringing it fully and appropriately to bear, studying the secrets of nature by way of experiment, offers the best promise of increasing our knowledge of mental illness. It is clearly mistaken to restrict the scientific method to that employed in the physical sciences: the biological sciences, and the sciences variously called 'social' and 'behavioural', have developed their own methods. In all these fields progress has been the outcome of controlled experiment, close observation, imaginative concepts and restrained intuition: have these methods and qualities of the inquiring mind been deployed on the problems of psychiatry?

So far as it draws upon the common fund of medical knowledge and the biological sciences basic to medicine, its scientific pretentions are relatively assured. It rests more and more upon such knowledge. But there remain large tracts of psychiatric experience in which little benefit has so far been derived from application of the methods and findings of these basic disciplines. Not that speculation has been stilled or research proscribed: but the problems are of a nature which makes them—or seems at present to make them—insusceptible of resolution by these means. To cope with such problems psychiatry has recourse to the comparatively young, tentative, but vigorous and expanding sciences which deal with behaviour and the interplay between man and the cultural environment in which he lives. They have no clear boundaries; they are still a long way, as Waddington [14] recently put it, 'from formulating for their field any principle as clear cut and incontrovertible as the principle of natural selection is in the biological realm', and they cannot yet in all their operations observe the rigour, nor hope for the consistency in their picture of the world of psychological and social phenomena, that has been attained in the world of the physical sciences. Nevertheless, the debt of psychiatry to these 'behavioural' sciences is increasing, partly because of the direct application of pyschological and social findings, but more through borrowing—and exchanging—methods for joint investigation, as by the so-called multi-disciplinary team.

DYNAMIC PSYCHOPATHOLOGY

The increment of knowledge that comes from this will meet scientific standards well enough. There is, however, a body of theory that psychiatrists draw on heavily for the interpretation and the treatment of mental disorder, but which falls short of meeting such standards. This is dynamic psychopathology, which serves to explain abnormal conduct and to steer its treatment. It is elaborate, intricate, and apt for every contingency. Yet comprehensive explanatory systems have been suspect in medicine, for good historical and epistemological reasons. We no longer feel disposed to embrace a set of related hypotheses, however illuminating and attractive, because we can collect many observations that confirm them: the grammar of science now dwells instead on refutation, whereby error can be detected and purged. Unless a generalization is stated in such terms that it can be tested and possibly falsified it may serve pragmatic ends but it is hardly a scientific hypothesis. Here dynamic psychopathology as we have known it largely falls short. It has a number of tenets stated in such a way that they could not be refuted; whatever evidence has been brought forward by experiment, criticism, or uncontrolled observation to falsify them, an alternative explanation or a recast phrasing served to reinstate the apparently refuted hypothesis.

This detracts from the scientific standing of psychiatry; but of course it does not mean that a clean sweep can or should be made of current psychopathology. Valuable concepts, penetrating and rightly discerned, may have to be expressed at a given time in language which poorly meets the need for refutable predictions. As technological advances are made, the available language for communication and testing becomes more serviceable, and the concepts and hypothesis may be found valid. The importance of technological

281

developments in all this is obvious: without the microscope Harvey himself could only conjecture about how the blood passed from the arterioles to the venules. The techniques available to the social sciences, such as the questionary and the interview, are at the pre-microscope stage. With better techniques of investigation and concomitant refining of central concepts (such as instinct), the loose tissue of psychopathology will doubtless be rewoven by degrees and made of more lasting stuff—always assuming, as we are entitled to, that society will afford the right facilities and that the prepared mind and alert observation of men of exceptional capacity will be forthcoming for the task.

A TEMPTING APPROACH

It is tempting for a psychiatrist who has lived through the last four decades, with their legitimate record of progress in his subject, to dilate upon this and extol our recent achievements. A leading teacher of psychiatry [15], for example, declared two years ago, 'for those who can accept this newer viewpoint, psychiatric illness becomes hugely and splendidly treatable. . . . For it is now accepted, not as an act of faith but as something clearly demonstrated, that there can be effective intervention in mental illness. . . . Today most psychiatric patients are cured . . . no one doubts the efficacy of psychiatric treatment.' And it is not only from psychiatrists that such paeans come. The President of the United States [16], in his message to Congress in February 1963, spoke of inaugurating 'a wholly new emphasis and approach to care for the mentally ill. This approach relies primarily upon the new knowledge and new drugs acquired and developed in recent years which make it possible for most of the mentally ill to be successfully and quickly treated in their own communities and returned to a useful place in society. These breakthroughs have rendered obsolete the traditional methods of treatment which imposed upon the mentally ill a social quarantine. . . .' Alas, these are exaggerated claims; any readiness to echo them is chastened by remembering how often physicians have supposed their own era to be one of momentous and unprecedented enlightenment. Osler [17], for example, in 1902, acclaimed in exultant language 'the colossal advance of the past fifty years: . . . never has the outlook for the profession been brighter.' Psychiatrists too have in the past congratulated themselves prematurely on major advances: indeed, the Harveian Orator in 1863 [18], himself a psychiatrist and the son of a psychiatrist, extolled the striking therapeutic advances in the cure of the insane made in his own and his father's day—advances which we must dismiss as nugatory.

It is as well, therefore, for us psychiatrists to try to keep a balance between wishful enthusiasm and sceptical judgment. We are not living through a period that marks a new epoch: there is no Galileo or Darwin, no Harvey or Newton, in psychiatry and psychology: nor—to put our aspirations on a more realistic plane—have there been discoveries during the last twenty years

282

comparable to those that have signalized the growth of therapeutics and surgery in other medical fields. Psychiatric advances have been less dramatic and less conclusive. Still, to those who have taken part in them, they have given the satisfaction and excited the hopes out of which enthusiasm is generated. Sceptical judgment is a rarer attribute, especially among those who listen to assurances that new drugs are specific and powerful, that psychotherapy is at its zenith, and that doubt is a clogging weakness.

To assess current trends and problems in psychiatry is more than a contemporary can trust himself to do impartially or within the compass of a lecture; but there are some matters which claim much attention, and they can be briefly stated.

ORIGINS OF MENTAL DISORDER

Successive generations of close observers have laboured to record the origins and aspect of mental disorder. Here doctors have done most, since they have seen most: but dramatists, novelists, historians, and biographers have brought subtle perception to bear on the inwardness of morbid experience and the springs of morbid conduct. In this century psychiatrists, influenced by the minute scrutiny of detail in psychoanalysis and by the exemplary thoroughness of the best German and French psychiatric descriptions, have diligently tried to set out the panorama of symptoms in mental disorder, coextensive with the infinitely varied picture of normal behaviour. Symptomatology is therefore a highly developed aspect of psychiatry—bewildering, as any minute study of human conduct and feelings is apt to be, but rich and instructive, in its tangled diversity. It has been the fashion, where the dynamic forces in psychopathology were the centre of attention, to belittle description, calling it superficial, and to use 'descriptive psychiatry' as a term of disparagement. Such a view takes for granted our knowledge of the forces that lie behind symptoms and appearances. It ignores the corrective power of direct observation, which can save dynamic psychopathology from its ever-present danger of mistaking metaphor for explanation, and giving to airy nothing a local habitation and a name.

Psychiatrists, like other people, used to look for single causes for single diseases: ideas about aetiology were therefore simple, one-eyed, and usually wrong. Now, seeing causation as a mesh of interacting forces, we are less ingenuous and less comfortable. Where hereditary influences and chromosome anomalies are prepotent in determining the form and the course of a mental abnormality, the problems of aetiology may be no more abstruse than those of alkaptonuria or retinitis pigmentosa; abstruse enough, even so. Where the onslaught of an adverse environment has been brutal or prolonged —an injury to the brain, for example, or an embittered denial of affection, trust, and opportunity—the aetiological problem may again, in its essentials, be like that of a broken femur or beriberi. Always individual responses will colour the clinical picture, and the individual environment will fashion the

283

outcome, even in such relatively simple sequences as these; but in the main they are among the less obscure aetiological issues in psychiatry.

But when it comes to asking how plastic a human being's mental constitution is at various phases of his life; how far training, and particular misfortunes, and physical events will mould and modify his personality; what characters are stamped in for good, and what can be reversed by such and such education, social influences, or chances of personal relationship: to questions such as these some psychiatrists are prepared to offer an answer, depending in substance and fullness on their doctrinal standpoint as well as on their experience and temperament. But to others, on sober review, such questions seem still largely unanswered. The driving forces of human conduct, shaping our minds for good or ill, are recondite; and though everybody forms opinions and working hypotheses on these matters many psychiatrists, on reflection, are ready to admit to much uncertainty and ignorance.

If we knew the answers to these questions, which men have been asking from time immemorial, then we should have moved a long way towards knowing not only how to prevent psychopathy but also how to bring up children and shape their personality along predetermined lines. It may be that such knowledge would put strength into the hands of those who want to mould men's minds into one pattern, and that it would augur ill for the future of that questing, free, adventurous quality of mind out of which the great human achievements have been born. If so, the dilemma will be no less fateful than that with which the progress of applied nuclear physics has confronted us. It seems, however, a good deal further away. But it is a reminder that, however firmly we concentrate our gaze, as we should, on the medical aspect of our patients' behaviour, we are still obliged to regard our own behaviour from another standpoint, since moral issues are there inescapable. Psychiatrists have no wish to be 'straighteners' who act, like medicine men in primitive communities, as the agents of organized society in getting 'deviants' to conform. If society asks psychiatrists to do this, with 'psychopathic disorder' as the thin end of the wedge, it may be predicted that they will refuse.

PATHOLOGY OF MENTAL DISORDER

The pathology of mental disorder was until lately divisible into pathology, as the term is ordinarily understood in medicine, and psychopathology. The division is wearing thin, but will not disappear so long as pathology depends closely on direct observation and experiment while psychopathology has a vast inferential superstructure, reared on a quivering raft of observation.

The somatic pathology of mental disorder is well illuminated in those conditions in which the mental disturbance is invariably associated with abnormal structural or chemical changes, of which it is a symptom; it is less clear when there are metabolic anomalies or fluctuations which are unspecific; and it is a very dark chamber, lit from time to time with tantalizing flashes, in the numerous 'functional' disorders. Schizophrenia is the outstanding instance of unremitting biochemical exploration, rewarded as yet with little harvest, but with much to suggest that the search will eventually succeed. In another area an inference about pathology can be drawn from the association between late effects of encephalitis and obsessional, hysterical, and sexual disturbances. More and more is being learned about the representation in central structures of psychological drives and states of awareness— for example, the mechanisms in the hypothalamus which control feeding behaviour, the activating role of the reticular formation in determining wakefulness, the oestrogen-sensitive neurones in the diencephalon which affect sexual behaviour. But it is a very far cry from such findings to a satisfying patho-physiology of 'non-organic' mental disorder. In any case such a patho-physiology will be yoked with a patho-psychology: the correlations that are now being discovered for the most part assume a double-aspect theory of brain and mind, or a psycho-physical parallelism—ultimately, no doubt, to be superseded.

We are still unable to speak intelligibly about the pathology of mental disorder except in two languages—the somatic and the psychological. The second of these—the language of psychopathology—has many dialects: too many for comfort. Most prevalent are those derived from psychoanalysis; most systematic those of the psychiatrist turned philosopher, like Karl Jaspers [19]. Less orderly and less crystallized but most promising are those which express, however haltingly, the linkage between the concepts of the physiologist, the experimental psychologist, and the sociologist, and which draw on the vernacular of studies as apparently diverse as those of animal behaviour, cognitive development, neural function, communication, and social transaction.

The dependence of the majority of psychiatrists upon Freudian psychopathology recalls the dominance of systems in medicine in the eighteenth century. This is not the occasion to review the grounds on which some accept psychoanalysis as a durable approximation to the truth, unrivalled in explanatory power, and comparable with the discoveries of Copernicus and Darwin, whereas others, like Karl Popper, regard it as a pre-scientific metaphysical scheme, and while they concede its explanatory power, deplore this as a fundamental weakness: the study of such theories, wrote Popper [20], 'seemed to have the effect of an intellectual conversion or revelation, opening your eyes to a new truth hidden from those not yet initiated. Once your eyes were thus opened, you saw new confirming instances everywhere: the world was full of verifications of the theory. Whatever happened always confirmed it. Thus its truth appeared manifest.'

Between these opposed judgments is a large body of indeterminate opinion, well aware of the great influence Freud's suggestions and conclusions have had upon Western thought, and well aware that some of his theory will endure, but unsure where the dividing line will eventually be drawn between premature synthesis and perceptive insight, between myth and model. Although psychoanalysis has been before the world, in developing guise, for more than half a century, it has not attained a stable resting point: the involvement of psychoanalysis as a theoretical system with psychoanalysis as a method of treatment, and with psychoanalysis as a method of exploration, has further clouded the picture. In such a situation the contemporary psychiatrist who is not a psychoanalyst can only pay it his tribute of wary respect and qualified gratitude, while he recognizes that the opinions expressed in the writings of leading psychoanalysts are dissonant, and that separating the wheat from the tares in this well-ploughed field has so far baffled many a reaper. Among psychoanalysts there are now people who recognize that the theory of psychoanalysis is in flux because the gap between observations and inferences has been too wide, formulations too vague, and the findings of other disciplines overlooked or treated with a selective bias. There seems much to encourage the view that a process of methodological cleansing is in train.

There are also the forms of psychopathology based on learning theory, or on conditioning and 'higher nervous activity': these are being developed *pari passu* with the psychological and physiological studies of the normal from which they derive. More abstruse and baffling is the form of psychopathology which draws its inspiration from existential philosophy, chiefly as Heidegger presented it, and which exalts subjectivity.

Obviously the number of diverse systems of psychopathology speaks against the survival of most of them as admissible elements in a medical discipline; they may merge, since at bottom they have more in common with one another than they have discrepancies, once their language has been pruned and translated into a plainer idiom.

PREVENTION

Our growing knowledge of prevention is more closely indebted to aetiology than to psychopathology. The area of direct prevention has expanded in the proportion that mental illness has been found to be dependent on avoidable or remediable somatic damage. There are, furthermore, the conditions for which heredity is partly responsible—for example, schizophrenia and manic-depressive psychosis—or is wholly responsible—for example, amaurotic idiocy, phenylketonuria, and Huntington's chorea. A significant but less definable and less certain group of preventable disorders derives not from malnutrition and other physical deficiencies and trauma but from deprivation of what seem biosocial essentials for normal mental development—affection, stimulation, protection, a dependable and consistent human environment.

Whether we regard the somatic or the psychological privations and noxae which contribute to mental morbidity, the means of prevention will be in part social. If society provided better obstetrical and prenatal care the incidence of defect through prematurity, birth-injury, anoxia and other perinatal damage might be reduced; and better conditions for the upbringing of children might lessen the chances of mental abnormality. No one can at present dog-matize on this matter; but it is clear that even when we know enough to specify the requisites for healthy mental development there will be need also for social action, and suitable public education, to get these requisites supplied.

Besides prevention through removal of major causes, there is the secondary sort of prevention which is effected by giving appropriate treatment to arrest or repair the damage done by disease. The alcoholic may be turned aside from the course which would lead to an encephalopathy or delirium; the schizophrenic may be so cared for that he has no chance to accommodate himself to a dependent, sterile, isolated way of life or to surrender the links with his family and occupation which would promote his mental health. What can be achieved depends not only on the nature of the illness and our ability to curtail or abate it by treatment, but also on the desires of the patient and his relatives, and the attitudes prevailing in society at large. The present drive to substitute community care for hospital care assumes that healthy people will understand the plight of the mentally disordered and can help them to become normal again: a legitimate assumption but unproved. Moreover, attempts to better people's knowledge and attitudes to mental illness by education and propaganda have not been quickly success-ful, or in some respects successful at all.

The office of medicine, said Bacon [21], is to 'tune this curious harp of man's body, and to reduce it to harmony'. And the physician, he went on, 'hath no particular act demonstrative of his ability, but is judged most by the event; which is ever but as it is taken; for who can tell, if a patient die or recover ... whether it be art or accident.' Something of this is the case with medicine still, and with psychiatry in particular. The increase in our therapeutic powers has been considerable, and is judged by the event; un-fortunately it is sometimes uncertain whether the treatment caused the out-come. Some methods are of great and unquestioned value, indispensable even to those who deplore their overuse; other methods, once high in favour, are dying out; and a few are vigorously championed by their partisans while other psychiatrists declare them grossly overrated. The method which is beyond all others manifestly effective is an empirical one; the most widely used methods—drugs and psychotherapy—still await the verdict that will follow dispassionate and controlled trial. The improvement in collective results that has taken place during the last thirty years is attributable not only to technical advances but also to the social changes in psychiatric hospitals and the concomitant changes in the minds and practice of those who work in them.

RESEARCH AND EDUCATION

From one standpoint the progress of psychiatry has been substantial and heartening: from another, there is a painful disproportion between the limited growth in our knowledge and the vast tracts of human distress which we still cannot account for or remove. Such a situation, in any branch of medicine, demands scrutiny of the influences and resources on which progress has depended in the recent past; and it invites speculation about the areas of psychiatric research and education where a more bountiful yield may be expected.

Medical education has an obvious place in the forefront of such scrutiny. We have lately had a thoughtful survey [22] of how medical students are taught psychiatry in the United States: much time is devoted to the subject there; it is taken very seriously, as though equal in importance to medicine, surgery, and obstetrics; and it has, in the last two decades, put most of its eggs in the psychodynamic or psychoanalytic basket. The results, surveyed by experienced American observers—or by the visitor—warrant only partial imitation. In the most recently published commentary a distinguished American teacher, himself a leading psychoanalyst [23] and not given to extravagant language, says that 'of all the subjects that the intern has been exposed to as a medical student he shows the greatest ignorance in the field of psychiatry ... our medical graduates show what amounts to an almost universal ignorance of basic psychiatry upon graduation'; and he says that it has been his experience, examining candidates for specialist accreditation by the American Board, that many of them 'do not seem to know how to examine a patient; that their so-called psychoanalytic orientation is a matter of utter confusion; that there is a mish-mash of vague conceptualizations—arising from many different sources—that passes for so-called psychodynamic psychiatry'. Such a verdict pillories the defects but overlooks the merits of American psychiatric education—its boldness in experiment, its zest for self-criticism, its enthusiasm, its receptive alertness to new ideas.

It is not for us, struggling and beset with problems, to behold the mote that is in our brother's eye while considering not the beam that is in our own. Hitherto in this country the direct clinical experience gained by clerking on psychiatrically abnormal patients has been too little, or too little supervised; or it has been too fortuitous in so far as it was uncertain whether the student, during the relatively short period spent in this way, would encounter a sufficient variety of disorders to make him at ease when examining such patients and enable him to acquire the broad principles of causation and psychopathology, and the rudiments of treatment.

The rudiments of treatment: even that will be too much, in the opinion of some; to others it will seem far too little. The dispute turns, of course, on the amount of psychological treatment that should be taught; physical methods will have the same sort of coverage and range as treatment in other branches of medicine, but psychotherapy has pitfalls and requirements peculiar to itself. Moreover, as Neal Miller [24] and others have pointed out, 'there is distressingly little rigorous proof that the average improvement of treated patients [by psychotherapy] is better than the spontaneous improvement of untreated ones.' This is hardly the pabulum for beginners. There is no evidence, from countries where medical students are introduced to active psychotherapy and encouraged to try their prentice hand, that they are, on the average, better doctors thereafter in dealing with their patients' psychological problems, open or covert, than if they had not had this early exposure to the elements. An analogy may be drawn with surgery: students do not operate and are not taught to operate. It is a postgraduate study, except on a very minor scale.

STAPLE ELEMENTS OF TEACHING

Close study of the phenomena of mental disorder, appraisal of evident causes, inferences about pathology, balanced consideration of prognosis— these are the preliminaries and the staple elements in the teaching of psychiatry to medical students. The students require a grasp and familiarity which will serve as the foundation on which treatment can be built at a relatively late stage. The medical student is being educated, rather than vocationally trained; and his education, at this stage of his life, will hardly be furthered by plunging him into the turmoil of psychological treatment, and getting him to engross himself in unravelling the emotional relationship of his patients to him and his to them.

Undergraduate education opens the way to postgraduate psychiatric studies, as specialist or investigator. Systematic and comprehensive teaching, fostered by the universities, is increasingly available to replace or supplement the once universal training by apprenticeship in mental hospitals. Besides those who intend to practise this specialty, general practitioners and public health doctors ask for appropriate postgraduate teaching.

There are also those non-medical investigators who are inquiring into some psychiatric matter and need a better acquaintance with the phenomena and problems of mental disorder than they can pick up as they go along. These are the converse of the psychiatrists who need further training in a particular scientific discipline in order to carry out clinical research. The Medical Research Council has here played a major part in facilitating the further education of those who will chiefly advance our knowledge. They work for the most part in universities and research units: and it is through the universities and the Medical Research Council (reinforced by the big foundations) that the development of psychiatry as a living branch of scientific medicine has been mainly brought about in this country. This is not to disparage the contribution of the mental hospitals.

SUPPORT FOR RESEARCH

It is sometimes said that the pace of psychiatric research has been too slow, the financial support too meagre, and that there are many able men, eager to engage in research, who are denied the means. It is not a contention that can easily be put to the proof. It is, however, reasonably certain that there is no bias against the furtherance of research into psychiatric problems: good will, rather, and eagerness to help. Psychiatry needs more money for research (including the buildings to house research), but it needs it on much the same grounds, and probably to much the same extent, as medical research as a whole needs more than it at present gets. The barrier to conspicuous advance in psychiatry has not been stinginess and prejudice on the part of those who decide whether a research project submitted to them should live or die; nor has it been lack of ability among those who are engaged in psychiatric research: it lies in the inherent toughness of the problems. 'The subtlety of the subject,' said an earlier authority, 'doth cause large possibility, and easy failing.'

As to the flow of suitable workers: the number of able people who come into psychiatry and occupy themselves with its problems has been steadily rising. The day may be fairly near when psychiatrists in academic posts can echo Billroth's [25] two-edged compliment to German medicine: 'I do not doubt that if we professors were all to die at once today, we should be replaced immediately, and so ably that the development of science would not be halted for a moment.' Who knows, it might be hastened.

If there had been seeming discrimination against psychiatric research, it would very likely have been concentrated on those areas which, in postulates and method, are least able to satisfy the criteria which prevail in the physical and biological sciences. That the sciences concerned with behaviour and social relations were for long given stepchild treatment in our universities is common knowledge: whether liberal support for research in these sciences would have yielded results of a kind applicable to research in psychiatry is harder to say, but probable. An economist [26], dismayed at the misuse and diversion of intellectual resources, has recently put the dilemma bluntly: 'Our major problems lie in the field of social systems: our major intellectual resource is still being devoted towards physical and biological systems.' But he does not maintain that, besides the unstinted support of good work in the social sciences for which he pleads, liberal assistance should also be given to weak projects and dubious programmes because the demands are so urgent and the hour is so late. The patent misery and the losses entailed by psychological disorder and social mischief naturally evoke loud calls for bolder measures of investigation and remedy. It is to be hoped that these demands will be met by much-increased aid and sustenance for the social sciences, by the encouragement of clinical research in psychiatry, and by boldly concentrating resources on those who can make good use of them, rather than by adopting a kindly but reckless bread-on-the-waters policy.

PSYCHIATRIC PROBLEMS

Many impersonal forces affect the direction of psychiatric inquiry and promote its spread. A trenchant example is afforded by the political changes in the world which have lately obliged people of emergent nations to adjust themselves to rapidly changing culture, new values, and unfamiliar material conditions. Such a situation raises psychiatric problems of an absorbing kind. Comparative study of the forms, causes, and course of mental disorder in different ethnic groups has been a subject of intermittent, languid inquiry since the latter part of the last century; but in the last two decades external events have directed research more energetically into this obscure, potentially rich area of inquiry. The recent survey of the Yoruba by Leighton and Lambo [27] is an informative study of the relation between a community's degree of social integration and the amount of mental ill-health in it: it demonstrates how indispensable for such studies are the techniques and theoretical equipment of the anthropologist and the sociologist as well as of the psychiatrist. Psychiatry borrows with laudable impartiality from many disciplines, and it cannot be gainsaid that the bulk of psychiatric discovery has been the product of assiduous cross-fertilization.

When we turn from factors that have brought about increase in psychiatric knowledge to those that have hampered it we may recall Allan Gregg's [28] summary: 'The three most powerful traditions of psychiatry are still, as they have been from time immemorial, the horror which mental disease inspires, the power and subtlety with which psychiatric symptoms influence human relations, and the tendency of man to think of spirit as not only separable but already separate from body. These are the inherent, the inveterate, the inevitable handicaps of psychiatry.' The third of these, the relation of mind and body, is indeed an ancient and obstinate difficulty. Cartesian dualism is disavowed, yet perforce implied, by nearly all psychiatrists: in this century it has been most conspicuously embraced, and repudiated, by those who concern themselves especially with 'psychosomatic' illness. The very distinction between physical and mental, which is implicit in the designation of psychiatry as a distinct branch of medicine, begs the question. If the dualism is denied, then the territory of psychiatry becomes theoretically coextensive with medicine.

FUTURE OF PSYCHIATRY

Can the trends now discernible in psychiatry be projected a little way into the future? Prophecy, it has been justly said, is the most gratuitous of all forms of error; but prediction is an inescapable exercise for doctors, and a short-term prognosis may be offered, hesitantly, of the relations between medicine in general and this ambitious yet diffident branch of medicine.

There has been a turn in medical thought and in public attitudes towards the use of hospitals in psychiatric treatment. The new goal is to reduce the institutional provision in mental hospitals, to re-locate it largely in general hospitals, and to improve the measures of support and rehabilitation which the community can make available outside the hospital. These aims are in keeping with liberal and permissive trends in society at large. If attained, they will strengthen the links between psychiatry and other branches of medicine. They will, however, cast a burden on the families of those mentally ill patients who are not in hospital, and may conduce to insufficient segregation of those who, because of their mental disorder, endanger other people. The ends are obviously good, the means imperfect: and, though the experiment succeeds, it may be only at a price—a price which society, collectively, is hardly willing to pay.

The respective functions of the psychiatrist and of other people who are professionally concerned with mental disorders are still unclear enough to make conflict between them possible. It is in the treatment area that dissension has arisen in the past and will arise again. An analogy pointing to the likely settlement of this clash of interests may be seen in the agreed role, *vis-à-vis* the doctor, of the biochemist confronted with inborn errors of metabolism, or the role of the microbiologist and the pharmacologist confronted with infections.

It would be eccentric to doubt that as knowledge accumulates, both about the bodily pathology of mental illness and about its psychopathology, medicine as a whole will be more and more penetrated with psychiatric discoveries and the application of psychiatric principles. The rate at which this will occur must depend on the cogency of the evidence and the acceptability of the methods and concepts on which the psychiatrist relies. It seems likely to be a steady rather than a rapid process. Phases of quiescence or spuriously impressive growth will bring their own Nemesis.

It is natural to wonder from which quarter our help will mainly come; which sciences will fertilize our field and enrich us, if we know how to apply them. Will it be from epidemiology, or biochemistry, or psychology, or genetics, or from all of these, or will it be from the application of some science as yet remote from our affairs; or will it be from great technological advances, as in automation and electronic computing? I cannot suggest the answer. More than once there has been joyous acclaim for a 'break-through' in psychiatric research, but after a while the rejoicing has been toned down to a whisper. On the other hand, no one, however farsighted, could have prophesied ten years ago how the modern study of chromosomes, or the development of chromatography and other separation methods, would elucidate some forms of mental defect.

CONCLUSIONS

A symposium on the future of psychiatry was recently held in the United States, and the contributors ranged from those who foresaw an explosion of discoveries along a wide horizon to others who uttered sombre warnings: 'unless our philosophy of science becomes more critical, experimental, more deductive and inventive, we will remain in the Renaissance period of medical history, awaiting a Harvey to catapult us into the seventeenth century' [29]. A less extreme view would take account of the volume of productive research into psychiatric problems now going on in many countries, and would draw comfort and hope from the exciting advances in the correlation of localized cerebral activity with behaviour, as well as from the study of psychological development, application of learning theory, knowledge of the action of chemical substances on neural areas, the growing use of epidemiological methods, and the steady accumulation of detailed experimental and clinical observations.

Psychiatrists, hitherto ardent, if not over-ardent, in the trial of new methods of treatment, are now much more aware of the common failing which Bacon adverted to: 'Even when men build some science and theory upon experiment, yet they almost always turn aside with premature and hasty zeal to practice, not merely on account of the advantage and benefit to be derived from it, but in order to obtain in the shape of some new work an assurance for themselves that it is worth their while to go on.' The many varieties of psychotherapy and of physical treatment now employed are being required to show their credentials, and reliance upon unchecked clinical experience for their appraisal is surely a dying illusion.

It is through its place in the roomy household of medicine, and its intimacy with many sciences, social and biological, that psychiatry can find the best assurance of increase by studying out the secrets of nature. So we may say with Bacon [30] 'that many excellent and useful matters are yet laid up in the bosom of Nature . . . quite out of the common track of our imagination, and still undiscovered; but they too will doubtless be brought to light in the course and revolution of years.'

REFERENCES

1 BURTON, R. *The Anatomy of Melancholy: Democritus Junior to the Reader*, London, 1621.

2 BROWNE, T. *Religio Medici*, Part the Second, Section IX. London, J. F. Spoor, 1642.

3 BERTOLOSO, E. *Acta med. Hist. patav.*, 1959, **6**, 17.

4 DODDS, C. *Brit. med. J.*, 1960, **2**, 182.

5 SYDENHAM, T. *Works*, London, 1742.

6 BURROWS, G. M. *Commentaries on the Causes, Forms, Symptoms and Treatments, Moral and Medical, of Insanity*, London, 1828.

7 HEINROTH, J. C. A. *Lehrbuch der Störungen des Seelenlebens oder der Seelenstörungen*, Leipzig, F. C. W. Vogel, 1818.

8 DUBOIS, P. *The Psychic Treatment of Nervous Disorders*, London, Funk and Wagnalls, 1909.

9 ALLPORT, G. W. *The Individual and His Religion*, London, Constable, 1951.

10 MOWRER, O. H. *Amer. Psychologist*, 1960, **15**, 301.

11 KANT, I. 'Anthropologie, in pragmatischer Hinsicht', in K. R. Rosenkranz, and Schubert, F. W. (eds.) *Gesammelte Schriften*, vol. 12, Leipzig, 1840.

12 WOOTTON, B. *Brit. med. J.*, 1963, **2**, 197.

13 ADRIAN, E. D. *Proc. roy. Soc. Med.*, 1963, **56**, 523.

14 WADDINGTON, C. H. 'Propagation of ideas', in S. M. Farber and R. H. L. Wilson's *Conflict and Creativity*, London, McGraw Hill, 1963.

15 MENNINGER, K. 'The Evolution of Diagnosis', in Brill, N. Q. (ed.) *Psychiatry in Medicine*, London, Cambridge University Press, 1962.

16 KENNEDY, J. F. 'Mental Illness and Mental Retardation', *Message to Congress*, 88th Congress, Document 58, 1963.

17 OSLER, W. (1902). *Chauvinism in Medicine*, An address before the Canadian Medical Association, Baltimore, Williams and Wilkins, 1902.

18 SUTHERLAND, A. J. *Oratio Harveiana*, London, Royal College of Physicians, 1863.

19 JASPERS, K. *General Psychopathology* (trans. J. Hoenig and M. W. Hamilton) Manchester, University Press, 1963.

20 POPPER, K. R. *Conjectures and Refutations*, London, Routledge, 1963.

21 BACON, K. 'Of the Proficience and Advancement of Learning', in Ellis, R. L. Spedding, J. and Heath, D. D. (eds.), *Collected Works*, London, 1858.

22 SHEPHERD, M. *The Teaching of Psychiatry in the United States*, London, Pitman, 1963.

23 KAUFMAN, M. R. *Psychiat. Quart.*, 1963, **37**, 340.

24 MILLER, N. 'Some applications of modern behaviour theory to personality change and psychotherapy', Unpublished, 1963.

25 BILLROTH, T. *Über das Lehren und Lernen der medizinischen Wissenschaften an den Universitäten der deutschen Nation*, Vienna, 1876.

26 BOULDING, R. E. *Proc. Amer. Philosoph. Soc.*, 1963, **107**, 117.

27 LEIGHTON, A. and LAMBO, T. A. *Psychiatric Disorder Among the Yoruba*, New York, Cornell University Press, 1963.

28 GREGG, A. *Amer. J. Psychiat.*, 1944, **101**, 285.

29 ROTHMAN, R. 'Future of genetic development and organic approaches', in Hoch, P. and Zubin, J. (eds.), *The Future of Psychiatry*, London, Grune and Stratton, 1962.

30 BACON, F. Novum Organum. In Ellis, R. L., Spedding, J. and Heath D. D. (eds.), *Collected Works*, London, 1858.

18

THE PSYCHOLOGY OF SHAKESPEARE

MANY HAVE tried to pierce the veil that hides Shakespeare the man from us. In his sonnets and his plays they have looked for his projected self, his half-disguised emotions and struggles. Sometimes their inferences about the changes that took place in Shakespeare's mind and personality are based on the general mood that pervades each of the plays, sometimes on the predominance of a single character or type of problem, and sometimes on the force and intensity of the poetic language.

Whatever the foundation upon which the attempt to trace Shakespeare's development is built, it remains a highly subjective construction, an inverted pyramid of conjectural biography, as a famous scholar called it. Neither the spiritual experiences of a great poet, nor the outward events of his life, can be inferred with confidence from his writings. In some writers the autobiographical material may be plentifully displayed, as it was by Dante, but in others ludicrous errors are the reward of those who read experiences and conflicts into the poet's words. A poet of our own day, T. S. Eliot, has put this in general terms: 'the more perfect the artist, the more completely separate in him will be the man who suffers and the mind which creates;' and he goes on, 'I am used to having cosmic significances, which I never suspected, extracted from my work (such as it is) by enthusiastic persons at a distance; and to having my personal biography reconstructed from passages which I got out of books or which I invented out of nothing because they sounded well; and to having my biography invariably ignored in what I *did* write from personal experience; so that in consequence', says Mr Eliot, 'I am inclined to believe that people are mistaken about Shakespeare just in proportion to the relative superiority of Shakespeare to myself.'

To avoid subjectivity—which, at its worst, results in telling us a great deal about the would-be interpreter and very little or nothing about Shakespeare —we have the statistical method; and to avoid superficiality we have the psychoanalytical method.

The statistical method is indeed objective in its primary treatment of its

This paper was broadcast in the European Service of the British Broadcasting Corporation in April 1964. It is reprinted from *Shakespeare, the Comprehensive Soul*, London, British Broadcasting Corporation, 1965.

material. Following the lead of the English statistician Udny Yule, who introduced the quantitative study of literary vocabulary, painstaking students have made numerical estimates of poetic word patterns of imagery, of references to colour, and of the number of lines given to the various characters in each play. From such statistics it has been inferred that Shakespeare was aggressive and strongly masculine, but with feminine elements against which he struggled; that he was suspicious and jealous, with a latent homosexual strain and a tendency to minimize the importance of sexual love as he grew older. Other conclusions, similarly tentative and general, emerged from scrutiny of the amount of talking allotted to the persons of the various plays. Interesting and probable though these interpretations are, they rest on assumptions which are unconfirmed.

Much the same must be said of the detailed inferences drawn by psychoanalysts about the deeper structure of Shakespeare's mind and the experiences in his childhood and in his later life which formed his mind. Freud himself, Ernest Jones, and several others have set about unravelling the conflicts in Shakespeare's unconscious which underlie the torments he dramatized in *Hamlet*. Studies of *Coriolanus, Lear, Julius Caesar*, and *Titus Andronicus* have been concerned with the same questions of dynamic psychopathology. One of the most ambitious of these interpreters discerns an alternating rhythm of tragedy and comedy, a recurring passage from depression to joyful 'reinstatement of the ideal', which can be traced through the whole sequence of plays: and this is linked to supposed discharges of emotion, as well as bodily discharges by the infant Shakespeare which, so the psychoanalyst maintains, laid the foundations for his successive descents into the abyss of depression and frustration, alternating with active fulfilment and regeneration.

The hardihood of these psychoanalytical speculations varies from author to author, but they postulate that the products of a poet's genius can be analysed like the fantasies of a child or the contents of a dream; and they imply that instead of the processes of free association and interpretation which are the normal requisites for psychoanalysis, careful study of the dead poet-playwright's words and themes can penetrate to their significance as symbols and expressions of unconscious conflict originating in the experiences of early childhood. The conjectures so arrived at are hazardous: in spite of the authority they derive from Freud's own cautious excursions into this sort of archaeological analysis, they cannot be relied on either as biography or psychology. Nevertheless they open up stimulating lines of thought: this is illustrated by the suggested relevance of the oedipus myth to the central problem in *Hamlet*, and the convergent influences in Shakespeare's life which led to a recurring emphasis on antagonism between father and son in the plays.

The Sonnets have always tantalized the would-be explorer of Shakespeare's inner life. Here the poet speaks, not through the characters he created, but in his own person; yet we cannot be sure when he is working wholly within a literary convention of his day, and when he is speaking with passionate sincerity. It is most likely that the Sonnets were written at different times, under the pressure of changing feelings, and with differing degrees of poetic intensity, but there are some amongst them which bespeak a melancholic disgust with himself, a sense of shame and misery which is no detached literary exercise but a depressive cry, a heartfelt utterance of shame and self-disgust. Take Sonnet 110:

> Alas, 'tis true, I have gone here and there,
> And made myself a motley to the view,
> Gor'd mine own thoughts, sold cheap what is most dear,
> Made old offences of affections new;
> Most true it is, that I have look'd on truth
> Askance and strangely:

or take the sonnet that follows it:

> O for my sake do you with Fortune chide,
> The guilty goddess of my harmful deeds,
> That did not better for my life provide
> Than public means which public manners breeds.
> Thence comes it that my name receives a brand,
> And almost thence my nature is subdu'd
> To what it works in, like the dyer's hand.

These are the authentic plaints with which psychiatrists are painfully familiar; they are immediately distinguishable from the contrived woe of such a sonnet as 66:

> Tired with all these, for restful death I cry.

There are of course, in the Sonnets, overt themes—jealousy, betrayal, love for a man, love for a woman: but it would surely be an error to picture Shakespeare as the helpless victim of fleeting emotions and passing events. No doubt his experiences entered into his poetry, but what separates the author of the Sonnets from a crowd of lesser poets and autobiographers is not the experience he translated into verse, but the personal and mingled elements of thought, imagery, rhythm and verbal music with which he clothed it, turning it into matchless poetry.

If we infer, as I think we must from the Sonnets, that Shakespeare passed through at least one period of severe depression, the question of his mental health may seem to deserve attention. It has been said that in *King Lear* and *Timon of Athens* there are symptoms of mental disturbance, and that the emotion which Shakespeare was able to express in the form of art in *Lear* had reached such a point that it overwhelmed him when he was writing *Timon*: or, again, it has been held that 'the transition from the tragedies to the romances is not an evolution but a revolution. There has been some mental process such as the psychology of religion would call a conversion'. These surmises and diagnoses are unwarranted. What little we know for sure about Shakespeare's way of life, his steady activities, his attention to business, and how he seemed to his contemporaries—all this speaks strongly against the assumption of instability and mental illness. He passed through a period of depression it is true, but it deepened his understanding without impairing his productivity or warping his technical powers, his command of imagery or his fine discrimination and balance. Moreover the later plays were produced at a time of insecurity and chaos in the Jacobean era of the Gunpowder Plot, so different from the assured, expansive, confident Elizabethan world. Inevitably this background affected Shakespeare's art: but not in the direction of mental disturbance.

How much, then, do we know, how much can we surmise about the development of Shakespeare's personality? Personality is, in everyone, a complex, elusive, unique totality, bearing many aspects: our knowledge and understanding of anyone else's personality—or of our own—must be incomplete, must be coloured and biased by our special relation to him and it must be largely based on our observation of his behaviour in a variety of testing situations. When we try to grasp the personalty of a transcendent creative artist, a poet of the highest order, we are clearly at a disadvantage; and this would be true even if we had lived with him, been admitted to his confidence, and explored his mind in intimate conversation. The attempt is, however, incomparably more audacious and more certain to fail when our judgments and impressions must be formed almost entirely from his plays and his poems. Only the broadest, most diffident conclusions can be drawn. It may be accepted that in his early manhood, when witty talkers, young lovers, and fiery adventurers predominated in his plays, Shakespeare himself was ardent and bold; later when deep moral problems, the crudities and sufferings that sexuality entails, the humiliations imposed by the imperious body and its desires, the meaning of death, frustration, and disillusionment—when these were the central themes of his plays, and the chief characters in them were powerful fathers and rulers who suffered defeat, we may, hesitantly, surmise that Shakespeare had himself an anguished maturity, to be succeeded at last by the relative serenity and renunciation which are expressed in *The Tempest*, his final play. There he had come to the time when he must break his magic staff and drown his book deeper than did ever plummet sound; he asked for solemn music, and he spoke his farewell nobly:

> Our revels now are ended. These our actors
> As I foretold you, were all spirits and
> Are melted into air, into thin air:
> And, like the baseless fabric of this vision,
> The cloud-capp'd towers, the gorgeous palaces,
> The solemn temples, the great globe itself,
> Yea, all which it inherit, shall dissolve,
> And, like this insubstantial pageant faded,
> Leave not a rack behind. We are such stuff
> As dreams are made on; and our little life
> Is rounded with a sleep.

BIBLIOGRAPHY

1926

With CAMPBELL, T. D. The aborigines of South Australia: dental observations recorded at Ooldea. *Aust. J. Dent.*, **30**, 371–6.

With CAMPBELL, T. D. The aborigines of South Australia: anthropometric descriptive and other observations recorded at Ooldea. *Trans. R. Soc. S. Aust.*, **50**, 183–91.

1928

Traumatic pneumocephalus. *Brain*, **51**, 221–43.

1930

An investigation into the clinical features of melancholia. M.D. Thesis; Univ. Adelaide.

1931

Paranoid disorders. *Gen. Pract. Fr.-Br. med. Rev.*, **7**, 311–15.

Genetic problems in psychiatry: and their solution by the study of twins. *Eugen. Rev.*, **23**, 119–25.

1932

The experience of time in mental disorder. *Proc. R. Soc. Med.*, **25**, 611–20.

1933

Inheritance of mental disorders. *Eugen. Rev.*, **25**, 79–84.

1934

Melancholia: a historical review. *J. ment. Sci.*, **80**, 1–42.

Melancholia: a clinical survey of depressive states. *J. ment. Sci.*, **80**, 277–378.

The psychopathology of insight. *Br. J. med. Psychol.*, **14**, 332–48.

Mental reactions to bodily injury. *Med. Press*, **188**, 511–12.

Acromegaly in one of uniovular twins. *J. Neurol. Psychopath.*, **15**, 1–11.

German eugenic legislation: an examination of fact and theory. *Eugen. Rev.*, **26**, 183–91.

Inheritance of mental disorders. In *The Chances of Morbid Inheritance*, ed. BLACKER, C. P. London: H. K. Lewis.

1935

Psychological syndromes in central nervous disease: a genetic interpretation. *Eugen. Rev.*, **27**, 213–15.
Neurosis and unemployment. *Lancet*, **2**, 293–7.
Prognosis in schizophrenia. *Lancet*, **1**, 339–41.
With MINSKI, L. Chorea and psychosis. *Lancet*, **1**, 536–8.

1936

Melancholia: prognostic study and case material. *J. ment. Sci.*, **82**, 488–558.
Prognosis in the manic-depressive psychosis. *Lancet*, **2**, 997–9.
Problems of obsessional illness. *Proc. R. Soc. Med.*, **29**, 325–36.
A case of apparent dissimilarity of monozygotic twins. *Ann. Eugen.*, **7**, 58–64.
Psychiatry and General Medicine. *Med. Press*, **192**, Symposium No. 2, 1–3.

1937

With SAMUEL, N., and GALLOWAY, J. A study of cretinism in London with especial reference to mental development and problems of growth. *Lancet*, **1**, 1505–9 and **2**, 5–9.

1938

States of depression: their clinical and aetiological differentiation. *Brit. med. J.*, **2**, 875–8.
The diagnosis and treatment of obsessional states. *Practitioner*, **141**, 21–30.
Some recent aspects of dementia. In *Festskrift tillägnad Olof Kinberg*, pp. 238–44. Stockholm: Asbrink.
Paranoia and paranoid states. In *The British Encyclopaedia of Medical Practice* (1st ed.), **10**, 292–301. London: Butterworth.
Alcoholic psychoses. In *The British Encyclopaedia of Medical Practice*, (1st ed.), **10**, 332–41. London: Butterworth.

1940

With JACKSON, J. Psychiatric comparison of artificial menopause and the effects of hysterectomy. *J. Neurol. Psychiat., Lond.*, **3**, 101–10.

1941

Psychological Medicine. In Price's *Textbook of the Practice of Medicine*, 6th ed. (and subsequent editions). London: Oxford University Press.
Psychiatric aspects of effort syndrome. *Proc. R. Soc. Med.*, **34**, 533–40.
With JONES, M. Effort syndrome. *Lancet*, **1**, 813–18.

1942

Discussion on Differential Diagnosis and Treatment of Post-contusional States. *Proc. R. Soc. Med.*, **35**, 607–14.
Incidence of neurosis in England under war conditions. *Lancet*, **2**, 175–83.
With SLATER, E. Neurosis in soldiers: a follow-up study. *Lancet*, **1**, 496–8.

1943

Social effects of neurosis. *Lancet*, **1**, 167–70.
Mental health in war-time. *Publ. Hlth., Lond.*, **57**, 27–30.
With GOLDSCHMIDT, H. Social causes of admissions to a mental hospital for the
aged. *Sociol. Rev.*, **35**, 86–98.

1944

Depression (In 'Recent Progress in Psychiatry'). *J. ment. Sci.*, **90**, 256–65.
The psychological aspects of indigestion. *Practitioner*, **152**, 257–60.
With GOODYEAR, K. Vocational aspects of neurosis in soldiers. *Lancet*, **2**, 105–9.

1945

The industrial resettlement of the neurotic. *Labour Mgmt*, **27**, 40–3. Also in
(1946) Suppl. to *Brit. med. J.*, **1**, 197–9.
Psychiatric investigation in Britain. *Amer. J. Psychiat.*, **101**, 486–93.
On the place of physical treatment in psychiatry. *Br. med. Bull.*, **3**, 22–4.
Psychiatric advice in industry. *Br. J. ind. Med.*, **2**, 41–2.
The treatment of alcoholism. In Interim Supplement to *British Encylopaedia of
Medical Practice*, pp. 11–12. London: Butterworth.
Sobre el lugo del tratamiento físico en psiquiatría. (i) *Revta. Asoc. méd.
argent.*, **59**, 1235–7, and (ii) *Gac. méd. españ.*, **19**, 494–7.

1946

Early recognition of disease; mental disorders. *Practitioner*, **156**, 459–63.
Ageing and senility: a major problem of psychiatry. *J. ment. Sci.*, **92**, 150–70.
Memorandum to the Royal Commission on Equal Pay. Appendices IX and X to
Minutes of Evidence taken before the Royal Commission on Equal Pay,
pp. 130–4. London: H.M.S.O.

1947

The education of psychiatrists. *Lancet*, **2**, 79–83.

1949

Philosophy and psychiatry (Manson Lecture). *Philosphy*, **24**, 99–117.
Postgraduate study in mental health in Britain. *Br. med. Bull.*, **6**, 185–7.
With DAVIES, D. L. Effects of decamethonium iodide (C 10) on respiration and
induced convulsions in man. *Lancet*, **1**, 775–7.

1950

Mental disorders. Section in *Chambers' Encyclopaedia*, **9**, 258–64. London:
Newnes.

1951

Henry Maudsley: his work and influence (Maudsley Lecture). *J. ment. Sci.*, **97**,
259–77.
Social aspects of psychiatry (Morison Lecture). *Edinb. med. J.*, **58**, 214–47.
Medical psychology. In *A Century of Science*, ed. DINGLE, H. London: Hutchison.

BIBLIOGRAPHY

1952

Classification of schizophrenia. *Proceedings of the first World Congress of Psychiatry (Paris 1950).* Part 2. Paris: Hermann.

With SLATER, E. Psychiatry in the Emergency Medical Service. In *History of the Second World War: United Kingdom Medical Series. Medicine and Pathology,* ed. Sir Z. COPE. London: H.M.S.O.

Paranoia and paranoid states. In *British Encyclopaedia of Medical Practice* (2nd ed.), **10,** 362–70. London: Butterworth.

Alcoholic psychoses. In *British Encyclopaedia of Medical Practice* (2nd ed.), **10,** 394–402. London: Butterworth.

1953

Health as a social concept. *Brit. J. Sociol.,* **4,** 109–24.

Letter from Britain. *Amer. J. Psychiat.,* **110,** 401–5.

Hysterical dissociation in dementia paralytica. *Mschr. Psychiat. Neurol.,* **125,** 589–604.

Research in occupational psychiatry. *Folia psychiat. neurol. neurochir. neerl.,* **56,** 779–86.

Advances in psychological medicine. *Practitioner,* **171,** 403–12.

Contribution to Points of Research into the Interaction between the Individual and the Culture. In *Prospects in Psychiatric Research,* ed. TANNER, J. Oxford: Blackwell.

1954

With FLEMINGER, J. J. The psychiatric risk from corticotrophin and cortisone. *Lancet,* **1,** 383–6.

Aspetti psicosomatici della medicina clinica. *Recenti Prog. Med.,* **16,** 434–53.

1955

Philippe Pinel and the English. *Proc. R. Soc. Med.,* **48,** 581–6.

Mental aspects of ageing. *Ciba Fdn. Colloq. Ageing,* **1,** 32–48. London: Churchill.

The relation between operative risk and the patient's general condition: alcohol, other habits of addiction and psychogenic factors. *Sixteenth International Congress of Surgery, Copenhagen.* Brussels: Imprimerie Medicale et Scientifique.

1956

Sigmund Freud, 1856–1939. *Discovery,* **17,** 181–3.

Statistical aspects of suicide. *Can. med. Ass. J.,* **74,** 99–104.

Rehabilitation programs in England. In *The Elements of a Community Mental Health Program.* New York: Millbank Memorial Fund.

1957

Social psychiatry. In *Lectures on the Scientific Basis of Medicine, 1956–7,* **6,** 116–42. University of London: Athlone Press.

The offspring of parents both mentally ill. *Acta genet. Statist. med.,* **7,** 349–65.

Jung's early work. *J. analyt. Psychol.,* **2,** 119–136.

La enfermedad obsesiva. *Acta neuropsiq. argent.,* **3,** 323–35.

BIBLIOGRAPHY

1958

Between guesswork and certainty in psychiatry (Bradshaw Lecture). *Lancet*, **1**, 171–5 and 227–30.
Resettlement of the chronic schizophrenic. (i) *J. all-India Inst. ment. Hlth.*, **1**, 22–8; (ii) (1959). In *Report of the Second Internat. Congr. Psychiatry: (Zurich 1957)*. Zurich: Orell Fussli. **1**, 223–8.
J. C. Reil's concepts of brain function. In *The History and Philosophy of Knowledge of the Brain and its function*, ed. POYNTER, F. N. L. Oxford: Blackwell.
Fertility and mental illness. *Eugen. Rev.*, **50**, 91–106.
A psychiatrist looks at a layman. *Oxf. med. Sch. Gaz.*, **10**, 124–6.

1959

Families with manic-depressive psychosis. *Eugen. Q.*, **6**, 130–7.
The impact of psychotropic drugs on the structure, function and future of psychiatric services in hospitals. In *Neuro-Psychopharmacology*, eds. BRADLEY, P. B., FLÜGEL, F. and HOCH, P. Amsterdam: Elsevier Pub. Co.

1960

The study of defect (Adolf Meyer Research Lecture). *Amer. J. Psychiat.*, **117**, 289–305.

1961

Agents of cultural advance (Hobhouse Memorial Trust Lecture). London: Oxford University Press.
Amnesic syndromes; the psychopathological aspect. *Proc. R. Soc. Med.*, **54**, 955–61.
The chemical treatment of mental disorder. *Biology hum. Affairs*, **27**, 19–26.
Psychiatric education and training. In *Psychiatrie der Gegenwart*, eds. GRUHLE, H. W., JUNG, R., MAYER-GROSS, W. and MÜLLER, M., Band 3. Berlin: Springer.
Current field studies in mental disorders in Britain. In *Comparative Epidemiology of Mental Disorders*, eds. HOCH, P. H. and ZUBIN, J. New York: Grune & Stratton.
Psychiatry in Great Britain. In *Contemporary European psychiatry*, ed. BELLAK, L. New York: Grove Press.

1962

Ebb and flow in social psychiatry (Bertram Roberts Memorial Lecture). *Yale J. Biol. Med.*, **35**, 62–83.
Inaugural speech of the scientific session. In *First Pan-African Psychiatric Conference 1961*, ed. LAMBO, T. A. Ibadan: Government Printer.
What are the foreigners up to? *Amer. J. Psychiat.*, **118**, 751–2.

1963

Medicine and the affections of the mind (Harveian Oration). *Brit. med. J.*, **2**, 1549–57.
Research and its application in psychiatry (Maurice Bloch Lecture). Glasgow: Jackson.

303

The psychoses. In *Cecil-Loeb's Textbook of Medicine*, 11th ed. (and 12th ed.), eds. BEESON, P. B. and MCDERMOTT, W. Philadelphia: Saunders.
Symposium: Training for Child Psychiatry. *J. Child. Psychol. Psychiat.*, **4,** 75–84.
Demographic aspects of mental disorder. *Proc. Roy. Soc.*, B.**159,** 202–20.
Henry Maudsley. In *Grosse Nervenaerzte*, ed. KOLLE, K. Band 3. Stuttgart: Thieme.

1964

Health in 1984: changes in psychiatric methods and attitudes. *New Scient.*, **21,** 423–4.
Health. In *A Dictionary of the Social Sciences*, eds. GOULD, J. and KOLB, W. L. London: Tavistock.
Depression. In *Depression. Proc. Symposium, Cambridge, 1959*, ed. DAVIES, E. B. Cambridge: University Press.

1965

J. C. Reil: Innovator and Battler. *J. Hist. Behav. Sci.*, **1,** 178–90.
A note on personality and obsessional illness. *Psychiatria Neurol. Basel*, **150,** 299–305.
The Medical Research Council Social Psychiatry Research Unit. In *The Organization of Research Establishments*, ed. Sir J. COCKCROFT. Cambridge: University Press.
The Psychology of Shakespeare. In *Shakespeare: the comprehensive soul*, PRITCHETT, V. S. *et al.* London: British Broadcasting Corporation.

1966

Dogma disputed: Psychiatric dicta. *Lancet*, **1,** 974–5.
Survivance de l'Hystérie. *Evol. psychiat.* **31,** 159–65.

INDEX

(Authors' names are in italics)